PEOPLE
MAKE THE
HOSPITAL

# PEOPLE
# MAKE THE
# HOSPITAL

## The History of Washoe Medical Center

ANTON P. SOHN & CARROLL W. OGREN

GREASEWOOD PRESS RENO

Greasewood Press / Pathology 350 / Reno, Nevada 89557

Production of *People Make the Hospital:
The History of Washoe Medical Center*
was made possible by a grant from
The Great Basin History of Medicine Program
of the Department of Pathology,
University of Nevada School of Medicine.
Jacket Design by Carrie Nelson House.

Library of Congress Catalog Card Number 98-34645

Library of Congress Cataloging-in-PublicationData
Sohn, A. P. (Anton Paul), 1935-
People make the hospital; the history of Washoe Medical Center by
Anton P. Sohn and Carroll W. Ogren
p.   cm.
Includes bibliographical references and index.
ISBN 0-9649759-5-5
1. Wahoe Medical Center—History. 2. Medical centers—Nevada
History. 3. Hospitals—Nevada—History. I Ogren, Carroll W. 1927-
II. Washoe Medical Center (Nev.) III Title.
RA982.R37W377   1998          98-34645
362.1'1'0979355—dc21          CIP

*For my brothers, John, Robert, and Stuart*
*and my wife, Patricia Ann Ogren*

*For my wife, Arlene A. Sohn*

# CONTENTS

Illustrations   xi
Preface   xiii
Foreword   xix
Abbreviations   xxv

1   Introduction: The Change in Healthcare   1
CARROLL W. OGREN

2   first Steps, 1862–1930   5
ANTON P. SOHN
    *Smallpox Outbreak*
    *The First Washoe County Hospital*
    *The Move to Reno*
    *The Move to Kirman and Mill Streets*
    *Beginning the Twentieth Century*
    *Multiple Reno Hospitals*
    *The Influenza Pandemic*
    *A North Wing*

3   Coming of Age, 1930–1957   17
ANTON P. SOHN
    *Reorganization Creates Washoe General hospital*
    *The Great Depression*
    *World War II*

*Post World War II*
*Washoe Medical Center*
*Tuberculosis and Physical Therapy*
*A Leader in the War Against Polio*
*After Polio*

4    Hospital Resident, 1957–1958    33
     CARROLL W. OGREN
     *Arrival at Washoe Medical Center*
     *The Scott Ranch Ditch*
     *The 1958 Building*
     *Duties of an Administrative Resident*
     *Clyde Fox, Administrator*
     *Nevada State Hospital*

5    Assistant Administrator, 1958–1964    43
     CARROLL W. OGREN
     *Television in Patient Rooms*
     *The Quonset Huts*
     *East Wing Addition*
     *Convalescent Unit*
     *Earl Horton, Administrator*
     *An Emergency Landing and Secret Service Visits*
     *1960 Winter Olympics*
     The Misfits *and* Lets Make Love
     *Psychiatric Ward*
     *Snack Bar*
     *The Hospital's District Attorneys*
     *The First* CAT *Scanner*

6    Administrator, 1964–1978    55
     CARROLL W. OGREN
     *The First Chaplain, Richard Engeseth, and the Kohl Memorial Chapel*
     *Planning for the Tower*
     *Tom Scully, Director of Education*
     *A Tragedy at Washoe Medical Center*
     *A Liver Transplant*
     *Slot Machine Thrombosis*

*Other Problems*
*The First Helicopter*
*Dedication of the 1973 Building*
*Open Heart Surgery and the Cardiac Care Unit*
*Poison Center*
*Incline Village Hospital*

7   People Make the Hospital: During Mr. Ogren's Tenure   69
    CARROLL W. OGREN
       *Nursing Staff*
       *Medical Staff*
       *Board of Trustees*
       *Department Supervisors*
       *Departments*
       *Women's League*
       *Philanthropists*
       *Maida Pringle, R.N.*
       *Larry Russell, M.D.*
       *Staff Secretaries*
       *Hospital Personalities*

8   Hospital Politics: During Mr. Ogren's Tenure   103
    CARROLL W. OGREN
       *Hospital Accreditation*
       *Relations with Hospital-Based Physicians*
       *Washoe Western School of Practical Nursing*
       *University of Nevada School of Medicine*
       *Our Relationship with Saint Mary's Hospital*
       *A leader in the Nevada Hospital Association*
       *Unusual Occurrences*
       *Media coverage*

9   A New Direction, 1978–1998   119
    ANTON P. SOHN
       *Mr. Ogren Leaves Washoe Medical Center*
       *Years of Conflict—Establishing a Residency*
       *Years of Conflict—Good Friends Compete*
       *Years of Conflict—Neonatology*

*Years of Conflict—Helicopter Service*
*Years of Conflict—Trauma Service*
*Laboratory Computer*
*Another Grand Jury Investigation*
*Pediatric Intensive Care Unit*
*The Second Reorganization*
*The Eleven-Story Tower Addition*
*The Cancer Center and Dialysis Unit*
*The Parking Garage Addition*
*Bone Marrow Transplantation*
*Into the Future*

Notes   137
Appendices
    I       Chronology of Reference Material   143
    II      1958 Medical Staff   177
    III     1967 Department Heads   181
    IV      Medical Staff   183
    V       Board of Trustees Chairmen   197
    VI      Administrators   199
    VII     Chiefs of Staff   201
    VIII    Early Reno/Sparks Hospitals   203
    IX      1998 Department Managers   205
    X       Directors of Nursing   207
    XI      Auxiliary Presidents   209
    XII     History of the Women's League   211
    XIII    C. W. Ogren, Early Years   213
Bibliography   221
Index   223

# ILLUSTRATIONS

*(following page 68)*
1948 Power house construction site
James Lamb, circa 1990
Redwood Pavilion, circa 1940
Mrs. Douglas Cloud, Clyde Fox, and Drs. Salvadorini and
    Sandars, 1958
Nurses Pat Blodgett and Vinette Blanchard, 1970
1958 Emergency room exterior with ambulance
WMC's first cardioscope—Dr. Hillstrom and Clyde Fox,
    circa 1955
County Hospital farm, Dr. Larry Russell's clinic, and
    Quonset huts, circa 1955
Two polio patients with breathing assistance, circa 1953
Iron lung and Nurse Bernice Lawson, circa 1953
Polio children in Hubbard tub, circa 1953
Aerial view of Washoe Medical Center 1973 Tower
Washoe Medical Center Professional Building, 1989
1998 Administrative staff
Twin Barbara Ruth Schelin in the nursery, 1950s
Baby in incubator, 1950s
Clyde Fox, Dr. Russell, Dr. Bart Hood, and Chris Kakoras,
    Christmas 1950s
Nurses Marge Adams, Virginia Campbell, Judy Benevenuto, and
    June Stevenson, 1978

*(following page 136)*
1973 Tower dedication with Carroll Ogren, Dr. Mack, and
   Mr. S. Ogren
Nurse Rose Costa and Dr. Larry Russell, circa 1960
Nurses Bobbie (left), Dianne Savage, and Madeline Guisto
   (UNR cap), 1970s
Mrs. Geraldine "Poison Lady" Staples, 1988
Nurse Jean Molde, 1973 Tower patient room
One of the first open heart surgeries, 1977
Head hemodialysis Nurse Charlotte Matthews, 1980
Chief of Staff Dr. Anton Sohn and Mrs. Maida Pringle, 1982
Nurses Esther Chalmers and Bernice Martin Mathews, 1970
Bob Burn, 1998
Patient room in 1906 building
Operating room in 1973 addition
Radiology technician Judy Miller (left) and Student Tomi Argoitia
   in 1958 building
1961 building at the corner of Kirman (left) and Mill Streets
Starting construction of 1961 building
Washoe Medical Center Blood Bank with bloodmobile, 1955
Nurse Evelyn Naeb, technologist Charles Chester, and Toni Negri,
   1955
1906 Hospital
Nurses Iva Haislip (left) and Jean Gans, 1971
Washoe County Hospital in 1901 with Joseph Odett and family,
   circa 1907
Dr. Mack, Mrs. Pringle, and Mr. Ogren honoring Mrs. Pringle,
   mid 1970
1959 LPN Graduates

# PREFACE

This history deals with humanity, a moving experience, from 1862 when smallpox created havoc in a small western Nevada community, to 1918 and the worldwide setting of influenza, to 1952 when children were stricken with paralytic polio, to the growing menace of human immunodeficiency virus (HIV) infection, and to 1998 when all healthcare needs are met by a corporate complex and a government that thinks it has all of the answers to healthcare problems, but usually creates more problems than it solves. For the earlier part of this history—beginning when a printing shop was made into a hospital, the records are incomplete and sparse; in the latter part of this history of a modern, high technology, teaching hospital, the records are voluminous and detailed. I have taken these records, along with various individual recollections, primarily Carroll Ogren's story, which forms the heart of this narrative and created the picture of the evolution of Reno's oldest hospital, the tertiary care provider of northern Nevada—Washoe Medical Center. The significance of Mr. Ogren's story is reinforced by two leading American historians.

America's leading historian on the military medicine, Dr. Robert J. T. Joy, states, "All history is local." Another premier World War II historian, Stephen E. Ambrose, emphasizes that he was taught "to let my characters speak for themselves by quoting them liberally. They were there. I wasn't." Both of these quotes go to the heart of this history, the story of Washoe Medical Center. The first one hundred years of the Hospital are fact—cold, hard, and without comment; the personal experiences are missing and not recorded. Few of the characters speak in this local drama. Thus, we will never know the whole story. I decided to not allow that to happen for the most recent years of one of Nevada's most important medical centers. During modern times, Carroll Ogren served the longest period of any administrator at Washoe Medical Center and was instrumental in its transition to a place of prominence. His personal reminiscences are told in this book. They will not be lost. They tell us what really happened. No punches are pulled, and these reminiscences create the story of *People Make the Hospital.*

Unfortunately, all of Mr. Ogren's predecessors are gone, but the part they played in the creation of Washoe Medical Center is not forgotten. Before 1934, the hospital's administrators created a home and health care facility for the elderly and indigent, a home that was usually a source of pride for the community. Mr. Joseph Odett was superintendent at the turn of the century when the hospital was known for "neat beds, neat wards, neat inmates and general air of good cheer." Mr. John Kenney was appointed to guide the hospital during its first reorganization in 1934. Mr. Clyde Fox came on the scene in 1949 and created the vision that resulted in a modern hospital associated with a medical school. Fox changed the name from Washoe County General Hospital to Washoe Medical Center and prepared the way for Mr. Ogren to guide the hospital to financial stability. In 1985 Mr. James Lamb led the hospital through its second reorganization and created a nonprofit private hospital with an enlarging campus designed to provide all healthcare needs to the community. The last chapter in the twentieth century is still being written as Mr. Bob Burn leads the hospital into the future. Thus, I have not tried to detail and evaluate the last few years of Washoe Medical Center's history.

The story of Washoe Medical Center is contained in two different parts of the book. The narrative to the story is found in chapters one through nine, while the details are outlined and referenced in Appendix I. Many of these details are only listed in the appendix, but they have important historical significance; therefore, I felt compelled to list them.

Furthermore, only the story of the hospital, Washoe Medical Center, is told in this book. No attempt is made to tell the story of the Washoe Health System. The medical center is one part of the system, and the story of the Washoe Health System requires another study.

Researching and writing this book was a pleasure for me. I have been closely associated with Washoe Medical Center for thirty years in positions ranging from Chief of Staff, to member of the Board, to Director of the Laboratory, and finally, to membership of the senior active staff. My daily relationship stopped in 1992 when I resigned from the Board to teach full-time at the University of Nevada School of Medicine. As I researched the history of Washoe Medical Center, I had a chance to revisit old friends and spend many hours at the hospital going through archives and Board of Trustees' minutes. An important part of this history was interviewing many of the people who helped Mr. Ogren make Washoe Medical Center the great institution that it has become.

I spent many delightful hours in Carroll's Las Vegas home, recording his story and enjoying his Swedish hospitality. These hours brought back my memories of his humor and zest for life. The following stories relate Mr. Ogren's relationship with the Sisters at Saint Mary's Hospital, his keen insight into human nature, and describe the ingredients that make a hospital great. Not to be forgotten are the small incidents that relate to the day-to-day operation of the hospital.

The important ingredients that make a hospital are found in Dr. Harvey Cushing's *Address at the opening ceremonies of the Neurological Institute at the McGill University, September 27, 1934.* Dr. Cushing , the father of neurosurgery, stated:

> So the measure of this fine Institute will not be what one can out-wardly grasp of its carefully planned body, for that is a mere matter off morphology—of its soma. The real measure will lie in its psyche, the intangible spirit of the laborers within; and for this…there is no standard yardstick.

Dr. Ernie Mack more succinctly stated this theme in the dedication of the new Washoe Medical Center tower in 1973, when he said "People make the Hospital." Mr. Ogren reiterated this sentiment in his oral history, and the logo of Washoe Medical Center emphasizes this theme by stating, "It comes from the heart." As we approach the twenty-first century one question remains, will medical care come from the heart or will it be based on the bottom line, the financial summary? If patient care does not come from the heart, physicians and nurses become healthcare providers and not physicians and nurses.

Mr. Ogren put the principle, from the heart, into action. He wasn't content with administrating the hospital, but was personally involved in patient care. On many occasions, he visited patients and saw to their comfort. He knew the names of all the employees at Washoe Medical Center, and made it a rule to visit the departments and personally hand out paychecks.

The people in the hospital form a complex organism: The nurses, the doctors, the administrators, the Board of Trustees, the many other employees, who operate the facility, and philanthropic individuals help the hospital achieve its goals. All are dedicated to humanity. To underline this point, the appendix contains the names of nursing directors, medical staff members, chiefs of staff, board chairmen, auxiliary presidents, and administrators. Also included are department supervisors, who with their employees go about their work in the hospital without recognition, providing the matrix that makes the Hospital function. The list of Mr. Ogren's supervisors compared with the list of the 1998 managers demonstrates the growing complexity of modern hospitals. When Mr. Ogren came to Washoe Medical Center, there were less than a one hundred physicians. Now, there are several hundred specialists and subspecialists.

Acknowledgments are an important part of any book about history because it takes many people to accomplish the task, open the doors to the past, and find the hidden facts. Without them, my job would be more difficult and maybe impossible. I am indebted to the administrative staff at Washoe Medical Center: Adele Showalter, Victoria Francis, Della Hoy, and Bonnie Squires, who, under the direction of CEO Bob Burn, provided access to old hospital records and accommodated me with office space. Numerous other Washoe Medical Center employees and departments were helpful. Medical Staff employees, Jo Ann Luckemeyer, Alsie Dalrymple, Joyce Jones, and Brenda Murphy, under the direction of Karen Massey provided crucial information on medical staff members. Sherry McGee, Washoe Medical Center Librarian, freely opened her files of old newspaper articles and records relating to the early days at the hospital. Jan Johnson provided information on the Women's League and lent me the hospital photographic collection. Steve Young provided the photograph of the present supervisory staff. Patricia Keough was particularly helpful with her knowledge of Washoe Medical Center by providing forgotten details.

Washoe County Librarian, Kim Raines, helped to locate newspaper articles in the reference section of the main library. Pauline Reese and Nancy Frost of the Washoe County Register's Office helped locate County Commissioner's records. Drs. Tom Brady, Rod Sage, Frank E. Roberts, Ernie Mack, Owen Bolstad, Tom Scully, Robert Myles, Leibert Sandars, and John M. Davis read the manuscript and offered suggestions. Dr. Bill Feltner (radiation oncology), Dr. David Johnson (renal dialysis), and Dr. Joao Ascensao (bone marrow transplantation), provided information about their units. Louise Russell, Kim Becker, and Bridget Becker Jensen, and Dr. Ernie Mack allowed me to use their personal photographs. Eva Rosenauer and Jean Myles provided information on the Women's League. My daughter, Kristin Sohn, edited the final manuscript, and Anton Phillip Sohn and Carrie House did the formatting. Dr. Eric A. Sohn also helped with the editing. Teresa Garrison spent many hours typing Mr. Ogren's history and Jeannine Funk helped with preparing the manuscript for publication. Others who provided information are Claudette Edmiston and Drs. William Conran and William Keeler who recalled the early days of the cardiac unit. Mike Hoover retold the early days of the helicopter service. Dr. George Forman helped with information on Dr. George Smith's research laboratory at Washoe Medical Center. Bob Burn read the manuscript, offered suggestions, and provided information about the hospital's more recent history. Mrs. Billie Bennett provided photographs of her great grandfather, Joseph Odett. Lynda Mulvey helped with preparing the manuscript for publication. Bernice Martin Mathews, who has been associated with Washoe Medical Center for over forty-five years, recalled names and helped identify individuals in archival photographs. And Rollan Melton offered valuable suggestions.

Anton Paul Sohn<br>*Reno, Nevada*

# FOREWORD

It is nearly forty-one years since my luggage was unceremoniously deposited on the tarmac on the south end of the Reno Airport, and I was scheduled to meet with Clyde Fox, administrator of Washoe Medical Center, for an interview. It would ultimately decide my acceptance as an administrative resident for one year starting in the summer of 1957. I had completed the first semester of graduate school in hospital administration at Washington University in St. Louis.

Before then, my first Reno trip was a stop-over on my way to Minneapolis, Minnesota. It was 1941; our family was returning to Minneapolis by car from San Francisco where we had visited with my brother, John, who was in the Army Air Corps at Hamilton field near San Francisco. We spent the night in a motel in Sparks where the rail line passed one hundred yards from the back door. More notable was the night long howling of the coyotes which seemed to surround us.

In 1941 Sparks was virtually a wide spot in the road. Before going to the motel, our visit to the gambling Mecca was cut short by the fact that my twin bother and I were only fourteen and could not enter Harold's Club. My perception of Reno then and on my second visit in 1957 was the same. It was a small town.

In 1957 my luggage, consisting of one small suitcase, was dropped on the pavement next to the airplane. The Reno terminal was a small, wood, frame building at the east end of Airport Road. It consisted of a snack counter with about ten stools and four to five square tables that sat four people each. The cab ride to downtown Reno confirmed my suspicion. I was in a small town. I checked into a motel one block northwest of the Riverside Hotel and headed to Virginia Street. The Riverside marquee was ablaze with light announcing Spike Jones and the City Slickers. I had dinner in the Riverside and then watched the show from a stool at the bar looking through a plate glass window. I had little money, didn't gamble, and went to bed early, tired from an exhausting day.

Before bed, I picked up a brochure from a souvenir shop and learned a few facts about the town that I would call home for twenty-five years. I read that Reno had a population of 29,000 and the entire State of Nevada had less than 300,000 souls. Moreover, it stated that Reno was larger than Las Vegas. I had a fitful night's rest, apprehensive about my meeting with Mr. Fox in the morning.

When I approached Washoe Medical Center by cab the following morning, my suspicion was confirmed; the hospital was a meager physical plant. Mr. Fox arrived at 9:00 A.M. He impressed me with his warm welcome and his courtly manner. I was ushered into his office where his secretary, Mrs. Dyer, brought coffee. For the next two hours Mr. Fox recited the history of the hospital, describing in some detail a rather dismal picture of its financial status and a deteriorating physical plant. Yet, glowing with enthusiasm, he had a plan to pursue a positive program of growth to match his outlook for Reno's expansion.

At 11:30 two men in white uniforms with tall chefs' hats appeared with attractive lunch trays. I would later come to recognize these men as Mike Leonardi and Bert Floyd. Mike was to stay with me for my entire career at Washoe Medical Center. He became a trusted employee and Director of Food Services. After lunch we toured the hospital, returning to Fox's office where we talked until 4:00 P.M. when it was time for me to go to the airport. On the way to the airport, we sealed our agreement that I would report for duty on August 1, 1957.

In late July I drove from Minneapolis to Reno where I spent two days looking for an apartment. I settled in a small one room apartment with a pull-down Murphy bed located in a private home on Airport Road. I was under the watchful eye of the owner, Mrs. Philpott, a heavy set lady in her 60s. She left no doubt that she expected me to be a gentleman tenant with no monkey business. She was never disappointed because my hours in the hospital dictated that my primary need from her was a place to sleep.

With a rent of $100 a month combined with a $200 monthly income, there was little money for social activity. I had exhausted my savings in graduate school and had no other source of support. My sole purpose in taking a residency was to gain experience in areas that I had learned from books. My experiences during high school and college, coupled with my tour in a Navy hospital during World War II and Korea, provided me with much practical experience, but no chance to put into practice what I had learned in graduate school. It was a huge benefit knowing hospital medical terminology and the needs of patients. What I needed now was experience in personnel administration and finance.

Mr. Fox involved me in these activities and all facets of medical staff organization. I attended all meetings of the medical staff from the executive committee down through all of the hospital's departments. I also attended all meetings of the Board of Trustees. My desk, during my residency, faced Mrs. Maida Pringle's desk (See chapter on Mrs. Pringle), and I gained an experience too rich to adequately describe. Her office was a hub; it afforded me practical experience in medical staff relations which no text book could provide.

With the expiration of my residency, Mr. Fox asked me to stay on as his assistant at a salary of $600 a month with an office and secretary of my own. I was euphoric over the prospect of staying with Washoe Medical Center and readily accepted his offer. Regretfully our relationship would only last until June 1959 when Fox resigned as a result of a bitter fight with the County Manager, coupled with little support from the County Commissioners.

Their conduct did little to foster my respect for the political process and left me with little hope that any governmental institution could effectively compete with the private sector. With the departure of Clyde Fox, I was made Acting Administrator pending a search for a successor. I thought the Trustee's approach to finding a successor was half hearted. They rejected a magnificent administrator, Ken Knapp from Utah, on the basis that his salary demand was too great. They selected Earl Horton from Sacramento, a fast talker who was willing to work for a minimal salary and too inexperienced to command more than he was offered.

Horton's lack of expertise made me feel uncomfortable from the very beginning. My feelings were shared by leaders within the medical staff and the hospital staff. There seemed to be a pervasive lack of respect at a time when there was a growing need to meet the demands of an explosion in medical technology, the methods of patient care, and the intrusive role of the federal government. Horton's term lasted from September 1959 to September 1963, when he was forced to resign. I was made acting administrator which lasted until April 1964 when my appointment to administrator was made permanent.

After fourteen years as administrator, my career at Washoe Medical Center came to an abrupt end on November 9, 1978, when the Board of Trustees, having failed to get my resignation, fired me because my long battle with alcohol addiction had left them with no other choice. They did what they had to do. As I departed the hospital that night I thought that it would have been far more humane for them to take me to the back parking lot and put a bullet through my heart. Washoe Medical Center had given me a good life; alcohol had consumed it. I spent over a year in a recovery mode with the help of a lot of Alcoholics Anonymous friends and a higher power. During my earlier years of denial, there were many who tried desperately to help me fend off my demon. Among those I tearfully and gratefully acknowledge are: my family, Dan Arrate, Drs. John Chappel, Dick Gilmore, Bill Mack, Kenneth Maclean, Roy Peters, V. A. Salvadorini, Don Soli, Bob Barnet, and Norman Barnstein, Jane Crooks, R. N., Pat Keough, Dawn Clearie, Dwight Nelson, Maida Pringle, R. N., Roy Sampson, Eva Steinbrunner, friends in Alcoholics Anonymous, and a multitude who remembered me in their prayers.

From the summer of 1981 through the autumn of 1992, I worked as assistant general manager of the State Industrial Insurance System and administrator of the Jean Hanna Clark Industrial Rehabilitation Center in Las Vegas.

My career at the Rehabilitation Center ended when I retired after a total of fifty years in government service. I live with one unshakable regret—my termination from Washoe Medical Center, an institution I believed in, and a hospital I loved. In the preparation of this book, I have had the privilege and honor to work with Dr. Anton "Andy" Sohn, a friend for thirty years. Andy has provided the stimulus to bring it all together. His dedication to saving the history of Nevada medicine for all to share has been unselfish. All errors are mine alone. Some can be attributed to the degenerative process of aging. To those

I have left out of the narrative, I apologize. They are not forgotten. I have not set out to deliberately hurt anyone, but history demands honesty and factual detail. finally to all of my trustee friends, the medical staff, and my beloved fellow employees, thanks for the buggy ride, though bumpy at times it got us a great hospital for a deserving public.

Carroll W. Ogren
*Las Vegas, Nevada*

# ABBREVIATIONS

| | |
|---|---|
| ACS | American College of Surgeons |
| BOT | Board of Trustees |
| CAT or CT | Computerized Axial Tomography |
| CC | County Commissioners |
| CICU | Cardiac Intensive Care Unit |
| CON | Certificate of Need |
| EEG | Electroencephalograph |
| EKG | Electrocardiograph |
| EDFP | *Elko Daily Free Press* |
| ER | Emergency Room |
| GNHSA | Greater Nevada Health System Agency |
| HMO | Health Maintenance Organization |
| HSA | Health System Agency |
| ICU | Intensive Care Unit |
| JCAH | Joint Commission on Accreditation of Hospitals |
| JCAHO | Joint Commission on Accreditation of Healthcare Organizations |
| LPN | Licensed Practical Nurse |
| NA | *Nevada Appeal* (Carson City) |
| NIC | Nevada Industrial Commission |

| | |
|---|---|
| NRS | Nevada Revised Statues |
| NICU | Neonatal Intensive Care Unit |
| NSJ | *Nevada State Journal* (Reno) |
| NSMA | Nevada State Medical Association |
| OR | Operating Room |
| REG | *Reno Evening Gazette* |
| REMSA | Regional Emergency Medical Service Agency |
| RG-J | *Reno Gazette-Journal* |
| SFH | Sparks Family Hospital |
| SMH | Saint Mary's Hospital |
| SNL | Sierra Nevada Laboratories |
| SOM | School of Medicine |
| ST | *Sparks Tribune* |
| TB | Tuberculosis |
| TDT | *Tahoe Daily Tribune* |
| UNSOM | University of Nevada School of Medicine |
| VAH | Veterans Administration Hospital |
| WCMS | Washoe County Medical Society |
| WMC | Washoe Medical Center |

PEOPLE
MAKE THE
HOSPITAL

# INTRODUCTION
## The Change in Healthcare

C. W. OGREN

Washoe Medical Center in the summer of 1957 stood poised on the threshold of massive expansion. The next twenty years would witness net income soar from deficit financing to millions of dollars in liquid resources and accounts receivable. It would grow from 190 beds to a physical plant capable of providing 650 beds, from 275 employees to somewhere in the neighborhood of 1,500, from a medical staff of 64 active staff members to over 300. In 1957, there were no CAT scanners, no ICU, no CICU, no renal dialysis unit, no open heart surgery, no nuclear medicine, no super voltage x-ray therapy, not much in the way of laboratory or x-ray equipment, and the emergency department was primitive. In spite of the lack of these future technologies, there was concerned, comforting care. The hospital staff was and still is made of dedicated people; they were truly underpaid relative to their training and ability.

In 1946 the Democratic majority in Congress—with the tax rates still high, but without the costs of war—looked for areas where surplus revenue could be used to enhance the material well-being of the American people. One such area was hospital care. It was noted that there were many communities that had no hospital beds. The Hospital Survey and Construction Act of 1941, better known as the Hill-Burton Program, was passed into law. It became federal policy that every community that wanted a hospital could have a one financed with taxpayer dollars. Washoe Medical Center benefited enormously from the program because Hill-Burton also allowed for expansion of existing facilities. The federal program, successful as it was, didn't solve the financial plight of running a hospital.

In 1957 Washoe Medical Center was in chronic financial difficulty. In community hospitals all over the land, those patients who could afford to pay, paid more than the cost for their care in order that the hospital could provide care to those who could not afford to pay. Washoe County tried to cover the balance of these deficits through self imposed taxes. From 1950–1960 angry creditors could have closed the hospital if they had demanded the payables due to them. The hospital struggled by through a combination of cooperative creditors, Women's League gifts, donations from the Fleischmann Foundation and Tom Dant, and emergency loans from the county. Later, the federal government came to the aid of the hospitals. Tax dollars were poured into building projects. These federal programs would spell the decline and eventual demise of the community hospital.

In 1965 Congress was generous with the nation's tax payers' funds. Title xviii or Medicare and Title xix or Medicaid were incorporated into the Social Security Act of 1965. With these additions, almost everyone but the working poor would have access to hospital diagnosis and treatment. Now, our hospital was truly gaining in financial integrity. The government's formula even allowed generous reimbursement for debt service. Can you imagine today getting federal reimbursement for your home mortgage payments? That's what the program did for hospitals. Even in 1998, most hospitals claim forty percent or more of their revenue from Medicare and Medicaid; other third parties make up the difference. Local tax support is no longer necessary, but federal tax dollars paid to hospitals supporting Medicare are climbing out of sight.

In 1967 the federal expenditures for Medicare and Medicaid were less than $5 billion; in 1976 they were over $33 billion. Congressional experts were getting worried about duplication, under utilization, waste, and bad management. Next, Congress amended the Social Security Act with Section 1122 of Public Law 92–603 in 1971, establishing regional health planning. These regional health planning agencies were almost functional when it was observed that new hospitals were still being built and equipment was still being purchased. It was during this period that hospitals in the United States went on a binge of buying CAT scanners and expensive heart/lung equipment. These binges caused expensive duplication and caused Congress to zero in on hospitals once again.

Congress responded in 1975 with PL–93–641: Regional Health Planning Agencies were dissolved and HSA's were established. Certificates of Need for new facilities and equipment would be required. The Bureau of Health Planning and Resource Development was created to fund and monitor the new program. It was common knowledge that CONs were bought and sold. During the late 1970s, over the objection of Washoe Medical Center and Saint Mary's Hospital, a CON was granted for Sparks Family Hospital even though the GNHSA voted against the hospital. The governor allowed his bureau chief to overrule the HSA and construction proceeded. At this time both Washoe Medical Center and Saint Mary's Hospital had empty beds. Once again, politics overruled good judgment.

For example, from 1946 through 1973, 403,000 short term beds were added to the nation's hospital care inventory. The capacity for hospital care was almost doubled. The decline or even demise of the community medical control seemed certain. The HMOs dominate the patient universe, merger mania has infected the hospital industry attracting for-profit corporations with their greedy appetite for profit, and therefore, perpetrating fraud with unnecessary hospitalization and laboratory work.

If there is a growing malignancy in the health care system today, it can be excised only by the voters. There is little chance of this happening with the likes of a recent Clark County, Nevada, primary voter turnout of fifteen percent. It appears that with growing apathy and the cry for entitlements, deserving or not, we will someday, in the not distant future, see nationalization of our total healthcare industry.

Perhaps there is hope Congress will appoint a commission to correct all the hospital health care ills, and the middle class, in the midst of their reverie, will pay the bill, convinced by Congress and the President that they got a good deal. Who named these programs "entitlement"? Can the public's opinion that everyone is entitled to the most expensive medical care be swayed, and can the government pay the bill?

# FIRST STEPS, 1862–1930

A.P. SOHN

## Smallpox Outbreak[1]

The first county hospital in Washoe County can trace its origin to a County Commissioners meeting on February 17, 1862 in Washoe City. At this meeting, the commissioners reviewed a document stating that "smallpox is prevailing" in the neighboring settlement of Watson's Mill. Watson's Mill was near the center of population in Washoe Valley and fifteen miles from the county seat in Washoe City. Although the county was sparsely settled, the "dreaded plague" threatened everyone. To meet the emergency, the commissioners levied a property tax of twenty cents for each $100 evaluation of property and placed the money in a hospital fund.[2]

Also in 1862, the Nevada Territory Legislature passed a similar measure to ensure that indigent patients received medical care. They levied a tax of four dollars on every man under the age of fifty and gave money to each county to establish a "pest house" for contagious disease.[3] Previously, most people with an illness received care from family members in the home; however, there were many single people—such as miners, domestic helpers, and cowboys—in the new territory who did not live with family. As a consequence, hospitals became a necessity.

Measles, diphtheria, cholera, typhoid fever, tuberculosis, and rheumatic fever were also nineteenth-century menaces in Nevada, and periodically, epidemics of these diseases swept through its mining and ranching communities. As a result of the 1862 legislative action, many counties built a hospital or pest house, and many had a poor farm, both dedicated to the care of medical indigents. On the poor farm, able patients worked to provide services for the hospital, and they received sun and fresh air, an important ingredient of nineteenth-century therapeutics.

Even though a vaccination for smallpox was available, the disease continued unabated in Washoe Valley and forced the commissioners on April 8, 1863, to authorize an ad in the *Washoe Times* requesting proposals to build a hospital. Four months later the request was rescinded, but they took the next step in creating Washoe County's first hospital: they "ordered that a committee be appointed to purchase the printing office building, or some other building, or build a new building, as they may think best for the interest of the County, and the same shall be paid for in script drawn on the hospital fund. Said script to draw interest at the rate of 3% per month until paid, in addition to the 10% per annum legal rate."[4]

## The First Washoe County Hospital

On August 8, 1864 the County Commissioners authorized the purchase of the Printing Office Building in Washoe City from E. B. Wilson for $1,000. This building became the first Washoe County Hospital, and Dr. A. Gideon Weed became the first Washoe County physician. He took charge of the "hospital" facilities receiving a fee of $2.50 per person per day to furnish supplies, medicines, food, fuel, and attendants.[6] This was not an isolated situation; many Nevada counties had a county physician, and in some communities, competition for the position was keen. When selected, the doctor took responsibility for sick indigent patients (outpatient and hospitalized). This practice persisted for one hundred years in Washoe County.

## The Move to Reno

Washoe County used the building in Washoe City as a hospital for three years and then sold it to D. R. Sturr in 1867 for $200. Also in 1867, Dr. Joseph Ellis was appointed county physician and received $1,000 to care for the indigent sick. Sometime between 1867 and 1869, the county moved the hospital (pest house) and farm to Second Street in Reno. Unfortunately, the facility was poorly managed and the living conditions were less than satisfactory. As a result, the Washoe County district attorney investigated the facility for criminal negligence. Three years later the allegations were still unsettled, and the Washoe County Grand Jury recommended that Reno change its way of caring for paupers and the indigent sick. The following year, the *Nevada State Journal* criticized the pest house, calling it "A hogpen—a poor one at that." As criticism increased, citizens became more concerned—it was time to eliminate the problem.

## The Move to Kirman and Mill Streets

On October 4, 1875, the commissioners bought the land and moved the hospital to its present location at Kirman and Mill Streets. This act established the campus that over the years and after several name changes, became Washoe Medical Center. They appropriated money for "a small tract of forty acres on the south side of the river [where Washoe Medical Center now stands], and one mile east of Reno, and 25 inches of water were purchased of A. J. Hatch for $1,000, to be used for a poor-farm. On April 17, 1876, a contract was let to Wm. Thompson for the construction of a county hospital on the poor-farm, to cost $5,253.

To raise construction money for the new hospital, the commissioners authorized bonds in the amount $5,000 to be issued April 10, 1876. The building was finished and is now used by the county, being in charge of a physician [Dr. Henry H. Hogan was the county physician in 1874] appointed by the Board."[7] An 1890 lithograph at the Nevada

Historical Society in Reno shows this to be a two story building. Located just outside of the east boundary of Reno, the property was bounded on the south by Glendale Road (now Mill Street), on the west by Washoe, and on the north by Scott. The Washoe County Treasurer held the bonds and cancelled them with money from taxes; therefore, no interest had to be paid.[8] Patients in the new hospital paid twelve dollars a month for a room, but after analyzing the costs, the commissioners reduced the charge to six dollars. In 1883 the superintendent, who paid for all the patient maintenance aside from the room, received $140 a month. The commissioners appointed him, the matron, and the county physician for two-year terms.[9]

In addition to the county hospital in Reno, it appears that the county had a second county hospital in Wadsworth. On March 11, 1889, the commissioners authorized $250 to purchase a house to be used for another hospital in Wadsworth.

As Reno and Washoe County grew, there were demands for additions and new structures on the hospital grounds. In spite of these demands, there were insufficient funds until 1896, when a one-story building was built for $600. Two years later the commissioners authorized[10] their chairman and the superintendent to erect a wood building, fourteen by thirty feet, sufficient to house six patients. The project's cost were as follows:

| | |
|---|---:|
| Lumber from George Schaffer | 45.00 |
| Lumber, doors, etc. (Reno Mill Lumber Co.) | 39.82 |
| Nails, etc. (Nevada Hardware & Supply Co.) | 25.35 |
| Carpenter work (W. W. Schaff) 2 days @ $3.50 | 7.00 |
| Carpenter work (C. Haily) 1 day @ $3.50 | 3.50 |
| Carpenter work (J. Odett) 5 1/2 days @ $3.50 | 19.25 |
| Carpenter work (E. B. Hancock) 5 1/2 days @ $3.50 | 19.25 |
| Total cost of building | $159.17 |

In 1895 the county commissioners left no question that they were in charge of the hospital. An individual had to have an order signed by a commissioner to be admitted to the hospital. Once in the hospital, the county physician or his assistant, the steward, directed activities. Patients, known as inmates, were assigned work in the hospital or on the farm if the county physician deemed them capable of physical activity. Also, nurses were not necessarily included in the inmate's treatment unless requested by the physician or the steward.

## Beginning the Twentieth Century

The turn of the century ushered in a new era in medicine—the microbial age—as bacteria had been discovered. Also at the turn of the century (1899), the Nevada Legislature required physician licensure. No longer could quacks and unschooled persons hang out their shingles, call themselves doctors, and practice medicine. The legislature took several other measures to protect Nevada citizens: they established a State Public Health Board and a State Hygienic Laboratory. Into this environment entered Dr. Moris Walker.

Dr. Walker lived in Reno for fifty years and wrote in his memoirs about the early days in Reno. He describes the town in 1901 as a raw western town, "a center of considerable importance," with a "main street well-dotted with saloons and gambling houses: no paved streets; the sidewalks were plain board walks when any were present...." Medicine in Reno, also in its infancy, was equally primitive. "Five or six doctors were doing the bulk of the work. All were general practitioners. Reno had no hospitals [open to town doctors]; consequently no surgery other than emergency was attempted." There were three drug stores, but the doctor did most of his own prescriptions. "Most...were of the 'shotgun' variety; if one ingredient did not hit the spot, possibly another ingredient would." The typical doctor's office consisted of bleak rooms with "plain kitchen chairs, a small stand with a few tattered magazines strewn over it, the room heated with a plain box stove."[11] Nevada's doctors slowly improved their image. They kept pace with the rest of the nation by admitting specialists to the medical community and taking measures to improve health care facilities. The county hospital was no exception, and new facilities were needed.

Joseph Odett worked as a carpenter on the 1898 building, and by 1903 when the new Washoe County Public Hospital was under construction, he was the superintendent. During this period, the steward sometimes functioned as the superintendent, in addition to being the cook, pharmacist, and handyman. Odett was originally named the steward by the Washoe County Commissioners, but by the time the following article was written, he was the superintendent. This article in the Reno Evening Gazette leaves no doubt that even though Joseph Odett was the superintendent, his wife, Linda Alice, was the "controlling influence" and enforced the rules:

> The other day a Gazette reporter strayed out to the county hospital where scores of people who are old and ailing, destitute and friendless, are enjoying the comforts such as could be supplied in the home.
>
> It was noticeable that there was no damask on the table, no costly coverlets on the beds, no luxuries such as are deemed necessary in these latter sybaritic days, but the corners were curved on rough comforts and the rugged edges on stern necessities were removed.
>
> "Joe" O'Dette, the superintendent of the institution, who retires late, sleeps with one eye open, arises early and bestirs himself all day, declined to claim any personal worth in the order of things. "'Ma' is the controlling influence here," he said.
>
> Jacob Oxholm, the steward and nurse, who is always on duty, modestly replied to a bit of congratulations: "You must thank Mrs. O'Dette for most of the care and comfort which is given the old boys and the people who are sick and injured. Mr. O'Dette is a most capable man, but she is the mother of the hospital.
>
> The writer may speak from his own knowledge. Once he was injured and contrary to the wishes of friends and relatives, he selected the county infirmary for a resting place while bones mended.
>
> Mrs. O'Dette came to him with a little salver, placed it upon a table by his bed and said: "Young man, rule 12 prescribes that there shall be no smoking in the wards."
>
> "Then why did you bring me this tray?"
>
> "That is for your cigarette ashes."
>
> Mother O'Dette's hair is now as white as the snow on the crown of Mount Rose. Her prospective years are not so many as they were once upon this earth. It is with less zest and vim that she participates in the work of the Women's Relief Corps for she is the wife of a soldier, but her smile is still as cheery for the old boys in the hospital, her hand just as soothing on their brows, her heart just as throbbing for humanity as it was when "Joe" marched away to the war and she waited through the weary years.[12]

When the Washoe County Public Hospital construction was started in November 1903, the Washoe County Bank financed the next addition by issuing ten $1,000 bonds at 2 1/2 percent interest. The architect drew plans for a new building, not to exceed a cost of $22,000, and "the Nevada Hardware and Supply Company put in the New County Hospital, a heating plant for hot water…"[13] After construction of this building, the 1876 building became known as the Old County Hospital, and the two hospitals were separated by the Scott Ditch.

When the Hospital was completed, its doctors also needed new surgical instruments.; Drs. Samuel C. Gibson and George Thoma were permitted to spend ninety-one dollars for surgical instruments and tape.[14] After completion in 1904, the county insured the building for $18,000. In 1905 a heating plant was installed by Savage and Sons for $100; then, no additional expansion of the Hospital was necessary for several years. In his "History of Washoe Medical Center," Carroll Ogren notes: "An aerial photograph (on display in the halls of the local Gazette-Journal Building) taken in 1906 clearly show the hospital as the most prominent landmark in southeast Reno. Two stories constructed of fine brick, complete with porches and walks, the building is surrounded by the fields and pastures of the poor farm and much other open meadow, as Mill Street was scarcely settled at the time."[15]

## Multiple Reno Hospitals

In a short time the new county hospital was one of several hospitals (Nurses', Adventist, People's, Red Cross, Roosevelt, and Saint George) in the Reno area.[16] Besides these small, privately owned hospitals, Saint Mary's Hospital came into existence in 1908. Since 1897 the Sisters of Saint Dominic owned and operated Saint Mary's Convent and School at the corner of Chestnut and Walnut Street, west of downtown Reno. They converted the building into the Sister's Hospital which became Saint Mary's Hospital.

By 1904 the population of Washoe County was approximately 8,000, and more doctors were moving in to set up practice.[17] In 1913 Reno had three principle hospitals and was a regional referral center for northern Nevada communities. A historian states: "Here the most modern treatment, medical as well as surgical, is to be had. The Reno hospitals are prepared to furnish operating rooms where thorough "aseptic" conditions may be secured. They have trained nurses...to enable the surgeon to perform the most difficult operations....[It included an] x-ray apparatus, and a thoroughly competent bacteriologist who not only makes examinations but prepares autogenous bacterins for the most modern and successful treatment of infections and contagious diseases....The hospitals are the County, Saint George and Saint Mary's. Hence, Reno has become the Mecca of the afflicted to which are turning not only those of Nevada, but our neighboring states Utah, Oregon and nearby sections of California."[18]

Indeed, this is a very optimistic statement; there are still many "infections and contagious diseases" that are not treated successfully. As new and powerful antibiotics are discovered to treat bacterial illnesses, organisms mutate and render antibiotics ineffective. Ironically, the above statement "successful treatment..." predated by five years the devastation of the 1918 influenza pandemic, by over thirty years the microscopic identification of viruses, and by almost eighty years the identification of the virus that caused the 1918 flu.

## The Influenza Pandemic

The worst killer epidemic since the Black Death (plague) in fourteenth-century Europe swept across the world at the end of the Great War and killed approximately 25 million people—more than one percent of the world's population. The pandemic of 1918 or worldwide epidemic of influenza—also known as flu, three day fever, or grippe—was probably the most explosive and devastating disease of the twentieth century. The war, with its massing and movement of people in unsanitary conditions, along with its gathering of soldiers in crowded encampments led to an increase in all communicable diseases, but in particular the spread of influenza.

HIV might ultimately be of a larger magnitude, but it has not circled the globe and killed as many so quickly as the 1918 flu virus. The two diseases have several similarities: both are caused by viruses, and both target young adults, probably because older individuals had immunity to the influenza virus while HIV infection targets the life style of young adults. Flu was also a threat to the very old .

Because of the sudden onset of flu symptoms and the virulence of the unknown organism, many experts in 1918 suggested a combined bacterial etiology—viruses had not been discovered. Even if the cause of the highly contagious malady had been established, the treatment and preventative measures would not have changed, thus the outcome most likely would have been the same.

Influenza swept the world in three waves. The "first wave" started in early March and spread through the military camps, factories, and diverse institutions such as San Quentin Prison. It began March 4, 1918, at Camp Funston, Kansas, and by the end of the month, 233 cases flooded the camp hospital and forty-eight died from the dreaded bacterial pneumonia that complicated the flu.[19] From there, the soldiers spread the flu to France, but no one really knew where it came from—did it start in China, Europe, Africa, or America?

The "second—more deadly—wave" began late August in France and was spread by ocean shipping and returning servicemen to all continents, and the third wave peaked several months later. The total number of deaths from flu will never be known, but it has been calculated that as many as 550,000 people in the United States—more than four times our military losses in World War I—succumbed to the flu and its complications.

The deadly fall wave was known as the "Spanish Flu" or the "Spanish Lady" because the knowledge and severity of the disease was uncensored in Spain and, therefore, more publicized than in war-torn, northern European countries. Also the disease was especially devastating in Spain, and it was popular to blame this plague on the Spanish.

What were the effects of the flu on Nevada citizens? Newspaper articles from Fallon (*Fallon Eagle*), Las Vegas (*The Age*), Reno (*Evening Gazette* and *Nevada State Journal*), Sparks (*Tribune*), Carson City (*Daily Appeal*) and the University of Nevada (*Sagebrush*) demonstrate the impact on Nevada.

In Fallon "about a dozen cases" were documented in the news on October 5, 1918, and on October 19, Hall Sumner, age thirty-seven, was the first victim to succumb to the virus. By the end of the month, the citizens had another "important" concern: prohibition and the menace of alcohol—"Saloons a menace to society and aid to the Kaiser…a parasite on the industry of others." In December preventative measures such as facemasks became mandatory in schools, and public gatherings were banned. Face masks were probably somewhat effective because they decreased the spread of air-borne organisms. By December 14, when servicemen were returning home, the epidemic was waning.

Las Vegas was harder hit and panic ensued. Although the flu arrived in mid–September, by mid–October there were 140 cases with five new cases a day. The symptoms were headache, backache, fever, and bronchitis. Sometimes, bacterial pneumonia was a complication of the respiratory viral infection, and it was a dreaded complication without effective treatment—antibiotics had not been discovered. As the number of cases increased, doctors and nurses were overworked, hospitals were full, caskets were in short supply, and the local undertaker, C. B. Faust, was in bed with the flu. By the end of November, new cases were ten per day and schools were closed. Public health officials recommended flu masks of "four to six layers of fine mesh gauze" to control the spread. By December 14, when the "Dry Law" was scheduled to become effective—it was delayed by a court challenge—approximately fifty people had died of flu in Las Vegas.

Before the local outbreak in Reno, University of Nevada officials on October 15 posted a quarantine. This did not stop the inevitable spread; by the end of the month there were forty-five cases of flu and one death—Private Wilbourn Stock's. The second death was Coach Ray Whisman, and the "girls of Manzanita [Hall]" made flu masks. By November 12, the situation had quieted down enough for military companies—wearing flu masks— to commemorate the end of the war, and parade down Virginia Street.

Off campus, in the Reno–Sparks area, the first case was reported on October 12, and a flag parade was called off. It was reported that eating "plenty of raw onions and food seasoned with red peppers" was a good prevention. This was excellent advice because people kept their distance from people with onion breath, reducing the spread of the virus. Within one week "everything" was closed except saloons; even churches were not exempt, and ministers were advised to hold a "sermonless Sunday" on October 14. On the next Sunday, ministers were advised to use "unpreached sermons." However, nurses could not take the day off; at the Washoe County Hospital they were stressed and overworked, and they wanted more money for their "increased risk." One could not find fault with their demands because these very factors caused exhaustion and susceptibility to the infection they were treating. Furthermore, nurses provided "tender loving care" and hope, which maybe was the most important ingredient in treatment of the flu.

*The Sparks Tribune* reported at least sixteen deaths in Sparks. None of the remedies worked, but there were many suggestions for prevention—sagebrush tea, an old Indian remedy which "breaks fever in hours," was recommended to fight the grippe.

The people of Carson City also got advice on how to fight the new enemy. *The Carson City Daily Appeal* reported that calomel, citrate of caffeine…along with well–lighted and ventilated rooms with wide–open windows might be an effective way to reduce the spread.[20] Dr. William H. Hood of the State Board of Health promised help at the state level, if needed. Help was needed, but unfortunately, nobody knew how to provide effective help other than advice.

Confusion was the order of the day during the epidemic. The flu pandemic of 1918 was remembered in this country more than the horror of World War I. The concern of Nevadans in 1918 can be understood when the following facts are considered: (1) the number of deaths worldwide (25 million) due to influenza was more than three times the war losses (7 million), (2) approximately twenty-five percent of Nevada's citizens were ill with the flu—and faced death, and (3) the cause of the disease was unknown.

Recently, an H1N1 virus related to Swine Iowa 30 virus was isolated in autopsy material taken in 1918, and it is thought to be the cause of the epidemic that was a national crises. Even though the flu epidemic was eighty years ago, and few remember its consequences, the present epidemic of HIV is causing a similar crisis and producing a search for a cure.[21]

## A North Wing

A North Wing, containing an isolation and general ward, was added in 1921 to the 1904 building.[22] George W. Mapes bought the bonds which financed the North Wing, for $35,000 with 6% interest. When they matured at twenty years, the interest amounted to more than $7,000. After the North Wing was completed, other improvements were made: "Changes for better supervision and care of patients were made gradually. The operating room was painted and cleaned and was opened to all physicians and surgeons of Washoe County. All attendants had to be graduated and trained nurses. An advisory board of three physicians to serve without pay was created. New rules were formulated. The county physician was paid $200 a month and given an assistant at a salary of $125 per month."[23] In 1923 the operating room was opened, for the first time, to all physicians and surgeons in Washoe County.

# COMING OF AGE, 1930-1957

A.P. SOHN

## Reorganization Creates Washoe General Hospital

In 1929 the Nevada Legislature passed a law allowing the establishment of a county hospital directed by a board of trustees in any
county where the population exceeded 10,000; to be put into effect,
thirty percent of the taxpayers in that county had to agree to the establishment of a county hospital.[24]

On November 4, 1930 in Washoe County, the vote on this issue
carried by a two to one majority. Following the provisions of the law,
County Commissioners J. C. Peckham, John C. Durham, and William
Kelly Klaus appointed Dr. LaRue Robinson, Mrs. Frank Ellis
Humphrey, Mr. G. W. Nottingham, Mr. William McKnight, and Mr.
E. C. Mulcahy to the Board of Trustees of the Washoe County Pub-
lic Hospital.[25] The Board then hired Mr. John J. Kenney as the first
superintendent.

This decisive action by the Legislature and voters of Nevada ensured the success, growth, and management of the hospital for the next fifty years, and it moved the hospital from serving indigents to also providing for private paying patients. Ogren writes: "The first year of the Board of Trustees was certainly a busy one, marked as it was by much controversy concerning the jurisdiction of the Board and correct manner for financing the authorized building expansion." An initial action of the Board was the notification that the new hospital complex was to be known as the "Washoe General Hospital" rather than the "Washoe County Public Hospital."

When the 1933–34 hospital was added on to the 1904 building, the complex known as the Washoe General Hospital would serve the paying public, and be open to private doctors in the community, while the Old Hospital (the 1876 Washoe County Hospital) would house indigent patients, who would be cared for by the county physician. The same administrative team managed both hospitals. Ogren describes the controversy surrounding the construction of the new building:

> When the contract for the new building was awarded to J. C. Dillard of Reno for his bid of $198,997.00 for the complete "Y" structure (the present South Wing), many repercussions were felt. Inasmuch as this was not the lowest bid received, several citizens obtained a restraining order upon the Board, causing all action to be halted. This action also caused one of the rejected bidders to institute a suit against the Board. At the same time an opinion was passed down by the District Attorney that the Board could not legally enter into an obligation greater than the amount of the funds immediately in sight; this being approximately $100,000 (comprised of the surplus then in the hospital fund and the proceeds of the eighty-three $1,000 bonds sold to the First National Bank, interest at 5%, to mature serially between 1935 and 1941; said bonds authorized by the election of 1930, with retirement funds to be provided by a 2 mill/$1.00 tax expressly for the establishment and maintenance of the county public hospital).
>
> Coincidental to these discussions was the fact that the County Indigent Fund became depleted, and the Commissioners attempted to require the Board to maintain the existing hospital (West and North Wings) from the above mentioned 20¢/$100 property tax.

None of these questions were actually resolved during the first year (1931), while the Board was actually in direct control of the hospital and its policies. The financial pictures issued after the first year demonstrated that the utilization of the hospital facilities continued to increase, yet, the operation under the leadership of the Board netted a savings of between $8,000 and $10,000 (depending on which non-comparable expenses are allowed), over the operation the previous year under the auspices of the Commissioners.[26]

## The Great Depression

The economic situation during the Great Depression put added financial pressure on the Washoe General Hospital; it provided hospital care for an increasing number of indigent patients. A 1931 article by George I. James in the *Journal Weekly* stated, "Depression Makes Washoe Co. Hospital an immediate necessity." The hospital's daily rate for a patient was four dollars per day, but few couldn't pay even a portion of that. The daily average hospital census was 111 patients, yet less than seven patients made some payment. The hospital's ledger revealed that the daily cost per patient for the year was $1.35, down from $2.04 the previous year. Also according to the *Journal Weekly* article, the taxpayers' cost for ten months of operating the hospital was $36,292, during which time receipts were $10,083.19 while the total paid out was $46,376.16.

Ogren describes the changes made to the DA's ruling: "At the beginning of 1932, the following three things happened: (1) the County Commissioners found they could not legally require the Board to run the hospital from the proceeds of their special levy, and it therefore became necessary to seek an Emergency Loan in the face of the empty County Indigent Fund; (2) Mr. J. C. Dillard, as a result of the court hearing about the contract he held, agreed to withdraw his acceptance of the same so that bids might again be sought, and; (3) the contract for a changed plan that was to include only two of the proposed wings to cost less than $100,000, in line with the requirements of the District Attorney, was let to Mr. William H. Kennedy for $93,165."[27]

Following the Trustees' instructions, F. J. DeLonchant, the famous classical architect who designed many buildings in early Reno, including the Courthouse, designed the new Washoe County General Hospital (the present South Wing), and William H. Kennedy finished the building, but the Board approval to add a maternity ward had to be rescinded in 1933 because of insufficient funds.

Besides economic hard times, 1932 was not a good year for the recently organized hospital. Mrs. I. McKay of Goldfield made a complaint against the hospital and Dr. Earl Creveling, and when the Board found that it was unwarranted, she filed the first known suit against the hospital demanding $25,000 for eye problems she sustained as a patient.[28] Also, the grand jury investigated a complaint against the administration, and on July 9 their report highly commended the management of Mr. Kenney. Unfortunately, new services could not be added because there was no money. In 1933, the financial picture improved, and the hospital began the process of organizing the medical staff and offering needed services.

A new administrator was necessary to carry out these programs and the Board's goals because they discharged the first superintendent, Mr. Kenney, for undisclosed "disloyalty" to the Board. They selected Dr. Alfred W. MacPherson as a replacement. MacPherson was a bargain; he provided anesthesia, ran the indigent clinic, directed the pharmacy, and was the hospital radiologist.[29]

On March 26, 1934, the Board and MacPherson opened a new surgery suite, which served both hospitals. During the first six months, approximately thirty-one percent of the 403 operative cases were tonsillectomies, twenty-five percent were appendectomies, sixteen percent were dilation and curettages (scraping the uterus), and three percent were hysterectomies. The remaining procedures as hernia repairs, gall bladder resections, ruptured ulcers, cataracts, and reduction of fractures accounted for less than two percent each.[30] Dr. MacPherson was the superintendent for less than two years when he resigned, and Mr. Kenney was waiting in the wings. He patched up his differences with the Board, and they forgave his "disloyalty" by appointing him Business Manager and, subsequently, Superintendent.

To organize the New Hospital's medical staff, the Board of Trustees turned to the Washoe County Medical Society; its members developed the first bylaws, rules, and regulations for the hospital. Recognizing the importance of nursing and a larger nursing staff, in 1934 the Board upgraded the job of head nurse to superintendent of nurses.

They hired Miss Teresa Hall of San Francisco for the job. Other new developments included a new clinic in the basement that was recommended by Dr. Thomas Bath, and the medical staff recommended pathology and radiology services for the hospital.[31]

By September 1934, funds were sufficient to allow the Board to act on the medical staff's recommendation, and they hired Dr. Alice Thompson, the first woman physician on the hospital staff and its first full-time pathologist. Dr. Lawrence Parsons also was hired as a consulting pathologist; however, the hospital did not have funds for a clinical laboratory.[32] They sent all bacteriology and chemistry testing to the State Hygienic Laboratory, now the State Public Health Laboratory directed by the University of Nevada School of Medicine.

The following January, the New Hospital had fifty-six employees, including Business Manager Mr. Kenney, Head Nurse Mrs. Wilkinson, Resident Physician Dr. MacPherson, two pathologists, and twenty-five nurses. And the Old Hospital had thirty-eight employees, including Mr. Kenney, Mrs. Wilkinson, Dr. MacPherson, the two pathologists, and eleven nurses.[33] The two hospitals continued to operate separately until at least 1942, and their financial outlook steadily and slowly improved. After the United States entered World War II, the economy was booming. Now, the Trustees could recognize the medical staff's "splendid cooperation during our financial distress," and authorize free hospitalization benefits for medical staff and hospital employees. This action underlined the frustrations of the medical staff when insufficient funds delayed the buying of medical supplies, replacing of worn-out instruments, and purchasing of necessities needed to provide quality patient care.

## World War II

Expansion of the hospital and services for the community continued into the war years. In 1941 the Board of Trustees made two requests for bonds; however, the district attorney ruled that the requests had to go to the voters, and the matter was dropped. Instead the Board obtained an emergency loan of $50,000 from Washoe County to finish Wing "B." The financial condition of the hospital was good, and the loan was quickly paid off. New services were added, including a dental clinic and a children's orthopedic clinic.

In addition to supplying new services and managing the hospital farm, many of the hospital's efforts were directed toward the war. These efforts increased significantly when, on December 7, 1941, the Japanese bombed Pearl Harbor and drew the United States into the war. Now, the war was close to home—the Pacific Coast was threatened. Four days later the Board ordered blackouts in the hospital. The next action emphasized the evolution of Washoe Medical Center from a home and healthcare facility for indigents, who had to work on the adjacent farm to produce food for the hospital inmates, to a modern hospital. The hospital decided to turn the hogs on the hospital farm into pork; this not only increased revenue, but it delayed wartime meat shortages. The cattle raising and milking operation continued to be an important operation. As the war expanded, shortages of gasoline, food, and clothing grew.

Nevertheless, the most serious shortage in the hospital involved personnel who provided patient care. There was a nationwide call to arms, and the nursing profession responded; subsequently, an acute nursing shortage developed. Administrator D. D. Stingley informed the Board of his efforts to recruit and keep nurses: he consulted other hospitals on the West Coast as to how they managed the crisis, and he offered special incentives of laundry services, free meals, and automatic raises up to fifteen percent, but the drain continued. In the same vein, many doctors enlisted in the military service, while others were drafted.

Perhaps the most surprising contribution of Washoe Medical Center to the war effort is buried in board minutes from September 1942. Today, many think that recycling is a recent concept resulting from the growing interest in the environment. Not so—in World War II, most neighborhood front curbs, from large cities to small towns such as Reno, were transformed into recycling collection points. Citizens provided everything from chewing gum tin foil to metal grave markers for defense plants to make into ammunition. In some parts of the country, prized Civil War cannons were contributed as scrap metal to the war effort.[34] All scrap metal was needed by the wartime industry. On September 10, 1942, the Board responded and contributed metal, including a brass dedication plaque at the main entrance, which most likely was made into bullets.

Moreover, bandages and blood components were needed. A call

went out for blood donors to contribute plasma and blood for wounded servicemen. The hospital created a blood bank in June 1943 and prepared for mass civilian causalities in case a sneak enemy attack occurred. Government agencies—the U.S. Army, U.S. Public Health Service and the Surgeon General—appealed to the hospital for help, if dependents of military personnel or injured trainees from local operations needed hospitalization.

By 1945 with the successful invasion of Europe and the end of the war drawing near, the Board ordered building plans for a new addition to be drawn by a San Francisco architect, Douglas Dacre Stone, a recognized leader in the field of hospital architecture. Also in 1945 one of Washoe Medical Center's first benefactors, C. V. Isbell, stepped forward and paved the hospital parking lot in a gesture of community spirit. And on October 26, Mrs. Maida J. Pringle was appointed supervisor of nursing, her first significant leadership role in the hospital.

Ogren notes that preparations for the war were still in place when he arrived:

> A relic of war hysteria fearing Japanese bombing was still in evidence in 1957. During the early stage of the World War II, the County Commissioners authorized the building of a three story aircraft observation tower on Second Street. Today, if one drew a line due east from the East Wing of the hospital to Second Street, one would hit the spot where the tower stood. It was sturdily built, supported by four wooden legs, topped by an enclosed cabin, surrounded by glass, and capable of holding two people. The cabin was accessible by a ladder which ran up the middle of the structure. During the war, volunteers occupied the cabin, and they could communicate by telephone with government agencies. On the tower was a huge warning siren which was used for many years after 1957 to signal 12 noon.

## Post World War II

After the war, employee demands for increased pay and benefits became an issue, and meetings occurred between the Board of Trustees and nurses. Also the laundry workers and the kitchen workers confronted the Board; feeling they needed protection from the hospital management, they met with union representatives. Even so, unionization of the hospital never occurred because the administrator and the Board responded to the workers' demands. For example, between 1942 and 1947, the number of employees increased from 208 to 318, a 53 percent increase, while salaries rose 179 percent.

While salaries rose precipitously, a steady, slow increase in patient beds and services placed stress on the existing facilities. The lengthy process of obtaining funds and approval for the building that was started in 1945 continued for several years. Mr. Henry Wallace, the superintendent, resigned because he was unhappy with the building process, but he also expressed displeasure with the medical staff and their chronic resistance to completing patient charts in a timely fashion. Wallace's replacement was a retired military veteran, Vlad Ratay. Mr. Ogren relates, "One interesting anecdote that Maida Pringle recited was that Vlad went to the pharmacy each week, and the pharmacist provided him with a quart of tax free alcohol—bourbon. It was an accepted routine."

To provide temporary relief from crowding in the hospital, in 1947 twelve Quonset huts were bought for $275 each from the Navy. The huts housed employees and provided needed patient wards, such as a pediatric ward and a ward for patients with rheumatic heart disease. In 1949, the hospital acquired from the Public Housing Administration two dormitory buildings which had previously been used by Southern Pacific Railroad employees when rooming quarters were not available in the community. Bob Beeks moved and relocated the structures to the northwest corner of the hospital grounds, next to the 1906 Administration Building. These buildings became the Redwood Pavilion. Although war surplus buildings and supplies were available at bargain prices, the financial condition of the hospital did not improve. In fact, Washoe County placed an even greater burden on the hospital.

The building program that was started during the waning days of World War II was now in full swing. The structure that cost $400,000 held the power house, boiler room, laundry, and dining room. Room was also left for future expansion. This was the first construction project since 1932. Even though services to the community were increased over 70% during this period of time, no new beds were added.

Between 1948 and 1949, the County Commissioners decreased the financial support to the hospital by $160,000 when they decreased the *Ad Valorem* tax from fifty-five cents to thirty-five cents per one hundred dollars.[35] The bill for hospital services was averaging $30,000 a month and the county didn't have the money to pay for its indigent patients. As a result of the gloomy financial outlook, Superintendent Ratay wrote his fatal report to the Board on April 14, 1949, recommending that the hospital terminate operations on September 30. The Board disagreed and terminated Mr. Ratay.

After Ratay left, the Board appointed Mrs. M. J. Pringle—who took most of the responsibilities—and Mr. H. Chester English, the hospital pharmacist, to share management of the hospital while a new superintendent was sought. Shortly after this decision, the top applicant, Mr. Clyde Fox, was invited to the hospital for an interview. Mr. Ogren recalls: "Mrs. Pringle accompanied Mr. Fox and a member of the Board on a tour of the hospital. During the tour, Mrs. Pringle was behind the board member who was facing Mr. Fox when he asked the board member if the hospital was in fair shape financially. The Board member replied, 'Yes, we don't foresee any real problems in that area.' Mrs. Pringle wildly waved her hands and shook her head, 'No.' Fox always got a kick out of reciting that story."

## Washoe Medical Center

Clyde Fox, another World War II veteran, was hired as superintendent in late June 1949 with the financial help of Harold Smith, Sr. owner of Harold's Club. Dr. E. W. Mack recalls that the hospital didn't have money to pay all of Mr. Fox's salary, and Mr. Smith personally paid part of the salary out of his pocket. One of Fox's first actions was to recommend that the Board change the name of the hospital to Washoe Medical Center.

On March 31, 1950 the Board requested an emergency loan of $100,000 to meet operating expenses. Six weeks later, the Women's Auxiliary was organized to help generate publicity and additional funds for the hospital; it immediately organized several events—a style show, a concession at the Reno Rodeo, and a banquet—to alleviate the financial crunch. The hospital was now looking to the community and philanthropists for help in balancing the budget and acquiring new equipment needed to move the hospital into the technology age.

Under Mr. Fox's guidance, the hospital acquired a more professional and positive outlook, but financial insecurity still smoldered in the background. Several long-lasting professional relationships were established as a result of Mr. Fox's leadership and vision: Dr. Lawrence A. Russell was appointed head of the indigent clinic; Dr. Vasco A. Salvadorini became the full-time hospital pathologist after a several year interval when the hospital had only part-time coverage; Dr. Ernest W. Mack received a contract to provide electroencephalography, and Dr. Leibert J. Sandars established a state-of-the-art radiology department.[36] All of these professionals provided leadership in their departments that would last over thirty years.

Unfortunately, these positive steps did not improve Washoe County's ability to pay for its indigents, and as the employees did not sympathize with the hospital's plight, they demanded more pay. In 1950, all employees got two free meals a day in addition to their wages. Fox and the Board realized that the employees would rather have the money in their pockets, and they substituted twenty dollars for the monthly meals, but there wasn't enough money to replace a six-day work week with a five-day work week. Fox also opened a cafe in the hospital for employees and visitors.

## Tuberculosis and Physical Therapy

After World War II great strides were made in the treatment of tuberculosis (TB). One of the Board's first actions at the end of the war was to get bids on a new TB and isolation ward. Although TB was on the wane, it was necessary to provide coordinated treatment and hospitalization for active cases of TB. In 1951, the Board agreed with the medical staff's recommendation that Dr. C. Robert Locke manage all TB patients in the hospital. Two years later, the TB ward was moved into two Quonset huts, and by 1957, the unit was moved into the hospital. Carroll Ogren notes:

> One other area where I rotated during my residency at Washoe Medical Center was the TB ward. It contained twenty beds for long

term TB patients, and was on Second East. When I studied the situation, I found the average length of stay was something like three years. The TB ward had both men and women, and it was a constant source of concern to us. There was a problem with alcohol, and coupled with that came sexual rendezvous.

We knew alcohol was being delivered via the backstairs by Reno cab drivers. We tried to stop it but the problem continued until the number of patients decreased. Antibiotics and improved treatment for TB allowed us to discharge patients earlier and eliminated the need for a separate ward. Therefore, after two or three years this problem went away.

In addition to eliminating the organism that causes TB, an important part of therapy is rehabilitation, including occupational and physical therapy. In 1951 a physical therapy department was established by the Board of Trustees. Other new services were developed. Plans were made to form a school of practical nursing; and a blood bank was established in a Quonset hut near the emergency room—the only emergency services in northern Nevada. As services to the community were expanded, building expansion was needed. Furthermore, the grand jury ruled that the Redwood Pavilion was inadequate. Subsequently, a bond issue was passed by the voters and plans were drawn to correct building deficiencies.

Not to be forgotten was the hospital's relationship with Saint Mary's Hospital. In 1950 the Board agreed with the Sisters to have the same room rates, and for the next two decades, the hospitals agreed to the same periodic increases. This cordial relationship lasted into the 1970s when Saint Mary's hired their first professional administrator and competition stiffened. As a consequence over the next twenty years, the hospitals competed for control of obstetrics, neonatal intensive care, open heart surgery, trauma, helicopter service, and other services that could establish dominance in the high technology age.

One new service that could not be predicted when Fox came on the scene in 1949 was the polio ward, necessitated by the polio epidemic that started in 1952 and peaked in 1953. Washoe Medical Center became the major polio treatment center in the state, and the polio ward filled to capacity.

## A Leader in the War Against Polio

Prior to the development of the polio vaccine by Jonas E. Salk in 1954, poliomyelitis was a dreaded disease of children. Patients were usually stricken between the ages of four and fifteen, and a few were under one. Worldwide, polio occurred in epidemic proportions, primarily during the summer. Reno was no exception, and during November 1952, twenty-five cases were brought to Washoe Medical Center. During all of 1952, 138 cases were treated at Washoe Medical Center, and eighteen cases were treated by other hospitals in the state. These 156 patients made Nevada the center of the worst epidemic of polio in the country. As a result, polio outnumbered all other reportable infectious diseases in the state.

During the height of the Nevada epidemic, extraordinary efforts were made to ascertain the source of the virus. Dr. Edward C. Rosenow, "the world's leading bacteriologist," erected a cylinder containing paraffin-coated pebbles on the top of the Mapes Hotel, the highest building in Reno, to determine if germs were in the air. This was a throwback to the nineteenth century when foul air or miasmas were thought to be the cause of disease. Dr. Resenow did not demonstrate disease in the air over Reno.

Realizing the magnitude of the epidemic, local communities came together to provide support and financial help. The National Foundation for Infantile Paralysis provided aid for patients, but the demand was too great and money was late coming. During this time of need, organizations and neighboring communities reached out to the hospital: the Veterans of Foreign Wars Post from Portola, California, donated a portable iron lung, the management and employees of Harold's Club donated $4,500 to buy an iron lung for hospitalized patients; and the local medical community formed a team to raise money and provide medical care.

The team was formed as the result of two near fatalities from bulbar spinal poliomyelitis, which paralyzes the breathing center. Members of the Washoe County Medical Society organized a representative team of hospitals, nurses, neurosurgeons, pediatricians, internists, general surgeons, orthopedists, otorhinolaryngologists, and anesthesiologists to manage future cases and intensify the war against paralytic polio. The Washoe County program became a nationwide model;

it included training, fund–raising, transport, ventilation, respiratory assistance—tracheostomy when necessary—and supportive care. The program is described by Dr. William A. O'Brien, III and his associates, Arthur E. Scott, Robert C. Crosby, and William E. Simpson in a book, *Diagnosis and Treatment of the Acute Phase of Poliomyelitis and its Complications.*[37]

To initiate the program, Washoe County Medical Society established a "Polio Equipment Fund," and a panel of society members appeared before service clubs requesting monetary support. Civic leaders were shown the status of care on the wards of Washoe Medical Center, where a shortage of equipment was demonstrated. Money also was needed to buy equipment for transporting paralyzed patients. Funds were quickly raised. The transport team—consisting of an otorhinolaryngologist, anesthesiologist, and hospital engineer—brought forty–one patients from as far as 300 miles to Washoe Medical Center. The ages of the patients ranged from seven weeks (David Whitlock from Yerington, who was cured) to fifty-nine years, and there were no complications during the transport. In fact, lives were saved by the earlier respiratory assistance that the team provided.

Transporation of patients was just the first step in treatment. Dr. Fred Elliott was the primary admitting officer for polio patients to Washoe Medical Center, and as a consequence of his dedication to his polio patients, he was stricken with paralytic polio. He practiced in Reno for over forty years with a small amount of residual paralysis.

After admission of the patients to the hospital, members of the team followed them and treated complications. The treatment often involved long weeks and months in an iron lung, followed by physical rehabilitation.

The success of the program was demonstrated by statistics from the first two years. During that period, 137 patients with polio were admitted to Washoe Medical Center, and forty required a respirator. During the first year, the mortality rate was 30%, and the second year it dropped to 17.3%.

The success of the polio team, when responding to a medical emergency, was due to the community, Washoe Medical Center, Washoe County Medical Society, and health care professionals, working together to finance and fight a nearly-hopeless medical entity—respiratory paralysis due to polio.[38]

Washoe Medical Center's successful treatment of polio was the defining moment for the hospital; it demonstrated that the hospital had the resources and talent to assume the leadership of Nevada hospitals. This talent, coupled with the vision of Administrator Clyde Fox, propelled Washoe Medical Center to the front, and it became a leader of Nevada hospitals. The success of treating polio launched the modern era of medical treatment in the Reno-Sparks area; we are all its legatees, but there were still obstacles to overcome.

## After Polio

By 1954 a new building was sixty percent complete, and discussions centered on establishing a school of practical nursing. The Nevada State Board of Vocational Education offered help, and the Reno High School Adult Education Division was interested in a cooperative effort. In 1957, the school became a reality. The hospital was growing: over eighty doctors were on the staff, and 190 beds were available for patient use; however, the hospital still depended on the county for one third of its budget, and this was not enough. The hospital owed over $100,000 to its suppliers, but bankruptcy was not an option because no other hospital would take Washoe County's indigent patients. In addition, there were no other services available for poor pregnant women.

Not to be denied, the medical staff demanded full obstetrical services, and surgeons dramatically increased the number of cases. These demands resulted in enlarged surgery suites, the establishment of a recovery room, and a larger blood procurement program as the hospital did not have the resources to supply the necessary blood for the emergency room and surgery. Dr. Salvadorini and the medical staff took the problem to the Washoe County Medical Society, and a committee was established to recommend a solution. They recommended that the hospital be part of the Southwest Blood Bank network, based in Phoenix, Arizona. Ogren recalls: "When we gave the Southwest Blood Bank the contract to manage the Washoe Medical Center Blood Banks in 1956, we provided one of the Quonset huts. They stayed there for the next seven or eight years. Later, they moved to their own facility in town, but we continued our association."[39]

Another major step forward in the care of patients in our community was the development of the Reno Cancer Center. Ogren relates: "The establishment of Reno Cancer Examination Center in 1956 was a big step in the evolution of the hospital. It was precipitated largely by the medical staff and the demands of the Joint Commission on Accreditation of Hospitals (JCAH).[40] The first director of the Reno Cancer Center was Lura Turlarski, a dedicated person who worked hard to ensure that this large record keeping operation succeeded. The Center recorded all of the malignancies in the community as to type and location of the tumor. This information is important to help in establishing the cause and epidemiology of various cancers."

# HOSPITAL RESIDENT, 1957–1958

## C. W. OGREN

### Arrival at Washoe Medical Center

I finished my year of didactic work at Washington University and arrived at Washoe Medical Center in August 1957, to begin work as an administrative resident. It was then that my twin brother and I split up for the first time in thirty years. We were orderlies together, we were in the Navy together three different times, we went to the University of Minnesota together, we went to Washington University together; now, we split up. I went to Reno, and Stuart went to Orlando, Florida. It was the most traumatic time in my life. I don't think I had ever been as lonesome, but I compensated by staying busy and working long hours in the hospital.

That year turned out to be profitable for me because Washoe Medical Center was reorganizing. There were plans for new emergency and surgery departments. There was upheaval in the ranks of the department heads over wages. Mr. Fox asked me to take over the medical records department when the supervisor quit in anger. Then, he asked me to run the laundry service when its manager quit in anger. I also had to take over central supply when that department head quit, and I worked to organize emergency services.

I spent the better part of two months training a woman to become the manager of the emergency services. I took her through the business office of the old emergency room, and I taught her all of the procedures. When we took our final tour of the department on the day before opening, she said, "I quit." Apparently she felt that the preparation hadn't been sufficient, and she was overwhelmed. Then, Mr. Fox ran me through, on a rotation basis, the business office and some other departments. He also asked me to assist him in making plans for a new surgery department, a new x-ray department, clinical laboratory, and so forth.

## The Scott Ranch Ditch

In 1957 the Hospital was a stockholder in the Scott Ranch Ditch, an irrigation ditch, that flowed out of the Truckee River. The ditch flowed through much of downtown Reno and entered the Washoe Medical Center property on the east by crossing under the Street, North of Mill; it flowed through the entire hospital property. The ditch exited the Washoe Medical Center property, flowed east along Mill Street where the Juvenile Detention Center is located, and flowed underneath, what is now, Kietzke Lane and irrigated farm land east of Kietzke Lane.

When the hospital was a shareholder in the ditch company, the quarterly shareholders meetings were held in the home of Mr. Scott. At these meetings we would discuss repeated efforts by people to takeover shares in this company because they recognized the growing shortage of water and the fact that the ditch might be a handy source of income for them.

As Washoe Medical Center expanded, it became obvious that we had to get rid of this ditch because it was not only an eye sore, but it was in the way of further expansion. The Board of Trustees voted to ask Sierra Pacific Power if they would be interested in buying our shares. They answered in the affirmative, and the shares were sold to

Sierra Pacific Power Company. Shortly thereafter the irrigation water was shut off somewhere west of the hospital property, and we filled in the ditch.

## The 1958 Building

I was kept pretty busy during my year of residency. I worked from sunup until late at night, working fourteen to fifteen hour days. My salary was two hundred dollars a month, and my rent was a hundred dollars, so I didn't have a whole lot of money. At least I got free meals in the hospital. Mr. Fox was generous and encouraged me to attend all the meetings of the medical staff, including the executive committee and the various medical department meetings. I developed an understanding of departmental organization, but I was also involved in the new building.

The building project was conceived by Clyde Fox in 1955, and Hill-Burton Funds provided generous dollars. The project involved building a new emergency room and surgical suites and rebuilding the laboratory and x-ray departments. The old surgical suite, composed of two major operating rooms, was in a wooden structure on top of the South Wing. Dr. Tom Brady recalls, "To access the ICU one had to go out on the roof and walk along a wooden walk." The old emergency room was facing Mill Street, approximately where the current emergency room waiting area is located. The x-ray and laboratory departments were grossly inadequate from the standpoint of both space and equipment.

On the day the new facility opened, we felt we had died and gone to heaven. It was the latest in building and technology. We thought that we had an emergency room facility that would last forever. The radiologists were happy with the facility, as were the pathologists, the admitting personnel, and so forth. It greatly enhanced our ability to handle our growing number of patients.

One memorable thing occurred in the new library that was located next to the emergency department. One morning, I went down to the emergency department and was advised that all of the new furniture in the library was gone. We investigated and the director of the EKG department who lived in one of the Quonset huts said she returned from a movie at 2:00 A.M. and saw a moving truck in front of the hospital loading furniture. I said, "Didn't you suspect something was wrong?"

She said, "No, I didn't."

What happened to our furniture was that someone came in the middle of the night and took it.

## Duties of an Administrative Resident

When I was a resident I took board material to various board members for review and signature. I made many trips to the home of Mrs. Ben Edwards on Lakeridge Drive. During that year, not once was I invited in while Mrs. Edwards signed and reviewed the papers; I was always forced to stand on the front porch. This was on instructions of the maid. It's interesting to note, that after I became administrator, if I had any reason to see Mrs. Edwards on hospital business, I was invited into the house to the living room.

Another highlight during my residency was sharing office space with Maida Pringle, who was Mr. Fox's assistant administrator. Maida spent over forty years with the hospital, and she was as much, or more of, a preceptor as Mr. Fox. She had been through the school of hard knocks and had the experience. Not only was she a leader, but was also a character in the true sense of the word.

While I was an administrative resident, doctors would arrive in Reno for divorce and seek employment in the emergency room. It was my job to drive them to Carson City to see the Chairman of the Board of Medical Examiners, Dr. George H. Ross.[41] He lived in a little white house a block west of the main drag. There, Dr. Ross interviewed the doctors, looked at their credentials, and provided them with temporary privileges to work in the emergency room.

I always got a kick out of recalling that while the doctors were being interviewed, I would often look over Dr. Ross' library that was outside of his office. I saw books etched with white ink, "WMC," which indicated that they were the property of Washoe Medical Center. Many of our books wandered to various doctors' offices and never returned.

Another phenomenon that occurred when we hired doctors to work in the ER was that several disappeared in the middle of the night, never to be seen again. We were convinced that they were being tailed by private detectives working for divorce lawyers, and it was time to move on.

It is interesting to note the method used to decontaminate hospital mattresses during my residency. The system employed cyanide pellets and sulfuric acid similar to an execution. We had a small wooden frame building to the southeast of what would now be the East Wing; it was in the county equipment yard. The building wasn't much bigger than ten by six feet, and we could stack mattresses in it six feet high. The mattresses or blankets were piled in, sulfuric acid was put into the pail on an elevated stand in a corner, and a cyanide pellet the size of a tennis ball and off-white in color would be dropped into the bucket. The door was shut and locked. The room would be left for several hours, and the storeroom man would open the door and vent the place through an eight to ten foot high stove pipe vent on the top of the building. That constituted our decontamination process.

One thing I have always gotten a kick out of was rescuing the old Board records from the basement of the 1906 Administration Building. I found the old Board records in boxes in rooms where sick prisoners were housed in the early 1900s. I put the records in chronological order and had them bound.[42] In the records I saw one interesting incident in the early forties, when Maida Pringle was a union member. She was urging reforms in salary scales and benefits for hospital employees. At that time, no hospital employee was entitled to a paid vacation. After much harangue, the Board decided to allow a vacation of one week per year without salary. After that initial step, vacation benefits became standard procedure, and the hospital became a leader in employee benefits in Washoe County.

The February 1957 Board minutes reflect the presence of Neil Humphrey of the Tax Payers Association. He attended primarily because of the difficulty being experienced by the hospital in getting the county to pay their bill. It became more serious by the month. Also, Fred Hill, a Nevada Assemblyman and attorney, was listed in attendance. His father owned the Hill Brothers Motel on South Virginia and was something of an eccentric. He was noted for parking his

Cadillac on the motel property facing South Virginia Street, and he would sit there by the hour honking his horn at good looking women who walked by. The Hill Brothers Motel was located where the Peppermill Hotel now stands.

Discussions at the April 1957 meeting were about discounts for doctors and their families, Washoe County employees, nurses, pharmacists, nonresident doctors, morticians, doctors' staff, blood bank employees, volunteers, and so forth. The administrator was authorized to make these special discounts. This was a hospital policy, which was rescinded because the amount of discounts got out of control, and it seriously impaired our financial status. It's interesting to note in hindsight that these discounts were made to patients before insurance paid their bill. If they had insurance they got a bonus. If a person had two health insurance policies, both policies paid the account in full. It was really quite a reward to go to the hospital. This practice contributed to overutilization of hospitals. Patients often went in for a three day stay, and only laboratory and x-ray examinations were done.

Several years after the discount policy was rescinded, word circulated that I, as administrator, authorized discounts to certain doctors and members of the Washoe Medical Center Women's League. As a result, I was subpoenaed by the grand jury to explain why I violated hospital policy. I asked the district attorney for evidence of special discounts. When I gathered all of the records associated with these admissions and discharges, I demonstrated to the grand jury that in no instance had any special discount been granted. The investigation was dropped; I was vindicated.

Towards the end of my residency, I was busy typing my thesis, and as a result still didn't have much of a social life. On one particular evening, Dr. Don Mohler, who was an obstetrician on the staff, felt sympathy for me and asked me if I would come home with him for dinner. We went to his home on Sharon Way, entered through the back-door, and were met by his wife who had recently had surgery on her ankle and was having difficulty walking. To compound the situation, the washing machine had overflowed earlier that day and flooded the house. Dr. Mohler walked in and said, "Honey, this is Mr. Ogren. He is here for dinner." She proceeded to work him over real good verbally, and after she settled down, dinner was put on the table and we ended up having an enjoyable evening.

Upon completion of my residency, because there was so much going on in terms of building and reorganization, Mr. Fox asked me to stay-on as an assistant, assuring me that he would raise my salary from two hundred to six hundred dollars a month. This was the genesis of a twenty-one year association with Washoe Medical Center.

## Clyde Fox, Administrator

Clyde Fox was an able administrator, but he had major problems with County Commissioner Benjamin Winn, which could not be resolved. Mr. Fox also had difficulty with the county manager, Alan Carter, who felt that Washoe Medical Center got too much of the tax dollar. They got into a bitter fight, and there was nasty publicity in the newspapers. The hospital was receiving a share of the *Ad Valorem* tax collections to cover operations. I don't recall how much, but the County Commissioners felt it was too much. Having three County Commissioners on the Board didn't do a whole lot of good because their response to Mr. Fox's request for additional funds was that we can't give it to you if we don't have it. Finally, Fox didn't feel he was getting the support of the Commissioners on other issues, nor enough support from other Board members, so he decided it was time to leave.

Those were really bitter days between the Commissioners and the Hospital Administrator. Carter could be just as vindictive as Fox, and the two of them fought tooth and nail. Fiscal management would have been a whole lot simpler, had the County been able to pay its share of reimbursement. Ironically, the way things turned out, if Clyde stayed another three months or so, the whole thing would have ironed itself out. Carter, the County Manager, became ill, suffered renal failure, and died at Washoe Medical Center.

Clyde Fox resigned in 1959 to assume the job of administrator at an unfinished hospital in Parma, Ohio. Fox wasn't at the hospital in Parma when the plans for the hospital were drawn. He got into a disagreement with members of the medical staff who were Board members, and as a result his services were terminated. He then moved to New York, where he became administrator of the Manhattan Eye and

Ear Hospital. Fox was hired on the recommendation of his old friend, Tony O'Rourke, who had been influential in hospital affairs in the southwestern United States. In fact, Fox had worked for Tony in Arizona, and it was through his influence that he became administrator of the hospital in Tucson, the post he held prior to his move to Washoe Medical Center.

Mr. Fox was also active in the American Hospital Association. He was a real bright man. He enjoyed playing the piano, singing, and was talented in many ways. But his Achilles heel was his sensitivity; he took problems personally, and as a result, was hurt when a decision was made against his recommendation.

Being an accomplished carpenter and handy with tools, Fox's home on Saint Lawrence Street was a show place. I helped him on weekends, building his backyard into a perfect place for entertainment. He enjoyed holding barbecues during the summer for members of the medical staff, hospital staff, and Board. In the late 1950s and early 1960s there was a pleasant tradition; Fox would have garden parties for the department heads and chiefs of the medical staff. He had a magnificent backyard; it was ideal for entertaining. On the morning of the party, dietary staff unloaded food from two hospital station wagons and served it for the party. Looking back, I often think that if we did something like that today, the press would generate adverse publicity; however, the party was a great morale factor.

Along with his carpentry ability, Fox was also an excellent tile setter. Fox, Pringle, and I laid all of the tile in the new kitchen on the ground floor of the old South Wing. He and I also assisted with small improvements in patient rooms. We both enjoyed working with the engineering staff. Having been present through all of the difficulty with the county manager, and looking back on it, I am certain Mr. Fox would have been happy staying at Washoe Medical Center. He just couldn't cope with his deteriorated relationships with the County Manager and County Commissioners.

Shortly before he resigned, Fox was elected president of the Association of Western Hospitals, which was a goal he set years earlier. He was an influential member of the association and took part in all of its meetings. In fact, after I came to Washoe, he insisted that I attend the meetings as well. The first meeting of the Association of Western Hospitals that I attended was in San Francisco; here, Fox insisted that

I play a role in the administrative residents' section. As a result, I was placed on the agenda to give a speech on my experience at Washoe Med. I will always look fondly on my days with Clyde Fox.

## Nevada State Hospital

The Nevada State Hospital, located in Sparks, Nevada, had 700 beds and was administrated by Dr. Sidney J. Tillim. Tillim's associate was Dr. Jules Magnette, an interesting character, who was a retired urologist and at one time also owned a circus.. While still an administrative resident, I requested a tour of the hospital. Dr. Tillim consistently denied my request, without giving me a reason. Back in the late 1950s the Nevada State Hospital operated on a daily cost of under eight dollars per patient. You may wonder how any hospital could operate on such a meager patient cost, but it was accomplished, similar to Washoe Medical Center in the early days, by the hospital inmates working a farm located on hospital grounds, and much of the food for the hospital, including the milk, was provided by the farm.

# ASSISTANT ADMINISTRATOR, 1958-1964

## C. W. OGREN

### Television in Patient Rooms

In April 1958, we installed television sets in patient rooms. This was accomplished by a southern California investor-promoter who came to Fox with a proposal to place television in patients' rooms at no cost to the hospital. The investor felt that there would be sufficient revenue to ensure that his investment would be a solid one. At a cost in excess of two hundred thousand dollars to himself, the installation of this system was accomplished.

We told our patients that television was going to be available at a cost of one dollar a day; however, in order to get this off to a good start, the owner agreed that for the first thirty days all patients would get free television. We controlled each television with an electronic device that could be disconnected by the business office. On the day free television was discontinued, I went with the investor to each pa-

tient; we asked them if they wanted television at the cost of one dollar a day. At the time we had something like 175 television receivers
in the hospital. When he and I completed our rounds, there were only
five patients who elected to have television.

As an end result, the investor lost everything he had invested in
the system. He instituted a law suit against the Motorola Company,
who had provided the television sets, claiming they had misrepre-
sented the system to him. Motorola won the suit. The investor lost
everything, and the television system was auctioned on the steps of
the county courthouse. It was sold way below cost to the Women's
League, and the patients were no longer charged for the service. We
couldn't have planned it better if we tried.

## The Quonset Huts

There were probably eight Quonset huts on the property when I arrived At Washoe Medical Center.[43] Later one housed the blood bank,
and another housed what was perhaps the first efforts in a Nevada
hospital of a child care center. This was a dramatic and radical approach from the standpoint of the hospital administrator. We had two
full-time employees who managed the child care center, and it went
well for three or four years. After a while it became an irritation;
mothers felt their kids were not being properly cared for, and communicable diseases were spreading through the center. Our patience wore
thin, we decided that it wasn't worth the effort, and we dumped the
whole thing.

Four of the eight Quonset huts were used to house employees. We
had two Quonset huts that were joined together to form Rose Pavilion. They were designed to house female employees and nurses. Two
others were joined together and housed primarily maintenance, laundry, and kitchen personnel. The housing of employees, particularly the
male employees, turned out to be a constant source of difficulty. It was
difficult to get them to keep the units clean. As far as the female quarters were concerned, there was a lot of fighting and jealousy over who
had what room; however, it succeeded for a number of years.

I think as salaries got better and people had an opportunity to get
apartments, the Quonset huts became more and more unpopular.

Eventually all of the huts were removed, with the exception of two, which were the genesis of the University of Nevada School of Medicine. There, Drs. George Smith and Richard Licata established the first School of Medicine research laboratory.

At that time there was a wood frame building, known as the Redwood Pavilion, that housed our long term patients. The Redwood Pavilion consisted of four Southern Pacific Railroad barracks that were moved to the hospital grounds and remodeled. Subsequently, they housed seventy nursing home patients, but they were never adequate because the hallways were so narrow that to get a bed out of the room, one had to take it apart. I don't think those hallways were more than four feet wide. Even worse, they were a fire hazard. How we were able to keep long-term patients in there as long as we did, I'll never know, but they passed the JCAH inspections. Nevertheless, in 1951 the grand jury had investigated and recommended that the hospital replace Redwood because of complaints that it was inadequate for the amount of elderly patients it housed.

## East Wing Addition

In 1958 Mr. Fox recommended that the Board raise $1 million to build a three-story addition. Ultimately, the building cost $750,000 and a combination of federal, state, county, and private funds financed the construction. We needed additional beds, and we were being pushed hard to provide additional patient services. The building became the East Wing, and I was involved in the effort to make an entrance through the wall of the old, wooden administration building.

The old administration building was so fragile that we had to string steel wire to wooden supporting columns on each side of the building to keep it from collapsing during the breakthrough. In order to save money I instructed our chief engineer, Ed Sontag, to accomplish this work with hospital help. It was something our men were capable of doing.

When we started, the work on the East Wing wasn't complete; finishing work still had to be done. When the union laborers discovered our men working, they objected to union authorities. I was paid a visit by a union steward, who advised me that if our men continued to work, they would stop work and put out pickets. The agent for the carpenters' union was Stan Jones, who is still in state government and has become a good friend. I first met him when he came to me about this problem. I advised him about our financial trouble, and he said, "Carroll, if you promise me that you will do this work at night, I will turn my head and won't say a word. I will get the union workers to abide by my recommendation."

We completed our work during night hours, and the East Wing opened with fanfare. With the addition of the first new beds in decades, we again felt we were on our way to becoming a great institution. The East Wing project was accomplished with the generous assistance from Hill-Burton Funds. We had good luck with the allocation of Hill-Burton money, primarily because of Don Baker who was the Chief of the Division of Hospital Services for Nevada. Don and I had become good friends, and he was most cooperative in seeing that the allocation funds to Washoe Medical Center were sufficient to take care of our patient needs. The Division of Hospital Services occupied one floor of a small building around the corner from the Supreme Court building in Carson City. I think Don had a staff of about three or four people.

The East Wing was the last project of any significance to be completed prior to the major addition, which was finished in 1973. On the other hand, we were always planning and improving the hospital.

## Convalescent Unit

The next project after the East Wing was the development of a convalescent unit. In 1959 we requested that the Board seek a $150,000 bond to construct a convalescent unit of twenty-six beds on the ground floor of the North Wing. Since convalescing patients require little nursing care, we felt that we could provide them with care for several dollars a day less than more acutely ill patients are charged. This would save money for the patient and release hospital beds for more intense nursing care.

This experiment turned out to be a failure because we usually couldn't get cooperation from the medical staff. Patients were referred to the convalescent unit in spite of the fact that they still required intense nursing care. With the failure of the unit, we turned it into a psychiatric unit.

## An Emergency Landing and Secret Service Visits

An incident involving an airline took place in the winter of 1959, when a flight originating in Minneapolis served squab that was tainted. By the time the flight was over Utah, passengers were getting sick with profuse diarrhea and vomiting. It quickly became an astronomical problem, and the pilot elected to make an emergency landing in Reno. I might add that by this time, as the only two toilets on the airplane had been occupied by those in distress, most of the remaining passengers had defecated in their seats.

The plane made an emergency landing in Reno, and somewhat over thirty passengers were brought to the hospital with acute gastroenteritis. Many of them were so sick that morphine was administered. The following morning Washoe Medical Center was teeming with agents from the airlines, who were there to ease the situation and decrease the anger of the passengers. No one died, but it did create one heck of an administrative problem for the airline and the hospital.

Over the years I was also paid visits by the United States Secret Service, each time before a Presidential visit to Reno. These became routine; they wanted to be sure the emergency room personnel were alerted to the fact that the President would be visiting, and they wanted to examine the emergency rooms to see that any potential problem could be handled and the facilities were adequate. They also made certain that we had blood on hand that matched the President's type. They also reviewed our security and had us issue identification badges to all medical staff, who would enter the ER if the President was admitted.

## Earl Horton, Administrator

There were sixty applicants for administrator after Fox left, and the Board selected eight for interviews. It's been my experience that members of the Board of Trustees looked upon the search process as an unwelcome task, and this was no exception. The Board selected two candidates: first was Ken Napp, a much respected administrator of a hospital in Ogden, Utah, and an ex-president of the Association of Western Hospitals; second was Earl Horton, an assistant administrator for personnel at Sutter General Hospital in Sacramento. He had never been a hospital administrator. Napp was overwhelmingly selected as the primary choice, but his salary demand was in excess of $25,000, and the Board didn't feel that they could pay that kind of money. Earl Horton agreed to take the position for $12,000 a year and impressed the Board when he said he would be a twenty-four hour administrator.

Mr. Horton was at Washoe Medical Center for four years. I noted early on that he wasn't entirely honest with the Board of Trustees. For example, the accounts receivable were rising at an alarming rate, and collections were poor. He assured the Board that collections were being made and there was nothing to be concerned about. It has been my experience that a receivable over 120 days doesn't stand much chance of being collected.

Their were other problems, and Horton resigned in September 1963. He went to San Francisco, where he took a position at French Hospital. It is curious that no one from French Hospital contacted anyone at Washoe Medical Center to determine why he had left. After Horton left I was appointed Acting Administrator, and I continued in that capacity for several months until April 1964 when the Board elevated me to Administrator.

## 1960 Winter Olympics

Shortly after Horton was hired, the 1960 Winter Olympics were held at Squaw Valley. We hadn't anticipated a whole lot of problems with the Olympics, with the exception of the crowds that would be coming through Reno. As things happened, it had quite an impact on the hospital for some time.

There was little snow in Squaw Valley prior to the Olympics. In fact, the sponsors and officials were quite worried about the lack of snow. We received several skiers before the opening because they skied on slopes, and then hit rocks that were a few inches below the surface. They suffered severe injuries. One Italian skier had a fractured femur, sternum, and humerus, and chest injuries. Another Italian skier had severe head injuries.

Ironically, the day before the Olympics a major blizzard hit the Sierra. It was so severe that the parking area couldn't be used for the opening day ceremony.

During the course of the Olympics, we had American skiers who had suffered fractures of the sternum, humerus, and tibia. We had a member of the Swedish team who was hospitalized with severe bleeding from a gastric ulcer. I enjoyed visiting with the Swedish trainer because I could speak Swedish. I think I made the team member's stay a lot more comfortable.

When the Italian and Spanish athletes were hospitalized, I put out a call via the newspaper for interpreters. The response was immediate, particularly on the part of Reno females, who looked upon this as an exciting opportunity to meet Olympic participants. One Italian skier had severe fractures, and the interpreter was the daughter of a prominent local contractor. She gladly took on the task of interpreting for him. I went up to see the Olympic patients about once a day. After the Italian skier had been in there for short while, I walked in one day to shoot the breeze in my pigeon English, and noted that he had lipstick smudges on his mouth. This was shortly after his interpreter had left. I got the message to him that I thought it was pretty funny that they had gotten that well acquainted with his interpreter. As things turned out the relationship blossomed and continued on after he had been discharged from the hospital. It wasn't many months later that the newspaper carried a story about their marriage. He became a partner in a ski-lift operation near Squaw Valley. They had several children and a great life together.

The greatest problem was collecting payment for the care rendered to the Olympic athletes. I dealt with the San Francisco consulates of the athletes' various countries, including Sweden, Italy, and Spain. It took a long time to get their payments resolved; it was about three years after the Olympics, we closed the last case. finally, we had gotten reimbursed. I felt particularly sorry for one pharmacy in Truckee that suffered a good deal of financial pain because they had been dispensing drugs of one kind or another, for all of these teams. He had an awful time making collections. In fact, a number of teams didn't pay their bills, and produced financial losses for the pharmacist.

## The Misfits and Lets Make Love

Several movies were filmed in Reno during my tenure at the Hospital. The best known were *The Misfits* and *Lets Make Love*. Marilyn Monroe appeared in both. In 1960 when *The Misfits* was being filmed in Reno, Marilyn Monroe, Clark Gable, John Houston, who was the director, and numerous others stayed in Reno. Clark Gable and wife, Kay Spreckels, stayed in the home of Dr. Henry Valenta on Greenridge Drive. The world premier of *Lets Make Love* was scheduled at the Crest Theater and ground work was laid to have a dinner sponsored by the Women's League. Arrangements were made to have the banquet at the Riverside Hotel on August 21, 1960. Marilyn Monroe had accepted the invitation, but about an hour before the dinner, Reno lost all of its power as a result of the Donner Summit and Dog Valley fire. We were without power for the better part of three days; one couldn't even pump gas. As a result I missed my chance to sit next to Marilyn Monroe for dinner.

Marilyn Monroe was staying at the Mapes Hotel on about the eighth or ninth floor. A Reno fire truck was parked on South Virginia Street on the side where her room was located and had a spotlight aimed at her window so she would have light.

Fortunately, the hospital had installed an emergency generator just a few months before the fire occurred, so we were able to power all of the essential functions such as surgery, laundry, and the kitchen. We didn't have any power in the hallways or in many of the rooms. Because we were one of the few institutions in Reno that did have power, we had an agreement with two supermarkets. They brought all of their meats over to our kitchen lockers. Also, we did the laundry for Saint Mary's Hospital. Our generators really proved to be a Godsend on many occasions because of the lack of dependability with the power company. I think that continued for the entire twenty years I was there. There were a lot of power outages in Reno.

## Psychiatry Ward

About 1962, Dr. Raymond Brown, a psychiatrist on the staff, felt that it was time for the establishment of a psychiatric ward.[45] Prior to this time psychiatric patients had been housed in private and semiprivate rooms before being committed to the State Hospital in Sparks. If they were violent, they were put in cuffs and tied to their beds, which was a primitive way to treat noncriminal psychiatric patients. The Board of Trustees went along with Dr. Brown's suggestion, but I was dubious because he wanted to establish the unit with both male and female patients in the Wyman Pavilion.[46] There were six beds on each side of a hall, and it was Dr. Brown's intention to house the females on the east side and the males on the west side of the hall. It wasn't long before we discovered this didn't work. There were sexual liaisons going on, and it created a nightmare. The experiment continued until we replaced Redwood Pavilion with a long-term nursing facility and a psychiatric unit in the same building

## Snack Bar

In the 1950s the snack bar was located on the second floor at the south end of the 1906 Administration Building. It had ten to fifteen tables, and the dish washing room was to the right as you entered the cafeteria. The wooden floor in the dish washing room had become so saturated with water over the years that it had a spongy feeling to it when walked on. At the opposite end of that hallway was a meeting room which was used for both the hospital personnel meetings and medical staff meetings. There was a medical meeting there every Monday morning. The man who worked there for many years under those conditions was Jimmy Jones, who did a remarkable job when you consider that he ran the snack bar, prepared the meals, and washed the dishes. Jimmy was loved by everyone in the hospital.

## The Hospital's District Attorneys

Sometime in the 1960s, District Attorney Bill Raggio felt there was adequate work at Washoe Medical Center to justify moving an assistant district attorney to an office in the hospital. "This was the first instance in which the District Attorney's Office had staff located outside the main courthouse."[47] We decided it would be appropriate for a deputy district attorney and a secretarial staff to be stationed at the hospital, to cover not only the hospital, but also all litigation involving child care. The office was first occupied by John (Jack) Mathews. Jack established a great relationship with the hospital and was a knowledgeable and compassionate individual. Jack later became a Municipal Judge. He was succeeded by John Gabrielli, who had left private practice and was a capable and experienced attorney.[48] John was a soft-spoken attorney on the staff of district attorney. He occupied the office for several years and did a magnificent job for us. John later went on to become a district judge in Washoe County.

John was followed by Bill Hadley, who was still in office when I left Washoe Medical Center. Bill and I had a great relationship during the years he was there. He was always available and attended board meetings whenever I requested.

One day I was walking by Bill Hadley's office when, to my surprise, I saw him standing behind his desk with a pistol in his hand aimed at a huge man standing at the opposite side of the desk. Bill was obviously in a mode to shoot him if he made one more step.

I bounded down the stairs and had my secretary call the police. One squad car with a single policeman responded immediately; I took him upstairs where he attempted to calm the situation, but it only got worse. The man that Bill was holding the gun on grabbed the policeman and with one swing slammed him against the wall. About the time that he was getting up off the floor more police arrived, and it took four of them to get this guy down on the floor and handcuffed. I am sure that had this situation proceeded for any period of time with Hadley alone with this man, he would have had a bullet in his chest.

## The First CAT Scanner

In March 1964, Dr. Becker asked about buying a cobalt radiation machine at the cost of $60,000, and this was never acted on. It was discussed because cobalt had become available in Las Vegas through a grant from the Variety Club, which donated a cobalt machine to Rose De Lima Hospital in Henderson. The Variety Club felt that a gift was due to the Las Vegas area because of the large number of entertainers that were appearing there. They made a mistake putting the cobalt machine in Henderson; this meant that cancer patients had to travel fifteen miles for treatment. The problem was resolved three or four years later when Southern Nevada Memorial Hospital [now University Medical Center] took out an emergency loan to purchase a Van De Graff accelerator and made it simpler for patients to get treatment in Las Vegas.

Several years later Dr. Becker returned from a vacation in Europe where he saw one of the first CAT scanners. Shortly after that, Washoe Medical Center obtained its first CAT scanner through a two million dollar emergency loan from the county. Then as the revenue came in through the use of the equipment, we paid off the loan. During my years at Washoe Medical Center, we were able to pay off all of our loans for new equipment by utilizing revenue from the equipment.

# ADMINISTRATOR, 1964-1978

C. W. OGREN

## Appointed Administrator

I was appointed Administrator in April 1964. By then several construction projects were going forward. The new x-ray, laboratory, and medical records departments replaced what were rather medieval facilities. The old surgery department consisted of four surgical suites on the top floor of the South Wing, and they were sad at best; however, the new surgery suites had all of the latest technology.

## The First Chaplain, Pastor Richard Engeseth, and the Kohl Memorial Chapel

In the fall of 1964, Louise Kohl Smith, the wife of an attorney, Lloyd Smith, donated the Henry Kohl Memorial Chapel. The Smiths lived on Skyline Drive in an elaborate home, which was one of the first in Reno to have a full scale bomb shelter. Built under the swimming pool, the shelter had provisions to feed occupants for months. The home also had a small theater in the basement and was the scene of fancy Reno parties. Louise was the adopted daughter of the Kohl family from the eastern United States, and was related to the Piggy Wiggly supermarket owners. She was generous in her gifts to Washoe Medical Center, and was somewhat demanding. She came quite often to look at the Chapel, and if there was so much as a cross out of place, she would be in my office. The same thing held true if Bibles were out of place.

In 1965 James P. Shaw of the Episcopal Church requested that a chaplain be appointed. This proposal was not met with support from the medical staff because there were doctors who said that no chaplain would be permitted to peruse the records of their patients. Their concern was patient confidentiality. Chaplain Richard Engeseth, who was an Episcopal pastor, became the first hospital based chaplain in 1966. As time went on, they accepted and supported him; even those who opposed the program now supported it. There were times when doctors requested the chaplain's participation in patient management. In fact, it became so widely accepted that after a couple of years we appointed a second Episcopal priest.

## Planning for the Tower

A $14 million bond issue was approved at the February 28, 1966, Board of Trustees meeting. It seemed like a large sum of money, particularly when one considers the size of previous building projects, and at the time, it was the largest building project in the state of Nevada. The bond issue was approved by a majority of the voters in the general election. This contrasted with a previous bond issue that was on the ballot one year earlier and failed miserably. I think the second bond issue passed because we worked hard promoting it. We talked to high school students and gave them bumper stickers. I made speeches everywhere, from service clubs in Reno to the Cow Belles organization in Virginia City. There was hardly anyone we missed.

Several architectural firms presented proposals for the design of the new building. This process was quite lengthy because there were several architects who were interested. They did a great job of tooting their own bassoons and trying to look like the greatest architect that ever lived. Roger Simpson and Bud Putnam, architects in a Reno firm associated with the firm of Welton Beckett from Santa Monica, had the winning bid. Welton Becket impressed us because the firm did the UCLA Medical Center, but it gained fame by designing the Disneyland Hotel in Anaheim.

## Dr. Tom Scully, Director of Education

I hired pediatrician Tom Scully, who had practiced in Las Vegas and was living in New Jersey, to be the first Director of Medical Education at Washoe Medical Center. Tom had practiced in Las Vegas from 1966 to 1969, but had taken a job in New Jersey, where he was Program Director for Saint Michael Medical Center. After he was hired by us, he directed and organized continuing education and provided support for the School of Medicine. Dr. Scully's greatest asset was his ability to get along with members of the medical staff. This took a rare bird, but he did a good job. Dr. Scully later became Dean of the University of Nevada School of Medicine following Dr. George Smith's resignation.

## A Tragedy at Washoe Medical Center

I hired Bill Rundio, who came from Portsmouth, Virginia. Bill was highly recommended by my twin brother, who at the time was the President of the Virginia Hospital Association. Bill had worked in the Tidewater area and had a good reputation. He arrived with his wife, Sylvia, who was a registered nurse, and his three year old son, Billie. Sylvia worked in the Riverside Convalescent Center on the Truckee River, and Bill rotated through the departments as assistant administrator.

He had been at the hospital for about a year when he told me he had problems with depression, and Dr. Montgomery, a psychiatrist, recommended treatment. He asked if I would permit him a leave to get treatment in the Los Angeles area. I replied in the affirmative. He was gone about a month, and when he returned to work he seemed to be in pretty good shape. Two or three months went by when he came to me and said he needed more treatment. I encouraged him to get the treatment, and assured him not to worry about his salary while he was away. He went again to Los Angeles and got electroshock therapy. I didn't feel he was in the best of condition when he returned. He had a flushed appearance to his face and he seemed to be depressed. Quite frankly, I was worried.

It wasn't long before I got a call about 9:00 one morning from Dr. Montgomery's office nurse who said Mr. and Mrs. Rundio were in his office and they were going to meet with the doctor. The Rundios asked if I would be willing to attend the meeting. I indicated that I would be happy to attend. I was putting some things together in the desk prior to going over to the office, which was in Dr. Jack Becker's building across the park from the hospital, when I got another call from the office nurse. She said, "Mr. Ogren, Mr. Rundio has a gun."

I said, "I will be over anyway."

I charged across the park, took the elevator to the fourth floor, and as I walked into Dr. Montgomery's office Mrs. Rundio was seated at a desk next to the receptionist. Bill Rundio was standing in the doorway with his hand behind his back. I asked him what he had behind his back and he said, "A gun."

I talked to him like a Dutch uncle and convinced him to hand me the gun. He handed me a box which contained the gun. I took it in my hands and told him that I thought we should walk back across the park to the hospital and have a discussion about this whole thing. All the time I was wondering what I was going to do when I got him there. My immediate thought was that when I got back to the office I would have my secretary call the police and we would get an emergency commitment for him.

We left his wife in Dr. Montgomery's office, took the elevator down to the first floor, and headed out of the office building and across the park. I was about four strides ahead of him with the box containing the gun in my left hand. He suddenly grabbed the box, turned and ran towards the doctors' office building. We got into the lobby, but he was far enough ahead of me that the elevator door slammed shut before I could enter. I turned to the receptionist and told her to call the police adding, "This man has a gun." I immediately headed up the stairs at flank speed. When I got to the fourth floor, Sylvia was slumped in the chair. Bill had fired three shots into her chest. As I arrived, he put the gun to his temple and fired. I went to my office; the press was there, I refused to talk; the police called; everything was in chaos.

The Reno police asked me to come downtown so they could take a statement. I called Sylvia's brother in Virginia and told him what had happened. Dr. Robert and Jean Myles cared for the Rundio's three year-old son, Billie, until Sylvia's brother arrived the next day to take him to Virginia. He asked me if I would act as executor of the estate, and dispose of everything that the Rundios had in Reno, which I did. I closed the estate.

Some years later Dr. Montgomery, who was Rundio's physician, strangled his wife on the floor of their home in South Reno and then shot himself.

Some twenty years after this, I attended a convention that my brother was holding as president of the Virginia Hospital Association when a hospital administrator from Roanoke, Virginia, came up to me. He introduced himself and said, "I know the whole story about you and the Rundios and the help you tried to give them. It may interest you to know that little Billie is a successful corporate attorney."

## A Liver Transplant

One incident that can't go without being mentioned concerns a Reno contractor who was severely injured in an accident near Truckee in 1969. He was taken by ambulance to the hospital in Truckee where they soon recognized that the extent of his injuries was such that they couldn't handle them. They called Dr. Robert Simon, who trained under Dr. Thomas Starzl, a world famous liver transplant surgeon in Denver. Dr. Simon proceeded to Truckee with a police escort and made an evaluation of the patient. The man's injuries were so extensive that he needed radical surgery. He was brought to Washoe with a State Trooper escort.

Dr. Simon called and asked me if I knew where he might get a fresh pig liver, which could be transplanted into the patient. The implanted liver would allow the injured liver to heal. I called a Reno Rotarian friend, Norman Olsen of Washoe Meat Company. He put me in touch with the manager of a slaughter house in Gardnerville, Nevada. I asked him if he could immediately provide a pig liver and assured him that I would have a Nevada Highway trooper escort the liver to Washoe Medical Center. I called Officer Neil Lunt who arranged a Nevada Highway escort. They picked up the liver, brought it to the hospital, and Dr. Simon installed it in the patient. Unfortunately, the patient expired within a couple of days.

The lighter part of this whole scenario followed the patient's death. Someone from the laboratory called Mrs. Pringle, and asked her what to do with the pig liver. Mrs. Pringle didn't give it a lot of thought, but felt that as this was a pig liver it should be sent to the dietary department. This was done, and as an employee named Walsh unwrapped the liver, he noted the sutures and tubing coming out of it and immediately fainted dead away and struck his head on the floor. That ended the whole problem of the pig liver. Where it went from the dietary department, I will never know.

## Slot Machine Thrombosis

In the late 1960s, the Chrysler Corporation held their annual meeting at the Convention Center on South Virginia Street. This attracted some, 5,000 Chrysler Dealers from around the country. It was really a big show. The Convention Center was decorated with huge chandeliers. It was made to look like a magnificent ballroom. At any rate, during this convention we had an increase in myocardial infarctions (heart attacks).

This would have been a natural occurrence because by the time that a man is a successful Chrysler dealer, he is probably beyond his 50s. He traveled a long distance to Reno, didn't eat properly, stayed up for hours at a time, and gambled. At any rate, we had a number of their wives brought to the Medical Center by ambulance from the various casinos.

On this one particular day, Dr. George Smith and Dr. Salvadorini were doing a postmortem examination on a woman who had died in Harold's Club. She succumbed after admission to the hospital. As they were doing the autopsy, Dr. Salvadorini mentioned to Dr. Smith that the woman had been brought from a casino where she had been found at the base of a slot machine. With this, Dr. Smith raised his head and said, "A slot machine thrombosis." The subject sparked Dr. Smith's interest, so he researched this phenomenon and wrote a paper with Dr. Salvadorini titled, "Pulmonary Embolism." They pointed out that the embolism (a blood clot) was due to the stasis of blood in the lower extremeties from standing in front of a slot machine. The woman also wore a garter belt that was popular at the time, and this also produced stasis and edema accentuating the production of a blood clot. The paper was published, and Dr. Smith presented the paper at medical conventions.

## Other Problems

There are strange occurrences that can give an administrator fits. When we had finished the new building in 1973, we had a built-in food delivery system that transported food to all the floors using small elevators containing tray caddies. The employees often left a note on the last tray for that floor. It read, "Last breakfast, last lunch or last supper." On one occasion, a tray was delivered to a patient on the cardiac intensive care floor, and he and his relatives noticed right off the bat the note indicating, "Last supper." It didn't go over well.

Another occurrence that gave me a fit was when the business manager, Bill Behncke, decided to make a public relations pitch and let the patients who paid their bills know that it was appreciated. He initiated a practice whereby when a bill was paid, the patient would receive a letter thanking them and hoping they enjoyed their stay. I was suspicious of this from the start because of the potential of sending this message to a deceased patient's relatives. Of course this happened, and the relatives of a patient who had expired got a letter saying, "Thank you for paying the bill. We hoped you enjoyed your stay."

Hospital bills recreate problems despite our good intentions. Each day we listed all of the supplies, drugs, and services a patient used. To do this, we had a posting machine, which noted everything a patient got, from central supply to any pill they received. We had consistent complaints from patients complaining about paying five dollars for Kleenex or did not understand the importance of the laboratory tissue examination.

About this time we started the procedure of sending a nurse or orderly with patients to their waiting car. This wasn't done only to help the patient, but because we learned that without a hospital representative the wheelchair was being put into the trunk, going home with the patient.

We experienced problems with the Tahoe Forest Hospital in Truckee, California. They were guilty of repeatedly bringing seriously injured or ill patients to Washoe Medical Center in an ambulance without giving us prior notification. It was against the law to make such transfers unless there had been prior notification and residency had been determined. If an indigent established residency, the place of legal residence was responsible for hospital care. Tahoe Forest Hospital dumped so many patients on us that I threatened to confiscate any equipment they used to bring patents to Washoe Medical Center without written prior authorization. Within a short time they brought an unauthorized patient, and I obtained confiscation papers for their ambulance. It was kept in the parking lot until the situation was resolved. This practice ceased, and we never had another problem.

In a similar vein, there were a number of ski bums who were brought to us with fractures and injuries. They were taken to Tahoe Forest Hospital and transferred to us. Some paid their accounts, but many did not. The difference between what insurance paid and what remained on the bill was always charged to the patient. They were billed for the balance whether it was $1.00 or $1,000. On one occasion we had a bill with a balance of $3.60, and we billed the patient for it. A few days later, we received in the mail a mason jar filled with honey and 360 pennies. After this, I changed our procedure and wrote off the difference if it was less than ten dollars.

An incident occurred in the delivery room involving one of our psychiatrists. Relatives were allowed in the delivery room and when the psychiatrist's wife was delivering, he turned off the lights to the delivery room as the head crowned. He felt the bright light would be emotionally or psychologically traumatic to the baby. Dr. Robert Myles recalled that the psychiatrist also wanted the baby put in a tub of warm water, but it was put on a respirator because its oxygen level was low. He removed the child and gave it to its mother for "bonding" and all hell broke loose. As a result of that incident, the delivery personnel and some physicians ridiculed him.

## The First Helicopter

In the 1970s, Bill Lear and I decided to try transportation with emergency patients. I got to know Bill when he was a patient in the hospital. He had eye problems, and it was always a kick to go up to talk with him because he was a great story teller. Moya, his wife, took an immediate liking to me because I told her that I could remember the days when her father, Ole Olsen, who was a part of the Olsen and Johnson comedy team, appeared at the Orpheum Theater in Minneapolis.

Bill and I talked about helicopter transportation and Bill said, "Let's give it a try. I'll stand the cost and the hospital doesn't have to worry." He provided the helicopter; we parked it in the park across the street from the hospital. For a six month period, we used the helicopter for emergency cases, particularly highway accidents and the like. After much discussion and juggling the figures, we decided it was wasn't going to pay. At that point, it was shelved. I imagine it was another five years or so before helicopters were in vogue in trauma hospitals. At least we had the farsightedness to give it a try.

Ultimately, as third party insurers grew and more people had insurance, we became less dependent on the county for our share of taxes. During my career as administrator, we did away with county support entirely. We depended on the county occasionally for such things as emergency loans, but we always repaid them. We also used the county as the bonding guarantor for our various bond issues, but we never had to fall back on the county for retirement of the debt service. We always had adequate funding out of our revenue.

## Dedication of the 1973 Building49

In 1973 when we dedicated the new hospital, we really did it up right. A number of celebrities visited the hospital before the Grand Opening. Bill Harrah came over in a red Ferrari with his chauffeur and asked for a tour. A short time later, his ex-wife came over and asked for her personal tour.

During dedication, we had the Reno Civic Band, and involved the Masonic Order. It was really quite an affair and was well attended. My twin brother had come from Virginia. As he made his way through the throngs of people at the dedication, there were all kinds of people coming up and shaking his hand and expressing their appreciation on the job he had done. He accepted their compliments without telling them that he was my twin brother. This went on for most of the morning. The program showed the community how proud we were of our new facility.

## Open Heart Surgery and Cardiac Care Facilities

Dr. Peter Rowe started cardiology at Washoe Medical Center and Reno shortly after he arrived in 1948. He was trained in internal medicine and cardiology at the University of Michigan Hospitals and served in the Army for five years during World War II before coming to Reno. He, Drs. David Thompson and J. Stephen Phalen managed the first EKG Department at the hospital.

The history of the cardiac care unit dates to January 1963 when Joanne Wessel, RN was appointed manager of beds where patients with heart disease were admitted. Iva Haislip, RN helped on the unit and re-called when Louis Armstrong was admitted to the unit for congestive heart failure in 1964. He was treated by his private physician who always traveled with him. Shortly thereafter Sammy Davis, Jr. was admitted with coronary disease, and after he left the hospital, he gave a private show for the personnel who worked on the unit.

The next step in cardiology came after Dr. Bernie Lown, a colleague of Dr. George Smith's from Boston visited Reno. He had established the first cardiac intensive care unit in the country at the Peter Bent Brigham Hospital. When he visited to consult on Dr. Smith's pace-maker research, he recommended that Washoe Medical Center build a CICU. As a result Washoe Medical Center's CICU was the second or third unit in the country. Establishing the unit was relatively simple because we had beds and space available. We had done away with the

TB beds on the second floor of the East Wing, and that area was available.

The first CICU opened in September 1965 and consisted of a single monitored bed. At the end of the first year, mortality for heart attacks in Washoe Medical Center dropped thirty percent. This small step placed Washoe Medical Center at the forefront of hospitals in the country. In 1966, Fleischmann Foundation funds allowed the hospital to expand to nine monitored beds on a seventeen bed graduated care unit that varied from acute intense care to stepped-down care. Also in 1966, a telephone service for interpretations of EKGs was provided to northern Nevada and limited California counties.

The next major step in cardiology in northern Nevada occurred February 14, 1977, when Dr. Theodore "Ted" Berndt did the first cardiac catheterization case at Washoe Medical Center. Mrs. Ethel Wright was the patient, and Mrs. P. Jeffers, RN. assisted Dr. Berndt.

The first open heart surgery in northern Nevada also occurred in 1977 at Washoe Medical Center. This was a major undertaking because there was no room for errors; bad publicity would sink the program. The hospital in the Bay Area where Reno patients were sent for bypass surgery had excellent results, and we could not afford to be less successful. Dr. Bill Keeler chaired the committee to investigate the technical feasibility of the surgery. His committee looked at the availability of blood components, blood gas determinations, nursing skills, and pump technicians. All major renovations to the facilities, including a cardiac ICU and cardiac ward were done with hospital personnel. The hospital established an education program for the patient and family. At that time Dr. Robert Nichols was the only surgeon in Reno with the technical skills to do the surgery, and he did the first case, but he only operated on three or four patients before Dr. Art Lurie arrived and took over the program.

Coincidentally, the first open heart surgery took place on St. Valentine's Day, and Dale Hart, age 65, was the patient; there were no complications. Dr. Nichols was assisted by Drs. Robert Simon and William Keeler, and Rick Russell and Pat O'Brien were the perfusionists (heart pump technicians). The nurses were Claudette Edmiston, Lyn Milligan Crosby, and Dorothy Murphy. Dr. Paul Gregory administered anesthesia. After Dr. Lurie assumed leadership of the program, he was assisted by Dr. William Conran who initially commuted from Sacramento, California. Dr. Conran recalled that for several weeks he would start the drive to Reno at 4:00 A.M. in order to be on time for the 7:30 surgery.

## Poison Center

Dr. V. A. Salvadorini started Washoe Medical Center's poison center in 1960, but before we signed on with the National Poison Control Center in Denver, Dr. Salvadorini asked me to go to the Bay Area and look at the Poison Center in Berkeley. I was impressed with their program and agreed that we should start a similar program in Reno. For the first few years, it was staffed by nurses Helen Steele and Helen Smith in the emergency room.

In 1971 we hired a full-time person, Mrs. Geraldine Staples, who came to be known as the "Poison Lady." She did a wonderful job of traveling to the schools and teaching the students about the dangerous poisons in the home. The center not only provided information to callers and other hospitals, but also educated the public about the dangers of toxic substances and drugs in the home.

## Incline Village Hospital

The Director of Civic Affairs for Bill Harrah, Maurice Sheppard, told me they had been asked for a sizable contribution to assist in the building of a hospital at Incline Village. I told him that I would evaluate the need for the hospital, but I would want to have Don Baker assist me. He agreed.

During our review, we found many problems with their proposal. We found that the consultant employed for the proposed project had a shady past in California. We also found that they put undue emphasis on people who made promises of sizable donations. We agreed that there was a growing need for hospital beds at North Lake Tahoe, but we recommended that they proceed a little slower. It took the Incline community another twenty years to get the financial support to build the hospital. After it was established, it subsequently went bankrupt and changed ownership several times.

We completed a thirty to forty page report which I presented to the Board of Directors of Harrah's. Mr. Sheppard asked me what I wanted for payment. I said, "I have never done anything like this before, so why don't you pay me what you feel it's worth."

He said, "Carroll we don't do things like that around here." He then took me down to the cashier's cage on the main floor of Harrah's and said, "Give me a figure."

I said, "Six hundred dollars would be an adequate figure." He wrote out a note and handed it to the cashier. She gave him six $100 bills which he handed to me. My immediate thought was, "Ogren, you idiot! Why didn't you ask for six thousand?"

1948 Power house construction site—Trustee Augus Cauble (*left*), Administrator Vlad Ratay, and Trustees A. E. Holgate, Carl Shelly, Ernest Kleppe, and James Peckham (WMC photo)

James Lamb, Chief Executive Officer, circa 1990 (Steve Young, WMC photo)

Redwood Pavilion beds, circa 1940 (WMC photo)

Emergency room
Nurses Pat
Blodgett (*left*)
and Vinette
Blanchard, 1970
(WMC photo)

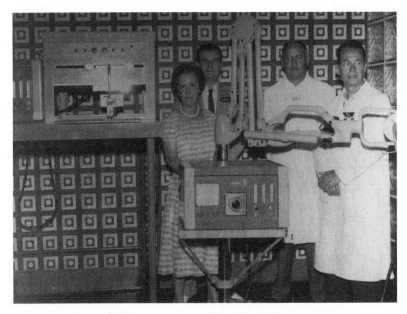

Mrs. Douglas Cloud, League President, Administrator Clyde Fox, Dr. V. A. Salvadorini, and Dr. Leibert Sandars with the first isotope counter in Nevada, 1958 (WMC photo)

1958 Emergency room exterior with ambulance (WMC photo)

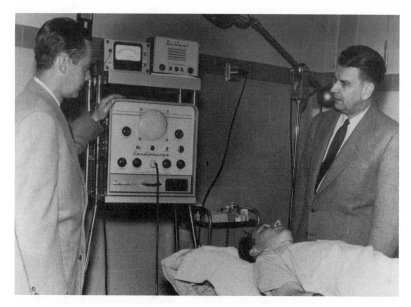

Washoe Medical Center's first cardioscope—Dr. Earl Hillstrom (*left*) and Administrator Clyde Fox, circa 1955 (WMC photo)

County Hosptial farm, looking east—Dr. Larry Russell's county clinic on the left and Quonset huts to the right, circa 1955 (WMC photo)

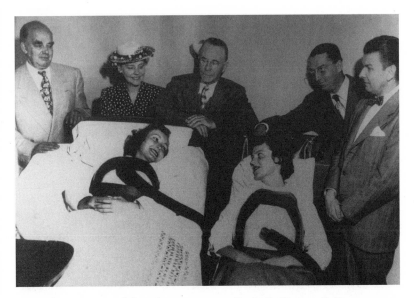

Two polio patients with breathing assistance: Dr. R. E. Wyman (*left*), 2 unknown persons, Trustee Bruce Thomas, Administrator Clyde Fox, and patient on the right is Mrs. William Ramsey, circa 1953 (WMC photo)

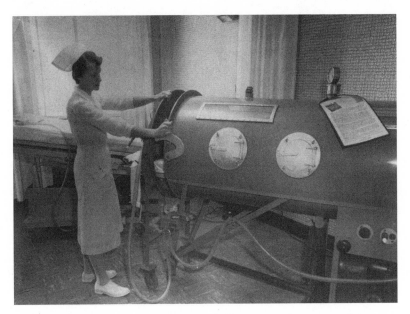

Iron lung and Nurse Bernice Lawson, circa 1953 (Gene Christensen photo)

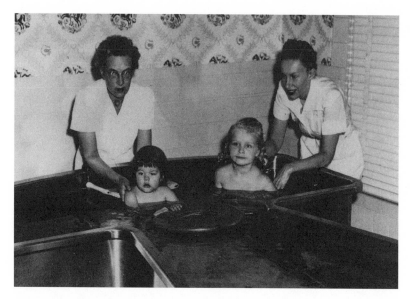

Polio children in Hubbard tub, circa 1953 (Mr. E. D. Mack photo)

Aerial view of Washoe Medical Center 1973 Tower (WMC photo)

Washoe Medical Center Professional Building, 1989 (Jay Graham photo)

1998 Administrative staff (*See Appendix IX for names*) (Steve Young, WMC photo)

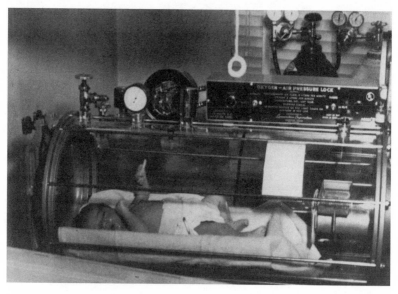

Baby in incubator, 1950s (WMC photo)

Nursery in the 1950s. (WMC photo)

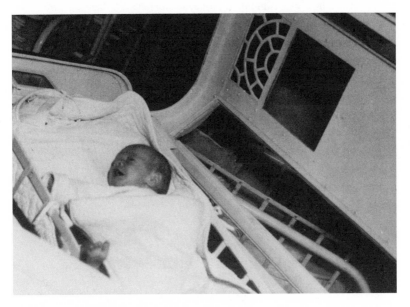

Twin Barbara Ruth Schelin (Sparks) (WMC photo)

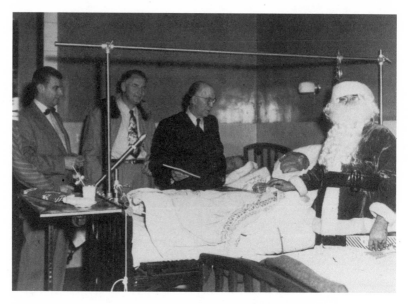

Christmas in the 1950s, Administrator Clyde Fox (*left*), Dr. Larry Russell, Dr. Arthur "Bart" Hood, and Chris Kakoras as Santa Claus (WMC photo)

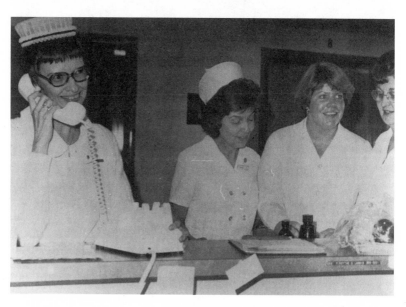

Oncology Nurses Marge Adams (*left*), Virginia Campbell (LPN), Judy Benevenuto, and June Stevenson, 1978 (WMC photo)

## PEOPLE MAKE THE HOSPITAL
### (During Mr. Ogren's Tenure)

C. W. OGREN

### Nursing Staff

One of the premier members of the nursing staff during my career in the medical center was Eileen "Mike" Jeffress. Mike was Irish and had the Irish map printed all over her face. Mike had many qualities, and one thing that made her stand out from other nurses was the nature of her nursing cap, which was a symbol of where a nurse had gone to school. Each school had a very distinctive nursing cap for its graduates. In fact, it might be noted that the cap for the graduates from the Orvis School of Nursing at the University of Nevada was a very distinctive cap fashioned after a cowboy hat, but non-University of Nevada graduates say it looks like a bedpan. If you see one you notice right off the bat that it resembles a very small cowboy hat, but Jeffress' cap was a round embroidered cap which was the picture of delicacy. She stood out from all others because of the nature of this cap.

I visited Mike on Nevada Day, October 31, 1996, because I had heard that she was ill with Lou Gehrig disease (amyotrophic lateral sclerosis), a degenerative central nervous system disorder ending in debility and death without affecting the mental process. I visited her at her home on Plumb Lane near the Presbyterian church. By this time Mike was walking with a cane and her speech was slurred, but she had an attitude second to none. I have never witnessed a person with a terminal illness who had a better attitude. She had made arrangements for most of her possessions to go to her children and friends. Her house was for sale. She mentioned that she had taken out a long term health care policy back in the '60s and this, combined with her retirement income, was going to be sufficient to pay for full care at the Manor Care Nursing Home.

Mike and I worked to compile a list of the nursing supervisors and head nurses she considered to make up the core of Washoe Medical Center through the '50s and into the '70s. I know it is dangerous to compile lists like this, because someone is going to be left out, but what we compiled included most of the staff. These nurses played a significant role in Washoe Medial Center: Pat Caldwell, June Stevenson, Anita Williams, Ellen Myers, Iva Haislip, Edith Rogers, Jean Molde, Joanne Sharigan Gould, Sandy Ballard, Edna Rix, Joanne Leigh, Mary Bailey, Mary Labuda, Vinette Blanchard, Evelyn Laws, Alma "Red" Johnson, Ava Drachulich, Martha Shea, Deanna Matthews, Alice Timerlake, Reva Cunningham, Evelyn Carson, Jerri Barr, Jackie Plowman, Pat Peer, Loretta Smith, Ruby Taylor, Bernice Chadwick, Ruth Hoffman, Bernice Martin Mathews, and Nancy Pleasants.

## Medical Staff

Generally, I had good relations with the medical staff, but on occasion, we disagreed. For example, I felt it was time to hire a physiatrist, a doctor of physical medicine, to provide rehabilitation services. This was met with reluctance by various specialists. Anyway the Board agreed to give it a try, and we hired the first physiatrist employed in the community and by Washoe Medical Center. Dr. Wally Treanor turned out to be an asset to the hospital, particularly from the standpoint of handling workers disability claims.

Demands made of the hospital by certain doctors groups didn't always work out in our favor. A prime example occurred when a number of surgeons, with Dr. Donald Guisto in the leadership role, demanded that we establish a burn unit. I believe this was early in the 1960's, and the Board approved pursuing the establishment of a burn unit. We renovated space outside of the surgery department, putting in four beds for burn patients and a specially designed Hubbard tank used for the debridement of burns. Firemen in Reno and Sparks raised much of the money for the unit. It didn't work out because Southern Nevada Memorial had established a good reputation with a more sophisticated unit in Las Vegas, and special air transportation was easily arranged. Patients with severe burns could be flown to Las Vegas or to Texas where the military had established the top burn unit in the United States.

We used the Texas unit when we got patients with serious burns, such as military personnel from Herlong, or when we got severely burned children. I would get in touch with one of the United States Senators. Their staff would make arrangements for transportation by military aircraft to San Antonio, Texas, where Brooke Army Hospital was located. When a military medical aircraft arrived, all other aircraft in the vicinity were diverted until the military craft had landed and loaded its patients.

In the early 1960's, I continued a practice that Clyde Fox had started; he displayed pictures of the members of the medical staff on the wall of the administration building. This was a fine idea. Most of the doctors liked it, but there was always some who wouldn't go along. At one point, only about half of the doctors had their pictures up, so I developed an idea. I invited the doctors' wives to lunch. After lunch I took them on a tour of the hospital, and I made certain that they went through the administration building to see our doctor gallery. These pictures were taken by Dr. Ernie Mack's father and later by Victor Anderson. The cost was borne by the hospital, so it didn't cost the doctors a thing. At any rate, I was pleasantly surprised to see a number of wives upset because their husbands' pictures weren't on the wall. It wasn't long before my secretary's phone started ringing and doctor's' secretaries were asking for appointments for the missing doctors to get their pictures taken.

From the early days, we always had difficulty in getting sufficient physician coverage in the emergency room. Originally, it was handled on a rotation basis by the medical staff. The Nevada Revised Statutes required the members of the medical staff in county hospitals to take care of indigent patients. This was done on a rotational basis, and it worked fairly well, but it created problems during the night and on weekends. One solution was to hire doctors to stay in the emergency room.

Mr. Fox hired the first emergency room doctor when a doctor came to Reno for a divorce. Not only was the doctor desperate for income, but he wanted to be busy and involved in patient care. From that point on, the interest in the position snowballed. Word got out around the country that Washoe Medical Center provided a good opportunity for doctors to have some income while in Reno for a divorce. It wasn't long before we were getting calls from doctors from all over the country who were planning to get a divorce and spend six weeks in Reno. It is interesting to note the number of doctors who came here for a divorce and stayed to practice medicine in the community.

Originally, we had a little difficulty with the medical staff buying into hiring doctors to work in the emergency room, but after several months they supported it because they got fewer night calls. The only time a doctor on service-call came to the emergency room was if the emergency room doctor needed a specialist.

Also, many new doctors on the medical staff enhanced their practices by working in the ER for thirty dollars a twelve-hour shift. This allowed them to acquire new patients and also receive referrals from other doctors.

In the 1950s and early 1960s there weren't a whole lot of malpractice cases. It seems that in the old days the doctors were family doctors; they were considered a part of the family, and you don't sue family. I can't recall a malpractice suit at Washoe Medical Center in the old days. There is terminology in the insurance industry that calls all suits initiated against an institution, the "prayer." Over the years that I was with Washoe, we had one "prayer" totaling $7 million. It is interesting to note that during the years I was there, actual claims paid totaled $320,000.

## Board of Trustees

In all of my years of being Administrator at Washoe Medical Center, the Board meetings were never dominated by one person. Board meetings were always dinner meetings. While the press was invited to the meetings, they rarely attended. They were not invited to have dinner, and this being the dinner hour, I think they preferred to be at home with their families. If there was something of significance on the agenda, we always gave them advance notice. The Reno newspapers usually had one or two persons assigned to the Washoe Medical Center beat, and they often dropped in to see me during the week. At that time, I would inform them what was going on and that seemed to satisfy them.

The Board meetings rarely lasted much over two hours. This was even preserved during the years when we were building and had long agendas. The Board members were well informed during their routine visits to my office, and as a result some subjects didn't need much discussion at the Board meetings. The only thing that took much time was the approval of policy. It was always amazing to me that we could accomplish what we did with short Board meetings. In the late 1970s, we had quite an influx of new Board members, and I noted that there was an increasing tendency of some of them to micro-manage the hospital. They wanted to get involved and second guess me, but that wasn't until late in my career. I had good relationships with most members of the Board.

Dr. Mack was the chairman for twenty-one years and was an effective chairman. We were told in graduate school that it wasn't a good thing to have doctors on the Board because they were self-centered and interested in their own behalf. I never found this to be true in my relationships with doctor members of the Board. Dr. Mack was particularly delightful to work with. He was interested in the growth of the hospital and joined me in all of the worries and concerns about expansion. He had a busy schedule, but he was always sympathetic and available to me when I needed him. Other medical staff physicians who served unselfishly as Board members included Robert Myles, Roy Peters, Mark Raymond, and John Becker.

Curtis Farr, I think, was the quintessential executive and Board member. He also was a successful Reno business man. He and his father ran the Coca-Cola/7-UP franchise in Reno. The bottle plant was located on South Virginia and Center Street. His wife was active in the Women's League, and they were both delightful people. Also Curtis Farr was a valuable Board member because he wasn't afraid to speak his mind.

Lynn B. Gerow, the father of the psychiatrist Lynn B. Gerow, Jr., was our general practitioner member of the Board. He made Clyde Fox's tenure difficult because Dr. Gerow never liked Clyde Fox, and there was always animosity between them.

Eddy Questa was president of the First National Bank of Reno when he was on the Board of Trustees. He was of Italian descent; and Mr. Fox requested that he run for the Board because of his business and financial acumen. Eddy was a quiet man who lived on Greenridge Circle where he had three Korean house people. Sigmun Rhea, the President of Korea, was a personal friend. This was obvious when one visited Eddy's home because it was a showplace of oriental furniture and memorabilia. His home was really a great place to visit because it was like visiting a museum. Eddy and Newt Crumley died in a plane crash in the early 1960s; their deaths were a real shock to the Board and the community.

When his death occurred, I was at a hospital meeting in Lovelock, Nevada, and we were in the midst of a first class winter blizzard. Word came that Mr. Questa and Newt Crumley, who was then owner of the Holiday Hotel, had gone down in Crumley's plane. The plane was a twin-engine Aero Commander. They went down somewhere between Las Vegas and Tonopah. Conditions for flying were so bad that commercial flying was grounded, but Crumley and Questa wanted to go to a meeting of the Chamber of Commerce in Elko. It was common knowledge that Crumley was an ex-Air Force hotshot pilot and didn't pay a whole lot of attention to weather conditions. He felt that he could surmount any bad weather. They got to 28,000 feet, and the wings iced up. They were somewhere in the area of Tonopah when Crumley advised the air controllers that he was going in. He crashed within miles from where he was born and raised.

Bryce Rhodes was a leading attorney in Reno and a positive member of the Board. He was truly a peacemaker, but also one who was willing to take a risk. He lived in southeast Reno near South Virginia, on Rhodes Lane, which was named after him. His home was a delightful place to visit. He entertained members of the hospital staff in great fashion. His wife was a prominent member of the Women's League, which made them another Washoe Medical Center couple. Because Bryce was legal counsel for the Nevada State Medical Association and the Nevada State Board of Medical Examiners, he knew medical issues and appreciated the concerns of doctors. This made him valuable to the Board of Trustees. He and Dr. Ken Maclean worked well together as a team on the Nevada Board of Medical Examiners.

Another valuable member was Mrs. Bea Edwards, who was married to Ben, a prominent land developer. They lived on Greenridge Circle. Bea was active in the Women's League. I remember her strained relationship with other League members because she let them know she was on the Board of Trustees and her word carried weight.

When I arrived, Ray Capurro, Ernest Kleppe, and Ray Peterson were the three County Commissioners of the Board. They were easy to work with. Of course, they could be outvoted by the five Board members elected at-large from Washoe county. It was always was a thorn in our side when the county bill was presented at monthly Board meetings, the County Commissioners would sometimes advise that there weren't sufficient funds in the county to pay what the hospital was demanding. That always exacerbated our financial problems, but the Women's League was able to raise funds to keep us solvent.

It's hard to believe that sometimes the only difference between closing the hospital and keeping it open was the fact that the Women's League had raised sufficient funds to pay the bills. Many months the dollars raised by the League made the difference between the hospital being in the red or being in the black. (See chapter on the Women's League.)

The issue of pay for Dr. Ben Drummer, a podiatrist, who successfully ran for the Board, hounded the Trustees for the better part of two years. Dr. Drummer became aware that NRS made provision for fifty dollars reimbursement per meeting for hospital Trustees.

Periodically, Dr. Drummer would ask that the compensation issue be on the hospital agenda, but it was invariably tabled because there was no support from the other Board members. This issue became something of a testy problem because I am aware that at no time in the history of Washoe Medical Center had any Trustee asked for compensation for their Board work. Finally at one meeting, Dr. Drummer brought his attorney, and much to the surprise of all us, not even the attorney supported his request for reimbursement. I think it was with a feeling of total disgust that the Board finally voted that Dr. Drummer could have his fifty dollars, and that closed the issue.

Howard McKissick Sr. was a County Commissioner and the father of Howard McKissick Jr., a Reno attorney. McKissick's family, at the turn of the century, owned the McKissick Opera House in Reno. Before Howard became a Board member, he was a federal marshal. One morning he and an assistant marshal went to a house on Moran Street to arrest a man for income tax evasion. Howard went to the door, and the man answered and asked him if he wanted to step in, which he did. The man then said that he wanted to go into his bedroom and get a shirt. He returned with a handgun and proceeded to shoot Howard McKissick in the chest and arm. Then, he went outside and started shooting at the other officer. Help arrived from the Reno Police Department and they captured the man. Howard later told me that when he realized he had serious gun shot wounds, it was the longest period in his life. He said that he was completely alert as the man looked at him and stepped over him to go out to the front porch in pursuit of the other officer.

Jack Cunningham also was a County Commissioner and had been Washoe County Treasurer for many years. Leo Sauer also was a county commissioner and came from a long line of Washoe Valley Pioneers. Sauer lived south of Reno, in an area known as Pleasant Valley. That whole area was owned by the Sauer family. Both Cunningham and Sauer were gentlemen and advocates for Washoe Medical Center. Sauer's daughter was an active member of the League.

## Department Supervisors

It didn't take me long to recognize that a hospital is only as good as the people who work in it, particularly the department heads. They take the brunt of the anxiety and uncertainty when the hospital is under construction or changing. I was blessed with department heads who were second to none. I will mention some of them, knowing that I will invariably leave some out, not deliberately, but because of advancing age and its effect on my memory.

In the dietary department, Jeanette Bankofier was the epitome of a professional and what I wanted in terms of a dietitian. Jeanette had many good ideas and was always on the job. I always appreciated her for keeping our food services running smoothly. She took the punches when the hospital grew from one hundred beds to six hundred and fifty. She got along well with her help and fit in well with the evolution of dietary practices. Her head chef was Mike Leonardi, and he lead a team second to none.

The store room had a dirt floor with shelving that extended back about one hundred feet through about four or five aisles. The store room chief was Ron Heidrich. Ron was a paraplegic who carried out his work from a wheel chair. I'll never forget that Ron had open contempt for anyone in the administrative office. He just didn't have any time for us. He was a cynic who obviously was a very unhappy person. The opposite was true of his one assistant, Clayton Graybill. Clayton was always upbeat, optimistic, and cheerful. He covered the entire hospital for many years with orders he filled in the store room. He was a delightful addition to the staff.

Ed Sontag, the chief engineer when I arrived, was another one who stands out. Ed didn't know the meaning of the word "No." His staff was competent in all areas of engineering—electrical, plumbing, and mechanical. He had a department that functioned smoothly. As with most good department heads, an indication of his worth was how little he bothered me. He was a self starter. After his death, he was replaced by Les McKay.

Les had worked in Dr. Smith's research in the Quonset huts as a biomedical engineer. He was an accomplished machinist. I watched him build an operating table by hand with his own milling machine. He came to my attention when he was the hospital representative for Medtronic, one of the first companies to produce heart pacemakers. On one of Les' early visits, it was determined that he would have to scrub for surgery and assist with our first pacemaker implant. This brought objection from members of the surgical staff, who said he had no business in surgery. After we discussed it with them, they realized they were defeating their own purpose because Les had the most knowledge about pacemaker implantation. He was permitted to scrub and supervise the installation of the first pacemakers in Washoe Medical Center and in northern Nevada. After that we had a smooth running operation.

When McKay took over as chief engineer, he was innovative, willing to take risk, and a self starter. In addition, the employees liked him. I particularly recall a problem we had with annual flooding of the laundry and adjoining departments. Frequently, water from Second Street backed up into the hospital. We had flooding so major that we were afraid it was going to come into contact with the steam rollers in the laundry and cause a major catastrophe. No one was able to find a solution until McKay came. He thought there was something he could do. He installed a butterfly valve between the main sewer lines on Second street and the hospital. When water came to a certain level the valve would close and there would be no further flooding of the hospital.

Among department heads of note was Jim Forrester, who took over as chief engineer after Les McKay. I met Jim on the carrier *U.S.S. Coral Sea* where he was in charge of the gunnery control division. He was a bright guy, and when he retired from the navy I asked him to come to the hospital. He agreed and turned out to be a mighty fine director of engineering. He was there during the major building project and helped the transition from the contractor to the hospital.

Genevieve, wife of sheriff Bud Young who died July 1996, was business manager when I arrived on the scene in 1957. Genevieve was really competent. She left Washoe Medical Center to work as a business manager for the orthopedic group of Herz, Sargent, and Teipner, where she worked for many years..

Jean Furler was our accountant, and she maintained her office on the second floor of the old administration building. Carl Bohall, Jean Bohall's husband, did a great job in the business and personnel offices.

Tess Larson was another business manager and her office was located across the hall from the physical therapy department in the old 1904 administration building. For many years Tess was the sole custodian of all payroll records. She was the one who prepared all the checks twice a month for the entire staff. I always regretted hearing her call for me to come and sign checks because all checks had to be signed by hand by two members of the administrative staff—usually the administrator and the business manager. Bob Foster was the next full-time business manager. Bob assisted me through all of the years of building with his expertise as an accountant and auditor.

The first man to come in as a full-time computer specialist under Foster was Gerald Bartley. He was made to order for the evolutionary process we were undergoing with computers. Jerry was instrumental in moving the computer department into a Quonset hut, but it wasn't many years before that became inadequate and we moved into a leased building on Plumb Lane.

The evolutionary process of the computerization is something that is of interest. When I started at Washoe Medical Center, the extent of our computerization was an old war surplus Remington-Rand posting machine. When charges where made in the various departments, they were written down in a charge book which used carbon paper. There was one book for each department. Toward the end of the workday someone in each department tore the charge slips out of the book, separated them, and took them to the switch board room where they were sorted. They were organized for the posting operator, who sat at the Remington-Rand posting machine and charged all of the patients accounts for the preceding twelve hour period.

We posted everything, from each pill to central supplies to surgical, laboratory, and x-ray charges; all hospital charges went on the patient bill. It was a lengthy process, made possible only by the fact that there weren't many patients; therefore, the posting machine was adequate. The evolutionary process continued, and we went to a peg board system. The charge ticket had round holes on the left border, and it was put on a peg board containing the ledger. As charges were made, the operator turned a wheel on the left, and it brought the next charge down to align with other charges. The charges made from the departments and the tickets were separated and sent to the switchboard.

The next step in the evolutionary process was to utilize magnetic cards. Much of the information on each patient was on a magnetic card, and this translated into the information needed to summarize charge data. From the magnetic card we went to the first humble beginnings of computerization. We started with a Burroughs system, and it didn't seem to work at all. Then, we went to IBM [International Business Machine] and didn't have good luck with that. We transferred to the NCR [National Cash Register] system, and for several months we used the NCR and the IBM simultaneously until we could eliminate the IBM system. We had a lot of problems, but at no time was the system completely down. The secret to our success with the final NCR 2000 system was that we proceeded slowly and cautiously instead of jumping from one system to another, and allowing for the probability of the whole thing collapsing.

The personnel director was Pearl O'Boyle, the wife of the under sheriff Dick O'Boyle. Pearl did a great job with the resources available. One thing that stands out in my memory was the day she came to Clyde Fox requesting authorization for more help and Clyde said, "What is our hospital compliment of employees right now?" She immediately replied, "290." Fox said that he would authorize five additional people on a priority basis. O'Boyle was succeeded by LuAnn Kamprath who was brought by Mr. Horton from Sutter Hospital in Sacramento. She resigned after three years to join the Kaiser system in Sacramento.

Her replacement as personnel chief was Roy Sampson, who was a retired Air Force Major. Roy was with me many years and was a competent manager. He was personnel director when the hospital was experiencing its greatest growth. We never had serious union problems, a credit to Roy because of the nifty way he looked after and anticipated the employees' needs. It was Roy who made the suggestion to me that upon retirement each employee should be entitled to their health insurance at the hospital's expense. We did a survey to determine the amount of retired employees, and it didn't seem to be too great a number; we could handle the additional expense. I went to the Board and they agreed. When employees retired they kept their health insurance until they died.

Leon Garrett functioned well as chief tech in the laboratory, especially at a time when the laboratory was experiencing phenomenal growth. Leon was the chief tech for over ten years and did a great job assisting Dr. Salvadorini.

The first laundry manager was an old Italian gent, Joe Zamboni, who spoke broken English, but had a department with few problems. Joe's wife, Rose, worked on the folding machine. We never had complaints about or from him, even under difficult circumstances. There was no air conditioning in the laundry, and all folding was done by hand. I worked with Zamboni for a week when I was an administrative resident. Clyde Fox wanted me to learn how to run the laundry in case I would be needed in the future. The thing that impressed me most about Zamboni was the fact that he didn't have any written instructions for the mixture of water and soap, etc. It was all in his head. It was a scoop of this and a scoop of that. At any rate I guess one measure of the efficiency of his system was that we never had any complaints about sore hind ends, on the newborns or anyone else for that matter.

Zamboni was replaced by Leonard "Roy" Hogan, who again was one of those department heads who got stuck with major expansion, the acquisition of major new equipment, and expansion of hospital beds. Roy was another self starter who never had to be told what to do. He rarely had any problems in his department and deserves a cluster of distinguished service crosses for the years of service he gave Washoe Medical Center. I respected him greatly and always will.

The department head in the x-ray department during all those early years was Eldon Phillips whose claim to fame was his fantastic knowledge of equipment—what made it go, how to take it apart, and how to get it working again. He also had a fantastic knowledge of mechanics. He ran an excellent x-ray department for the radiologists. Phil took a leave of absence for one year to go to the Middle East on the hospital ship, *U.S.S. Hope*, which had been in mothballs for years. Phil went as the chief tech of the x-ray department, and after they were underway he discovered that the x-ray equipment was still in the boxes from the manufacturer. It fell to him to get it unpacked and up and running, which he did. He and his relatively inexperienced crew accomplished an almost impossible task.

Our chief pharmacist was Sam Roberts, a mustachioed man about five feet six inches, but he was a skilled pharmacist and an efficient manager. When he retired, Howard Epling, a registered pharmacist who had owned DuPont Drug Store in Elko, Nevada, replaced him.

Epling was referred to me by Dick Rogers, who knew Epling when Dick was a surgical supply detail man. Howard had tired of the small town life and wanted to move to Reno. He took on the jobs of Chief Pharmacist and Director of Purchasing. He proved to be one of the greatest hires that I ever made. I came to love him greatly.

The purchasing agent prior to Howard Epling was Chet English, who was there when I arrived on the scene. He must have been in his mid-seventies, and he was an irascible old goat, but he got the job done and that's all I wanted. He came to work at about 6:30 in the morning, and his first job was to sort the sack of mail that had been deposited at the front entrance of the Administration Building on Mill Street. He took the sack into the Board Room which was to the left of the entrance, sorted it, and distributed it within thirty minutes. That included patient mail. Contrasting that with what it must take today, Chet did it in just a few minutes.

Dick Rogers came to the hospital from the Eugene Benjamin Company, where he had been a detail (sales) man for many years. I was elated when he agreed to come to Washoe Medical Center because I respected Dick. We had a wonderful relationship for all the years that he was with me as Purchasing Director.

I had only one uncomfortable experience with Chet, and that was when I was an administrative resident. I worked in the cashier's cage during vacation periods. There were only two employees, and they covered the hospital for twelve hours shifts, so it made a seven-day week, twelve-hour day for me. One morning Chet came and asked for something out of the cashier's cage. I responded and said, "Good morning, Dad." He gave me the most stern stare that I have ever had in my life, and said, "Goddamn you, Ogren, nobody ever calls me 'Dad.'" That taught me a lesson.

One of the early assistants was Norm Peterson, who got his graduate degree from Trinity University in Texas. Norm was an intelligent and capable guy who was with me through many of the difficult years. I know that I made life more difficult for him by my problem with the "grape," and I will always be grateful to him. He was joined by Mike Newmarker, who was Mrs. Pringle's grandson. I assisted Mike by giving him summer work. He worked in various departments of the hospital, and after he graduated from the University of Nevada, I was instrumental in getting him in the School of Hospital Administration at Washington University in Saint Louis. Mike was my successor when I left the medical center.

Bill Sthultz was my controller for a few years. He came on a recommendation from Dr. Don Mohler who knew him when Shultz was credit manager for Zales Jewelry store. He did an outstanding job in bringing the business office operations into the computer age. In those days it was still quite medieval when compared to what we have today. He left Washoe Medical Center to move to Las Vegas where he became Administrator of Rose De Lima Hospital in Henderson.

Of the long line of surgery supervisors, I would say that Ruth Hoffman was a standout. She had a job that required the patience of Job and the authority of labor boss George Meany. She had to keep the surgeons corralled, not only from the standpoint of scheduling, but from the standpoint of carrying out the rules and regulations of the department. She walked this thin line for years without a misstep.

During the years, there were two or three occasions when we were without a surgical supervisor; sometimes we made the changes, and other times people quit. When this happened we called on Maida Pringle to take charge. I knew that she hated it, but she would put on her green scrub uniform and run the department. It was always nice to know that we had her for a backup.

My Chief Nursing Supervisor, Daphane Green, was also incomparable. Daphane was a fiery red head who would say it like it was. She ran an efficient nursing department, and was with me for many years. Her husband was an American Indian who was in the roofing business. He was a delightful person. Daphane was one who enjoyed a party, and if she got a little high, you learned in a hurry exactly what she thought, but it was all forgotten the next day. As a nursing supervisor she was without a peer. She had some great nursing department heads with her in those days. She had floor nurses and charge nurses who were a great asset to her; she recognized it, and so did I. One who stands out was Red Johnson who supervised Second East. Red had known Pringle for thirty or forty years. She was a no-nonsense nurse who ran an efficient floor. She was missed when she left.

Another department head who stands out was Helen Nichols in medical records. Helen was a thin, acerbic, anxious women with a high pitched voiced. At that time medical records was on the second floor of the Administration Building. Her relationship with Mr. Fox deteriorated during my residency year. She quit, and I was forced into running medical records. Helen Nichols was succeeded by Juanita Skaggs, and she was replaced by Ida Vivian McCulley. These women can be credited with the maintenance of our accreditation success over the years because valid, quality record keeping was the linchpin of the accreditation process. I always marveled at how the transcribers successfully translated thousands of pages weekly. They endured a dozen different foreign accents and recognized nomenclature representing every medical and surgical specialty. Moreover, there was rarely any transcription lost. They tolerated the chronic, aching problem manifested by a small group of doctors who consistently failed to maintain records on a timely basis. The same thing happened in the central supply department. Mrs. Cunningham grew increasingly more dissatisfied with Clyde Fox. She came to me one day and said, "I am sick and tired of this job. In fact, I am so tired of it I have my resignation in my purse."

I said, "If you have it in your purse, why don't you give it to me." She did, and I accepted her resignation and informed Clyde Fox. He said, "Fine, you're going to run the department until we get a replacement."

. . .

The first Director of Public Relations at Washoe was Dick Rhyno who came from the TB association where he had been a public relations director. Dick performed in an admirable way. I gave him a picture of me that he copied and asked me to inscribe on it for his memory book. I wrote, "To Dick Rhyno who made me look good, Affectionately Carroll."

Barbara Lindh was in the admitting department for twenty-four years when she retired. How she took over that job is of some interest. When I first met Barbara, she was working for the Washoe County Welfare Department along with Corinne Thomas and Irene Darlington. They would come into the hospital from their offices in the County Building to review patient applications for county assistance. These were patients the admitting department deemed to be indigent and incapable of paying for their hospital care. Barbara Lindh was always critical of the way this whole operation was handled, feeling that there was not close enough coordination between Washoe County and the hospital. As a result, one day I told her to stop complaining; if she thought she could do better, I would give her the opportunity to takeover the Admitting Department. She agreed, so subsequently Barbara was hired to take charge of the department. From that point on, our problems decreased. She did a stellar job. I never regretted putting her in that spot. It taught me a valuable lesson: If you get a complainer, give them a chance to correct the problem.

Other department heads with long distinguished records include Sari Nash, who headed the EKG department, and Clare Talbot, who directed the EEG section. In the early years, the physical therapy department was in the 1906 building and was headed by an English lady, Joan Lewis. She was succeeded by Lawrence Mooney who presided over tremendous expansion of the department. He was also responsible for the cardiac rehabilitation program. Del McConnel oversaw the inhalation therapy department and shepherded its expansion.

Our first diener (autopsy assistant) in the morgue was Jim Holdridge, who had worked as a laboratory assistant and diener for Dr. Salvadorini.[52] Jim had a lot of ambition. He demonstrated he could do a lot when given the responsibility. He developed an interest in photography by photographing specimens for the laboratory and surgical departments. He took on the task of heading the first photography department, which was based in the pathology laboratory. After Washoe Medical Center, he went to Redding, California, where he is still employed in a hospital as the assistant administrator. Jim was replaced in photography by Gene Spoon, who performed admirably, not only in photography, but in supervising the utilization of the multitude of meeting rooms in the Hospital.

## Departments

During the sixty and seventies, due to the generosity of many gift givers and the steadily increasing improvement in medical center finances, we established the following departments: epidemiology, hemodialysis, infant intensive care, coronary care, cardiac surgery, cardiac catheterization, telemetry, nuclear medicine, respiratory therapy, pulmonary function, physical medicine and rehabilitation, social services, chaplain program, audio visual department, data processing, employee health service, optometric photography, poison control center, child abuse center, public relations department, general intensive care, speech therapy, endoscopy, obstetrics operating room, and security and investigation, to name a few.

Many of the above departments deserve special mention. For example, I encountered resistance when I felt it was time to hire a social worker. There was a particular need in the emergency department because we had such heavy traffic with tourists. A social worker could be of valuable assistance to people from out of town who had a loved one hospitalized. In other cases, a visitor to Reno would die, and the family had no one to assist them in this time of need.

When I hired our first medical social worker, Mike Hoover, the resistance was largely from medical staff who felt that a social worker had no business looking at patients' charts. After a few months on the job, Mike proved to be a tremendous asset to the medical staff, and they welcomed his assistance. Mike was followed by several other social workers, over the years which was a good demonstration that they were needed.

· · ·

Generally, the nursing staff was not a problem, and certainly they are
the backbone of hospital care. We had an emergency when a nursing
committee came to me and told me they wanted permission to wear
pants suits. When I took this to Mrs. Pringle, I thought she was going to go into orbit. After much discussion we decided we would give
it a try because, after all, the nurses were required to do lifting and
bending. Pant suits were white, clean, and well fitted; there was nothing wrong with them. Of course, it wasn't long before pants suits
came in vogue for nurses.

The next big crisis came when the nurses came to me saying they
no longer wanted to wear their caps. Again this brought loud cries
from the old-time nurses who felt that a cap was a sign of dignity and
put them in the same category with Florence Nightingale. After much
discussion, it was agreed that if they wanted to do away with caps,
they were welcome to do so.

## Women's League

When the Women's League constitution and bylaws were passed in
April 1950, the first president elected was Gladys Mapes, mother of
Charles Mapes, the general manager and owner of the Mapes Hotel.
I will always believe that Gladys was elected to this position because
of her wealth and influence in Nevada. She never did a lot of volunteer work, but she was always at the meetings. The League's ability to
raise money was important to the hospital. When we were losing
$20,000 annually in maternity, the League always helped out. At that
time the daily rate for a maternity patient was eight dollars.

Norman Biltz's wife was a loyal member of the Women's League.
She was the daughter of Hugh Auchincloss, Jackie Kennedy's stepfa-
ther. She arrived in Reno for divorce back in the forties and stayed at
one of the dude ranches. In the course of her stay, she met Norman,
who was an itinerant cab driver, and they ended up getting married.
Norman had inherent intelligence and the ability to turn her money
into additional millions. (See History of the Women's League in Appendix XII)

### Philanthropists

There were times in 1957 and 1958 that if it hadn't been for money raised by the Women's League, the hospital would have gone under. We were really in sad shape financially, but I think when it came to being Santa Klaus, the Fleischmann Foundation best fit the bill. Members of the Foundation had known Max Fleischmann during his early days in the Reno-Tahoe area. As I understood it, Mr. Bergin, chairman of the Foundation, had been Max Fleischmann's accountant. One of the other members of the Foundation, Sessions Wheeler, had been his hunting partner. Fran Breen had been a house boy for Max Fleischmann before he became an attorney. I got to know Leo Bergin through membership in the Reno Rotary Club.

While I was a resident, Mr. Bergin wrote a letter to Mr. Fox asking him for a list of things needed by the hospital. Fox immediately complied, and the list ran to well over a million dollars for x-ray and laboratory equipment and new beds for the entire hospital. Most of our beds were old and without automatic controls. We were in dire need of x-ray and laboratory equipment. This list was given to the Fleischmann Foundation, and the week before Christmas we got a check for the total amount of the request. The Fleischmann Foundation requested that every ninety days we provide them with a status report on what we had purchased and whether it was in operation or not. We were fussy about complying with their wishes, and it apparently pleased them because each year for at least four or five years I got similar instruction from the Foundation to provide them with a list of things we needed. It was always answered in full, and I religiously followed their instructions on informing them of what we had done with the money. I even invited them over to see what we had done with the money. It turned out to be a real bonanza for us when we were short of funds.

After the first year, other county hospitals in the state, along with Saint Mary's Hospital, were included in this program. Some of the small county hospitals throughout the state benefited greatly from this program. Many of these hospitals were constantly on the ropes financially.

Max Fleischmann, who lived at Lake Tahoe, was diagnosed with brain cancer, and committed suicide by shooting himself. The provisions of his will indicated that the corpus of the foundation he had established be spent within twenty years of the death of his wife, Sara. After Mr. Fleischmann's death, we continued to benefit from the terms of the will until the termination of the Foundation Trust.

Another of the hospital benefactors back in the late' 50s and early '60s was Mabel Isbell, the wife of C. V. Isbell who was the president of the Isbell Construction Company. He also had extensive copper mines in Arizona and had a corporate airplane. I think it was my first year as a resident when I got to know Mabel through Maida Pringle. They were fast friends. Mabel was a member of the Nevada State Legislature and introduced me from her desk on the floor during a session. Mabel also made generous gifts to the hospital.

Isbell Construction Company built many of the highways and bridges in Nevada's highway system. Moreover, in 1914 Isbell built the first graded road from Carson City to Lake Tahoe, using mules and Fresno scrapers. Before the new road was built, C. V. Isbell wanted the contract so badly that he underbid it. At any rate, Isbell got the contract and completed the road over Spooner Summit. Before the new highway opened, Mabel called me and asked me if I would like to see it. I was a resident so it would have been in the neighborhood of 1957. At any rate Mabel picked me up in her Cadillac, and we drove down to Carson City where we had dinner at the Carson City Nugget. We pro°ceeded to the new highway, where the foreman recognized Mrs. Isbell; he pulled the barricade aside, and we drove up the unopened highway all the way to Lake Tahoe.

Mabel was a real rugged character. When they were building these roads, she had a bunch of little kids; I think she had four or five children. She cooked for the road crews from a tent at the construction site; that's how versatile of an individual she was. Coming back down the highway that evening we were somewhere between Carson City and Reno when Mabel turned to me and said, "These Goddamn teeth." She pulled her uppers and lowers out of her mouth and put them in her purse. Then, she was more comfortable. She was a character, but she had a heart as big as all outdoors and thought the world of Washoe Medical Center and everything that it was trying to do.

Mabel took ill with heart disease and was scheduled to go to San Francisco to get one of the first pacemakers. She told Mrs. Pringle and me that she didn't want to go, that she had lived long enough, and that it was an unnecessary trip. She was scheduled to leave by ambulance the following morning, but that night, in accordance with her wishes, she expired.

Tom Dant was a man who turned out to be a good friend of the hospital. He lived on Greenridge Drive in a big, sprawling green house that was later bought by casino owner Leon Nightingale, whose wife was a pediatric nurse at Washoe Medical Center. Dant accumulated his fortune through three sources: Cunard Shipping Lines, Singer Sewing Machine, and Dant Liquor Company. He was a huge man and must have weighed all of 400 pounds. It was difficult for him to get around. He had a big round face with huge jowls, but nobody was more generous. He had an office across the street and just south of the court house. He would periodically call me over to his office and say, "Carroll what do you need real bad right now?" I would tell him we needed a certain piece of equipment, and he would say, "Okay, I will write you a check." He would write a check, and we would buy the equipment.

## Maida Pringle, R.N.

One of the highlights of sharing office space with Mrs. Pringle was the fact that it gave me the opportunity to meet everybody who was anybody in the State of Nevada or the City of Reno. She had a steady stream of visitors through her office, from U. S. Senators to local politicians. One politician I met in her office was Charley Cowen, a powerhouse on the City Council and a Reno barber. In her office I met the likes of U. S. Congressman Molly Malone, Senator Bible, and University of Nevada officials. It also gave me an opportunity to meet the bulk of the doctors on the staff. All of them seemed to come into her office at one time or another to register a complaint or sit and visit. It was accepted practice to stop and visit with her. Some came for the primary purpose of seeing her, but many were coming to visit their patients in the hospital. Many people visited Mrs. Pringle or made phone calls to her asking for favors, everything from getting a relative a summer job to arranging a better bed for a patient.

I think the reason these people went to Maida rather than going to the administrator was first, the administrator didn't have the time for prolonged visits; and second, he didn't have the contacts in Reno or in Nevada that Maida had. The feeling was that one could get action a whole lot quicker by going to her than going to the administrator.

While I was an administrative resident, I shared office space with Mrs. Pringle even though I reported strictly to Clyde Fox. (Mrs. Pringle was in Reno a fair amount of time before Clyde Fox, who arrived in 1949.) After I finished my residency, I got my own office and still reported to Mr. Fox.

During the twenty-one year period of my relationship with Mrs. Pringle, we became close friends. I learned a lot from her. Maida was an assertive person. She graduated in nursing from White Hospital School of Nursing in Sacramento and started work at Washoe Medical Center in 1941 and became director of nursing in October 1945.

Mrs. Pringle was married to Johnny Pringle, who owned a bar in Reno, and she had two children with Johnny. He was noted as a real practical joker in the Reno community, but he was well-liked and his nickname was "Knothole Pringle." The local Reno baseball team he played on at the Moana Stadium gave him the nickname when he hit a home run that went through a knothole in the fence. Maida and Johnny had a difficult marriage, and it finally ended in a divorce. The divorce bothered Mrs. Pringle. It wasn't long after the divorce that Johnny died in 1947.

Their son Jack was a popular all-state basketball player at Reno High School, and in 1950 he was killed in a car accident west of Reno. This was a real blow to her. Her daughter, Pat, was married to Len Newmarker, and Maida lived with them for many years. When Pat died it left another void in Mrs. Pringle's life. She has a grandson, Mike Newmarker who currently is an insurance broker in Reno, and a granddaughter, Jackie.

I got to know Mike when he worked summers in the hospital, and I asked him if he would be interested in a career in hospital administration. He answered in the affirmative, and I recommended him to Washington University; he was accepted and graduated in hospital administration. He returned to Washoe Medical Center where he worked in the business office until I made him assistant administrator.

When Dr. Mack advised Mrs. Pringle that he wasn't going to run for the Board, Maida went down that same afternoon, filed for the office, and of course, she won by a wide margin. It was said that any doctor or person with a hospital background didn't have much difficulty in winning a Board seat, but Maida won on her own popularity.

Through all the years I was associated with Maida Pringle as assistant administrator, a couple of incidents are worthy of mention. Maida's office was always considered sacred territory. If her door was closed, you did not walk in because she was engaged in some highly confidential meeting with a doctor. On one particular occasion I had to see her, so I opened the door; Mrs. Pringle was seated away from her desk and a psychiatrist was seated in a chair near her. She had rolled her chair over to him and was sitting in her unique manner with her hands on her knees. This was her favorite way of sitting when addressing people's problems. At any rate Mrs. Pringle was sitting there consulting with this psychiatrist. He was sobbing profusely, and I thought what a sight, now here's Maida Pringle consulting with a psychiatrist, and the psychiatrist is the one receiving therapy.

Another noteworthy and comical experience involving Mrs. Pringle occurred when the University of Nevada Psychology Department had a chimpanzee named Washoe. This chimpanzee was taught how to recognize sign language and names in connection with a social experiment. On this one particular morning the researchers, Beatrice and Alan Gardner, brought Washoe into my office. She was fully diapered and was a friendly little gal. I asked if I could take her down to meet Mrs. Pringle. They said, "Sure."

I put my arms out, the chimp came to me, put her arms around my neck, and we headed down the hallway to Mrs. Pringle's office. Now keep in mind that no animal of any kind was ever allowed in the hospital, let alone a chimp. Pringle's office door was closed, and again I didn't respect it as I should have. I opened the door, walked in with Washoe, and said, "Maida this little gal wants to go to work." I thought that she was going to jump out of her chair, but after she got over her initial shock, she agreed the chimp was mighty cute, but she wouldn't go along with any talk of employment for the little gal.

On another occasion, a Reno bank president was sitting in her office talking with her. I happened to be in on the conversation. It was part of the morning visitations that occurred in her office. The banker felt that he was God's gift to women and was always reciting tales of his exploits and seduction of the fair sex. He was reciting one of his conquests and Pringle looked at him with a stern eye and said, "You know, what you ought to do is blow your nose, it's all in your head."

There are too many stories associated with Mrs. Pringle to relate. One involved Jay Barker, who headed a small company that provided homemade printing systems for various businesses. Jay worked with me early on at Washoe Medical Center. We were going through the evolutionary process of getting a more sophisticated accounts receivable system set up. He provided us with the departmental booklets upon which charge tickets were made out for every service rendered. He related the following story to me.

Jay's future wife, Connie, was a registered nurse at Washoe Medical Center before they ever became acquainted. It seems that Jay had been injured in an auto wreck and was pretty seriously hurt. He was brought to Washoe Medical Center where he was put back together and spent several weeks as a patient. At one point he was in an oxygen tent. Of course in those days it was actually a tent which was composed of canvas and plastic and covered the patient from the waist level out over the head. There were always very serious problems from the standpoint of anyone attempting to smoke a cigarette or get anything with a combustion nature near to them.

On one particular night after Connie had been taking care of Jay for a few weeks, she had completed his evening care, and before she shut the flap to the oxygen tent she leaned in and kissed him. They had become fast friends by this time. Much to Connie's surprise, standing in the doorway watching this procedure was Maida Pringle. She said, "My, you do give efficient patient care, don't you?" With that she asked Connie to report to her office when she was finished with the patient. She went there scared half to death. Maida Pringle instructed her that from now on, her patient care would not include a good night kiss.

Following are the highlights of Mrs. Pringle's career. Maida Jasper Pringle was born and reared in Wheatland, California. After graduating in 1924 from the last class to attend White Nursing School in Sacramento, she worked at Children's Hospital in San Francisco,

Sutter Hospital in Sacramento, and Riverside Hospital in Susanville. In Susanville she married John Pringle, a Reno Native, and had two children. In 1930 the family moved to Reno, but Mrs. Pringle didn't start working at Washoe Medical Center until 1941.

After starting at the hospital, she served as night supervisor, afternoon supervisor, and surgery supervisor, and then in 1945, she was appointed Nursing Supervisor. After moving up to Assistant Administrator in 1952, she had been the acting administrator on at least four occasions. In recognition of her leadership and dedication to Washoe Medical Center, the street leading to the main entrance of the hospital was named Pringle Way, and the medical staff bestowed honorary membership upon her. The following article in the *Nevada State Journal* relates some of her accomplishments:

"Among the civic and professional groups Mrs. Pringle has been active in during her career at Washoe Med is the Quota Club International. She was president of the Reno chapter and then lieutenant governor and governor of the Northern Nevada and California district from 1969 to 1971.

"She served as a member of the Governor's Committee on Hospitals under former Governor Charles Russell and on the Nursing Home Administrators Licensing Board under former Governor Paul Laxalt and Governor Mike O'Callaghan.

"She was a member of the Orvis School of Nursing advisory committee from 1958 to 1972 and served as its chairman in 1968. She [was] chairman of the advisory committee of the Washoe Western School of Practical Nursing at Washoe Med.

"In 1972 she received the Meritorious Service medal from the Nevada Selective Service for her work during 15 years as a member of the Advisory Committee on Medical, Dental and Allied Medical Personnel."

Mrs. Pringle is the only person who served in all major capacities in the hospital. She was Director of Nursing, Administrator, Chairman of the Board of Trustees, and an Honorary Member of the medical staff. —No one exemplifies the spirit of Washoe Medical Center more than Maida Jasper Pringle, R.N.—

## Larry Russell, M.D.[53]

In looking back over the years, I think one of the most valuable people that Washoe Medical Center ever employed was Dr. Larry Russell who in the early days took care of all the indigent patients all by himself. Before he came to Washoe Medical Center, he was in Eureka for a short time; Clyde Fox heard from a detail man (drug company salesman) that Dr. Russell might be interested in coming to Reno.

He was hired in 1949, and he was one of the last county physicians. Washoe County eliminated the job two weeks after he was hired, but he continued to be the doctor for indigents and was the Director of the County Clinic. He saw his patients out of the little white house which was in the middle of the parking lot, just east of the old 1904 Administration Building. His nurse was Rose Costa, an Indian lady who had the same compassion for indigent patients as he did. Both of them were much loved by their patients and the medical staff.

Larry and Louise told me about the time they stood up as a witness for Dr. George Smith, dean of the medical school, when he married Norice Conant. They climbed down a cliff at Lake Tahoe and stood barefooted in the sand for the marriage.

Larry was married to Louise Russell, a registered nurse, but when they arrived in Reno, Louise didn't work as an R.N.; she was strictly a homemaker. One of my favorite reminiscences about Larry is the time we were sitting and chatting in his office. We both noticed a Catholic priest who parked in the lot, and had been there for some time in his car all alone. It got to be quite a long time, and we both became curious. Suddenly, a white Cadillac convertible appeared and pulled up next to his car; he got out, took off his collar; a blond lady in the Cadillac handed him a cardigan sweater; he climbed into her car, and off they went. We didn't attach a whole lot of significance to this, but it was one of those incidents that are not forgotten.

## Staff Secretaries

Narrative about my years at Washoe Medical Center would be incomplete without giving credit to Pat Keough, who was my secretary for eighteen years. Pat came to the hospital from Transwestern Insurance Company, and went to work as Earl Horton's secretary. It happened that Horton was out of town when I interviewed Pat, but I was impressed with her. I hired her, and she worked for Earl Horton. Some time later Pat indicated to me that she was having difficulty with Horton. I needed a secretary, so I went to Horton and asked if it was all right if I took Pat to work for me. He agreed and that began an association that lasted for many years.

Never, in all those years, did I see her come to work in any skirt or dress that was not neat and professional. She always looked as though she had stepped out of a catalog. Not only was she professional, but she could do correspondence without being told. I think one of the best indices of her ability and her trustworthiness was the fact that she didn't tell anyone about administrative business. She kept everything in confidence; for this reason she was respected by hospital staff and her peers.

I remember Pat's never ending struggle with the transcription of Board minutes. This was a job that weighed heavily on her at times, but she did the job with competence. I am sure that if these records are reviewed historically, they would be found in perfect order from the standpoint of what actually went on in meetings. I was really honored to be invited to say a few words at Pat's retirement party. I will always remember her as a trusted friend, and I have a great fondness for her.

Some mention should be made of the other secretarial staff from my days in the administration department. The first secretary for Mr. Fox was Mrs. Dyer, who was a respectable lady in her early 60s and did a fine job for Mr. Fox. I recall that many years later Mrs. Dyer was killed when struck by a car in an intersection in Carson City.

Mr. Fox's second secretary was Gay Hotchkiss, a very attractive young woman whose father was Jess Hotchkiss, the bass player for Kay Martin and her Body Guards—a small musical group that appeared in the casino lounges around Reno. Kay Martin maintained a lodge in South Reno which was a motel of sorts.

Later on, Jackie Hollar did some service as Mr. Fox's secretary. Gay Hotchkiss was the last secretary for Clyde Fox. When I was made assistant administrator, my first secretary was Bertha Pepper. She was married to an executive with Bell Telephone of Nevada and had five daughters. I remember one of her daughters had the first name of

Ginger and the last name of Pepper. My second secretary was Jackie Hollar, who later went to work for the Reno College of Trial Lawyers. Jackie was followed by Pat Keough.

From the standpoint of medical staff secretaries, Jean Bohall was the best, who knew medical staff business forwards and backwards. She got along well with the medical staff and was called by them "Washoe's BBC" (Bohall Broadcasting Company). When you consider that she worked with doctors representing every specialty, and doctors who had their own personal problems, she related extremely well to them. Jean had the confidence of the medical staff. She spent as much time listening to their personal problems as she did to their professional problems. She was another one to whom I was indebted. I am glad she was with me until I left Washoe Medical Center.

## Personalities

I knew several real characters at Washoe Medical Center. Kris Kakoris, an old Greek gentlemen and the transportation orderly in the surgery department for over forty years, was a hospital institution. Kris spoke broken English. He was married to Helen Hall, who was one of our two cashiers and a delightful lady. Kris was always in his hospital greens pushing patients to and from surgery. I think the most remarkable thing about Kris was the magnificent manner he had with making patients feel at ease. One of the first things he would ask them as he was wheeling them to surgery was who their surgeon was. And regardless of who it was, regardless of the surgeon's ability, Kris would pat them on the head or stroke their forehead and say, particularly with the women, "Honey, that is the best surgeon there is in this country." I am sure he put an awful lot of people, frightened to death of surgery, at ease. He was a guy who was also much loved by the surgeons and anesthesiologists. He carried their meals from the cafeteria to the surgery lounge; he knew all of their names and what they liked and disliked. Another surgery orderly who did a great job curbing patient's anxiety was Laconsey "Bob" Ponciano.

Another real character was Warren "Shorty" Holcomb. Shorty was a "little person" who lived in Redwood Pavilion for many years. He was a familiar fixture in the halls of the hospital with his wheelchair that operated on a ratchet system with handles that he controlled by hand. He propelled the wheelchair by pushing the handles back and forth. A year or two before he died, the Women's League gave him a magnificent new electric wheelchair. Then, Shorty had the finest transportation available.

For many years Shorty covered the entire hospital selling newspapers. He appeared at every patient room throughout the hospital, not only selling newspapers, but being an effective hospital spokesman. Everybody loved Shorty. He was a descendent of the wealthy Reno family after whom Holcomb Lane was named. He was hospitalized in Redwood Pavilion because of his inability to walk. When Shorty was finished with his route in the hospital, he would return to Redwood, and they would transfer him from his wheelchair to a small, three-wheel scooter. It was on this scooter that Shorty made his way around Redwood Pavilion.

Another loyal hospital personality was our gardener, Caesar Lombardi. He was a fine old Italian gentlemen and did everything possible to keep our yards and gardens looking ship shape. Each spring Caesar trucked in steer manure from a nearby farm, and with his little Case tractor distributed steer manure over all of the lawn areas, ensuring that as summer came we would have the most beautiful lawn in town. I will never forget one unfortunate incident that he provoked.

One lovely spring morning, I got several particularly angry calls from members of the medical staff. On this particular day, the steer manure was all in place when a helicopter came in from Herlong with two soldiers who had been injured in an explosion. It had to be one of the Army's largest helicopters. It was so big it could carry a jeep, and it had a crew of eight. The chopper came in and made one pass around the hospital to ensure a proper landing in the park across the street. In doing so it not only tore a lot of branches from trees but it also scattered manure for hundreds of feet. As luck would have it, the area hit the hardest was the doctors' parking lot where many had left their car windows open and a few convertibles had their tops down. Of course, they were covered with manure from front to rear. I took the brunt of the blame for that.

We had a character who regularly attended the medical staff meetings. He was a psychiatrist who also taught a philosophy course at the

University of Nevada. He had an alcohol problem. He would come to the hospital in an old rust colored Renault; I am sure it was probably the only one in the entire State of Nevada. He would arrive in his Renault with two standard size poodles. One was dyed pink and the other one was dyed blue. He would take the poodles out of the small back seat of the car and lead them to the railing of the old 1906 Building where he would tie them up while he was in the meeting.

He would generally arrive under the influence and would not say a thing in the meeting, but nonetheless he was there. The thing that I remembered the most about him was at the conclusion of the meetings, he would untie his two poodles and then walk back and forth in the parking lot trying to find this rust colored Renault. It was the only one within a thousand miles, but he always had trouble finding it.

At one point he hadn't appeared at the hospital for several days, and I remarked about this to Dr. Russell. He and I went out to his apartment, which was on St. Lawrence Avenue, one block west of South Virginia. We looked in the window and saw him lying on the floor with nothing on but a pair of jockey shorts. We contacted the manager and gained access to the apartment. He was lying unconscious on a floor covered with wrappers of chocolate Hershey bars and a number of empty quarts of vodka. We took him to the hospital where he was placed in the critical care ward. He recovered and his sister came from the East to take him there for recovery. I don't know how long he lived after that, but he never did return to Reno.

Early during my residency at Washoe, I became a fast friend of Dr. Salvadorini, who was the pathologist in charge of the laboratory. Dr. Vasco "Sal" Salvadorini was the only pathologist at the time. Of course, the laboratory staff was small. I helped with weekend projects at Dr. Sal's home on Pheasant Lane. On one occasion, he and I were clearing his pasture of rocks; it seemed that his place manufactured rocks during the week so we could clear them on the weekend. Dr. Sal borrowed a manure truck from Ben Caramella who was the owner of the Reno Disposal Service. Ben lived on a small ranch off of South Virginia Street. We would go there to pick up the manure truck on Saturday mornings.

On one particular weekend, we had half filled this truck with rocks. We were in a jovial mood and thought we would pull a trick on Larry

Devincinzi who lived in an exclusive Reno neighborhood about one block from Dr. Salvadorini. We drove the truck down to Larry Devincinzi's property and parked it right on the periphery of the front yard. I went to the door to get Larry to answer the door bell. When he opened the door, Dr. Sal hit the lever on the truck and dumped this whole load of rock in Larry's front lawn. Of course, we paid the price in that we had to pick up the rock.

The manure truck had sides on it that were quite high, permitting them to load the manure beyond the normal capacity of the truck. At any rate, we had finished our work on this one Sunday. It was always our procedure to take the truck down to the Standard Oil Station on the corner of Plumb Lane and South Virginia to fill it with gas. Dr. Sal was driving and we went zooming into the gas station not making provisions for the canopy over the gas pumps. Not only did we wreck the sides of the truck, but we tore down the canopy of the gas station. Dr. Sal had to pay for fixing both the truck and the station. He would have been better off if he hired someone to do the work in his yard.

We had a medical staff outlaw in the early 1960s named Dr. William J. Bryan. He was a heavy set, or I should say fat, gynecologist. He came into the hospital to make rounds on the weekends wearing a one piece USAF jumpsuit with two six shooters, one on each hip. Often times he brought his young son with him. The six shooters put fear into some of the staff members, because they all recognized that he was something of an eccentric. At any rate I confronted him and told him that he would no longer be permitted to wear his six shooters while making rounds at the hospital. He was forced to leave them with the switch board operator and pick them up on his way out.

In addition to his private practice, Dr. Bryan did physical exams for some of the brothels in the area. What made him even more famous, and resulted in him leaving town was an incident involving a minor girl. He ran for the Sparks City Council, and during the course of the campaign, he had a high school girl working for him in the office stuffing literature in envelopes. On this one particular occasion, he allegedly fed her alcoholic beverages and she became intoxicated and passed out. Dr. Bryan had been there with her and when she passed out, he locked up the office and went home. The girl woke up and called her boyfriend. He came down to pick her up, but couldn't get into the office, so he called the Sparks Police. They went in and took her to the hospital for further examination.

In 1961 Dr. Bryan was tried and convicted for contributing to the delinquency of a minor and agreed to leave the community. He left our area and moved to Los Angeles. Sometime later I saw a brochure and an article in a newsweek magazine describing a sex conference that Dr. Bryan was putting on in the Los Angeles area. It became quite a big thing. He received a lot of publicity.

# HOSPITAL POLITICS
## (During Mr. Ogren's Tenure)

### C. W. OGREN

### Hospital Accreditation

Hospital accreditation didn't come along until after World War II when the American College of Surgeons decided it was time for some sort of system to improve the quality of hospital care. For example, they were concerned about unnecessary surgery on teenage girls who were entering menarche and had abdominal pain. Some surgeons would do exploratory surgery and remove a normal appendix. In other instances, the pathologist's report indicated removal of a normal uterus. In fact, pathologists throughout the country were indicating that normal tissue was being removed. This was the spark behind the establishment of the Joint Commission. It was called the JCAH because several agencies went together to form this inspection body. I believe the first surveys were done in the 1955–'56 era, and Washoe Medical Center was among the first to be accredited. Our first accreditation was provisional because some corrections had to be made in medical staff and hospital records.

Looking back on the accreditation process, it was pretty scary because we feared that we would not become accredited. It was truly a mark of distinction if you gained accreditation. Failure marked you as a hospital that wasn't fit to care for patients. In the early days the accreditation team was made up of a physician and a hospital administrator. Both were retired and spent their retirement days surveying hospitals. They would come in for two or three days, examine medical records, surgical records, housekeeping, and numerous other departmental practices, and make a determination of denied or accrediation. The primary focus was medical records, where they made their determinations on the quality of care rendered by both the hospital and the physician. They also spent considerable time reviewing surgical procedures.

We were contacted by the accrediting team's physician six months before our accreditation survey. He would make certain demands for his stay. Most of the inspectors arrived in motor homes or trailer homes. They would write us to make provisions for an electrical supply to their recreation vehicle.

It became a common practice for hospitals throughout the country to lavishly entertain the survey teams. It seemed that there was a direct correlation between the entertainment provided and the success of your accreditation. For instance, at Washoe Medical Center we always provided two magnificent dinner meetings for the survey team where we would invite all of the medical department heads and the hospital department heads. This was always a special dinner and one that impressed the survey team.

We also saw to it that they attended one of the better shows available in Reno. It almost amounted to a bribery situation. In fact, the situation was out of control throughout the United States. When the accreditation survey was finished there was an accreditation closing conference. What was recited by the members of the survey team didn't always jive with what was later formally received in a letter delineating deficiencies.

The situation became so bad that a great number of hospital administrators and medical staffs objected to the way it was handled. As a result, a rule was instituted by the commission which required that all minutes of the closing conference be recorded to assure accuracy. We were later advised by the commission, as it evolved into a much better survey organization, that we were not to provide elaborate entertainment.

Once, we had a doctor survey member who impressed all of us as being something of an eccentric, senile old man. During the course of his survey, he went off the deep end, and we had to secure psychiatric help for him. We hospitalized him and released him to his wife who took him home in his trailer.

As the accreditation process evolved into what it is today, it became mandatory for hospitals to pass if they were to continue to receive full benefits under Medicare. One of the evolutions I was happy to see was the demand on the part of the accreditation commission that hospital medical records be completed in a timely period and not exceed ninety days. I was happy to see this evolve because it was always a thorn in my side as administrator to see the way these requirements were ignored by certain members of the medical staff.

There seemed to be a direct correlation between timely completion of medical records and how stern the Chief of the Medical Staff was in enforcing them. There were Chiefs of Staff over the years who were lax in enforcing this requirement. A few members of the medical staff were up to a year behind in the completion of their records.

In fact, one neurosurgeon, on several occasions while I was administrator, took one to two months off from his practice to do nothing but complete delinquent medical records. I remain convinced to this day that no doctor can review medical records that are a year old and recall exactly what he did in treating that patient. At another end of the spectrum, we had three surgeons who lost medical staff privileges because they were dictating progress notes immediately after dictating the surgical note at the end of the surgery procedure. These are just a few of the ways that hospital records were abused.

## Relations with Hospital-Based Physicians

A discussion in the July 1958 Board meeting was about the income of the pathologists, something that was jealously viewed by Mr. Fox, who felt that pathologists had no right getting a percentage of the revenue from laboratory procedures such as urinalysis. He was adamant about this even though pathologists perform supervision and are responsible for quality control of the procedure. Later, these heated discussion involved radiologists who wanted their patient income separated from the hospital bill. They wanted to do their own billing. Their argument centered on the fact that the American Medical Association agreed that they were like other physician and were responsible to the patient, and not the hospital, for medical treatment and diagnosis. In 1966 when Medicare became law, the government stepped into the fray and allowed pathologists and radiologists to bill and collect separately from the hospital for patient services.

When I was administrator, I think the one thing that guaranteed the success of deliberations with pathology and radiology was the fact that they both had Bill Raggio as their legal representative. In addition, Raggio was legal counsel to the County Commissioners and was able to see all sides of the deliberations. Mr. Raggio had good knowledge of the financial arrangements between the hospital and its radiologists and pathologists. The discussions that he led during these negotiations were always conducted on a high professional level, and it was his expertise that prohibited some of these meetings from becoming vindictive. We always ended the meetings with these two professional groups on a good level, but there were stormy times.

For example, in late 1966 before the radiologists obtained separate billing, Trustee Ben Drummer said that we should fire the radiologists. After they achieved separately billing, it was several years before the pathologists asked for and received a similar contract. They realized that it would be more difficult for them to submit smaller bills on procedures such as urinalysis.

## Washoe Western School of Practical Nursing

At one time, most large hospitals in this country had some type of a nursing education program. Unfortunately, the financial pressures of the 1960s and 70s forced many hospitals to cancel these vital programs. We all recognized that the basis of good nursing care depended on our nursing staff, their attitude, dedication, and ultimately their education. Washoe Medical Center was no exception. Our doctors also recognized this, and many of them volunteered their time to teach in our School of Practical Nursing.

In 1957 we started the school in order to take pressure off our registered nurses; to relieve them of duties that could be handled by less trained individuals. This was a pertinent step in the pursuit of good nursing care in Reno. Establishing the program proved to be a wise move on the part of the Board of Trustees. The school was cosponsored by the Nevada State Department of Vocational Education, Washoe County School District, and Washoe Medical Center. Initially Mrs. Geraldine Melady was the coordinator/instructor and Miss Lois Hartland was the clinical instructor. The first director of our school was Mrs. M. Esther Chalmers, who was ideal for the job. She always succeeded in getting a full class, and their year of didactic work was well organized. Later, Mrs. Edith Rogers was an instructor and was well liked by the students. In 1973 our School of Practical Nursing was transferred to Western Nevada Community College, and Mrs. Bernice Mathews who taught in the school at Washoe Medical Center continued as the Director.

When we had the practical nursing program, we had magnificent support from the University and the Community College System of Nevada (UCCSN); they helped in securing grants. One person who provided tremendous help was Alan Dondero, brother of Don Dondero, a well-known Reno photographer. Another was Mr. Vernon Erdley who was with the community college system, but he didn't like to be called by his first name. If he ever sees this mentioned, he will send me a nasty letter. Anyhow, he was an effective liaison between the UCCSN and the hospital. Erdley, later became Chairman of the Board of Regents of the University.

Students in the program benefited from scholarship given by the Women's League and other civic groups such as the Auxiliary to the Washoe County Medical Society.

## University of Nevada School of Medicine

In January 1958, Clyde Fox mentioned to the Board that a University of Nevada Medical School would be a great addition to the State. It was at this meeting that the Board asked Mr. Fox to prepare exhibits that might support his eagerness for establishing a school, and he agreed that this could be done in a few months. Fox had the maintenance department provide a model of what the hospital would look like twenty years in the future, and this was something we carted around to various service club meetings and hospital association meetings. This exhibit became quite a road show; it was an elaborate exhibit. Built on a table ten feet long and five feet wide, all of the buildings were built to scale. It included trees, grass, and detailed lights in the parking lots. For a long time the model was in the lobby area of the hospital

In Fox's dreams, Washoe Medical Center was to be a university style campus with the medical school building on the hospital grounds. There would be a separate hospital building for patients who would be under the care of university physicians. It was the wildest of dreams, got a lot of attention, and was of assistance in our pursuit of a hospital bond issue.

On January 16, 1967, members of the pathophysiology laboratory, Charles Armstrong (President of the University), Chancellor Miller, Dr. Fred Anderson, and other Regents met with our Board to discuss formation of a medical school. This was the genesis of what would become the two year medical school. It also marked the beginning of the effort to get a research project, which was initiated and ran by Dr. George Smith in the Quonset huts.

When planning was undertaken for additions and alterations to Washoe Medical Center in 1966, we included in our plans a medical school, and we never lost hope. This was manifested in the preoccupation with adequate classrooms, auditorium, cafeteria, and space for interns and nurses on the teaching wards. We expanded the medical records department to include provisions for interns and residents. We established the library on the ground floor for their use.

Those doctors who were the most eager in the promotion of a medical school were Louis Lombardi, Vasco Salvadorini, Fred Anderson, Bill O'Brien, Arthur Scott, Ernie Mack, and Bryce Rhodes, a Reno Lawyer who made a tremendous contribution in pursuing this dream. For many years, Bryce was the chairman of the Board of Washoe Medical Center.

I will never forget my experience in going to the Nevada Legislature along with Drs. Mack, Anderson, and O'Brien. At this session Dr. Anderson and Dr. Mack made a few remarks to a joint session of the Nevada Legislature. I remember the doctors had their wives in the gallery to hear their presentations.

At this meeting, the Legislature passed an enabling law providing money for a medical school feasibility study. When the meeting was over, Dr. Mack and I were standing in an anteroom talking with Floyd Lamb who was then the leading Senator in the State of Nevada. He was the Senate Majority Leader and without a doubt the most powerful man in the Senate. Unbeknown to us, he was also peddling his influence using Nevada State Retirement money. Later he was convicted of taking a bribe and sent to a federal prison. After the Senate had acted, Dr. Mack and I were speaking with Senator Lamb, and I will never forget as long as I live when he pushed his finger into Dr. Mack's chest and said, "Don't you dare ever come back here for more money." After the Legislature approved money to start the two year medical school, the only other state in the country with a two year school was North Dakota.

Within months after the legislature passed the bill authorizing the two year medical school, we hired Dr. Tom Scully as Director of Medical Education. His salary was split between the hospital and the school, and he acted as a liaison between the two by coordinating teaching rotations for students. He continued in this capacity until 1972 when he became full time at the medical school.

Another thing that helped the school be successful was the willingness of the Board to provide office space for medical school professors. I had empty space in the old South Wing, and most of that space was taken up by the University after we remodeled. We provided space for the chairmen of the departments of OB/GYN, pediatrics, and surgery.

There were negative feelings from the beginning generated toward the medical school. There was jealously on the part of faculty in other schools within the University, who felt that another college was going to be a detraction from their budget, and there were negative feelings from members of the medical staff in the hospital who resented the competition.

I think what gave me the greatest satisfaction in watching the growth of the medical school was the fact that the graduating two year students did so well. There were accepted by many first rate medical schools to finish their last two years of medical education. Some Reno physicians predicted that our students wouldn't do well. At all of the schools where they went to complete their last two years, they stood up well.

When the first class, the charter class of the two year medical school, finished in 1972, George Smith signed and presented me with a book entitled *A Way of Life* by William Osler; a treasured book in my library to this day.

## Our Relationship with Saint Mary's Hospital

When I was at Washoe Medical Center, we always had good relations with Saint Mary's Hospital. On a few occasions, I had sensitive items to discuss with the Trustees that involved competitive strategy. They were too sensitive to discuss in public. This was before there were rules stating that Board meetings had to be open to the public.

Open meetings became difficult when we had strained relations with Saint Mary's Hospital. Bud Reveley, the administrator, and his assistant would attend all of our meetings. They were curious as to our future intentions relative to equipment, acquisitions, and building plans. We had other disagreements with Saint Mary's Hospital. The essence of one disagreement was the fact that they were transferring indigent patients without notifying us. We demanded that Washoe County have an opportunity to interview patients before they sent them over.

Generally, our relationship with Saint Mary's Hospital was always the best. In fact, looking back on my early days as administrator, Sister Seraphine and I would get together before the beginning of the year and decide the minimum increases in hospital rates. Today, I guess you would call that price fixing, but in those days we weren't searching for profit, we were just trying to keep costs and price increases down.

Sister Seraphine was a tiny little lady. I don't think she was more than four feet two inches, and could not have weighed over ninety pounds. I always got a big kick out of telling a story of when Sister Seraphine was present at a meeting at Washoe Medical Center. She and her hospital chaplain came to the meeting, and it fell to me to me drive them home to the convent. On the way back we stopped at the Little Waldorf Saloon on North Virginia; went around to the back entrance, and sat near the bar.

The cocktail waitress came over and said, "What will you have?"

I said, "I'll have a scotch and water."

The chaplain said he would have a bourbon and soda, and Sister Seraphine said, "Well, I'll have a martini, but put it in a tea cup."

The cocktail waitress yelled back at the bartender "One scotch and water, one bourbon and soda and one martini, but put it in a tea cup."

The bartender yelled back, "Is that little Sister in here again?"

I always got a big kick out of that, and it always brought a laugh to her.

Another time, I was telling Sister Seraphine about an occurrence in our emergency room when an eighty year-old man had been brought in by ambulance from Mustang Ranch. With him was his seventy-six year-old friend, both were immaculately dressed and obviously men of means. The man was dead on arrival, and everybody noticed that his fly was open. I recited this story to Sister Seraphine and she said, "Mr. Ogren, did he have a smile on his face?"

Yet, on another occasion, I was driving Sister Seraphine and Sister Dominga to a meeting in Lovelock. Sister Seraphine was seated next to me in the front seat knitting when she looked at me and said, "Mr. Ogren, Do you have a pocket knife?"

I said, "Yes." I dug into my pocket and handed her the knife so she could cut her yarn. Sister Seraphine turned to me and said, "You know my father told me that any boy who carried a pocket knife was a good boy." She always called me Mr. Ogren; she never called me by my first name.

I met with Sister Seraphine and Sister Dominga and other staff members often. Our relationship was so good that each year when the Sheriff's Posse sponsored an annual outing for the Sisters, I was always invited. An interesting incident happened to me at one annual outing with the Sheriff's Posse. The jeeps and wagons were lined up outside Saint Mary's Hospital loading all the supplies, and I was talking to Sister Eugene, who was very attractive. Of course, they were all in their habits at that time. When it got to hill-climbing and so forth at the outing, the sisters would always hike their habits up a little bit and put rubber binders around their legs. I said to Sister Eugene, "Why don't you wear a pair of black shorts underneath that habit, so you can be a whole lot more comfortable when it comes to climbing?"

And she looked at me with a sly grin and said, "What makes you think we don't, Mr. Ogren?"

At one of these outings, while Sister Dominga was at Saint Mary's Hospital, she proposed marriage to me on leap year, February 29. She said I had to make a decision on that day. When I hesitated, she looked at me and said, "The proposal is no longer valid." I waited too long to answer.

Some time after that, Sister Dominga and Sister Carl, who was the personnel director, decided to leave the Dominican order. They left Reno and moved to Carson City where they both had state jobs. I saw Sister Dominga on several occasions after that and was always surprised to see her in civilian clothes and a classy blouse and skirt. She remarked to me, "When I was in the order you always called me Mary Joe Gleason because that was my name before I entered the order. Now that I am out of the order you always call me Sister Dominga."

I think that it is also interesting to note that Sister Dominga's father was Scoop Gleason, who was a famous Columnist with the San Francisco Chronicle. He was nicknamed Scoop Gleason because during the 1906 earthquake in San Francisco, he was in a row boat in the bay from which he made all his notes describing the earthquake from his unique vantage point.

We maintained a similar cordial relationship with Saint Rose De Lima Hospital in Las Vegas. They also were a great bunch of people.

## A Leader in the Nevada Hospital Association

Mr. Fox established the Northern Nevada Hospital Council in late 1957. We brought the county hospitals and private hospitals together, and we met at least every ninety days. The first members included administrators: Helen Allison (Carson-Tahoe Hospital); Andy Mettee (Ely—White Pine County General Hospital); Dave Brandsness (Elko General Hospital); Willeta Whomes (Fallon—Churchill Public Hospital); Ed J. Hanssen (Winnemucca—Humboldt General Hospital); Audrey Smith (Hawthorne—Mount Grant Hospital); Mildred Sebbas (Lovelock— Pershing General Hospital); Sister Seraphine (Saint

Mary's Hospital); Clara Barnett (Yerington—Lyon Health Center); and Tonopah—Nye General Hospital where Dr. Joy was the only physician in town. We contacted Dr. Joy if we had a problem. We could always find him in the one large casino in Tonopah because he was an inveterate slot machine player.

From the very beginning I was the volunteer executive secretary because I handled all of the correspondence. All of the correspondence was addressed to me at Washoe Medical Center, where the secretarial staff helped me. As other Hospitals demonstrated an interest, we gradually started including hospitals from Southern Nevada into the organization and changed the name to the Nevada Hospital Counsel.

The counsel expanded to include the Las Vegas Hospital, which has since been demolished. It was administrated by Mr. Les Edwards. Then the North Las Vegas Hospital, administrated by Bill Bennet, came in. Even representatives from the Owyhee Indian Hospital showed up for a few meetings. Southern Nevada Memorial Hospital joined, with Jack Staggs as the administrator, followed by Saint Rose De Lima Hospital, the Catholic Institution in Henderson which was administrated by Sister Georganne. The Schurz Indian Hospital took considerable interest and worked with us. The administrator there was Jim Verhey. The Veterans Hospital, administrated by James Harrison, also joined.

During the years that I was the administrator at Washoe Medical Center, our sister hospital in Las Vegas, Southern Memorial, had quite a change in administrators. Jack Staggs was followed by George Fleigh, who was an anesthesiologist and didn't last more than a year. He was followed by George Reitz, who was followed by Sam Crucilla, who was an osteopath. Dr. Otto Ravenholt, who at one time or another held about every major health responsibility in Las Vegas, took over temporarily as administrator.

In 1969 it was deemed appropriate to get a full time executive secretary for the organization. Sharon Green became the first paid executive director. She started in the summer of 1969 at an annual salary of $6,000, and was in the position until June of 1975 when she resigned to marry Dave Brandsness. By that time, the association had reached an annual budget of $125,000.

In 1964 and '65, we watched the evolution of Medicare and Medicaid into law. These were busy years in the Association. We were particularly busy in 1965 because there was extensive debate in Congress. I think it was in July of 1966 when Medicare went into law, but we did a lot of planning before it was implemented. The largest job was to find a fiscal intermediary who would act for the hospitals and process the Medicare bills.

One day, Bill Reed who was a representative of the Aetna Insurance company in Baltimore came to my office and asked if I could get the Nevada hospitals to recommend Aetna as the fiscal intermediary. The State Hospital Association was still in its infancy. I called the administrator of Southern Nevada Memorial Hospital, Jack Staggs; we constituted the two largest hospitals in the State of Nevada. After investigating Aetna we went to the State Association members and recommended Aetna to be the fiscal intermediary. After two or three meetings the other association members agreed. Aetna was appointed and subsequently did a good job for us.

## Unusual Occurrences

On reflections and observations over the years, some of this stuff is really crazy, but it is of general interest and shows some of the incidents in the life of an administrator. I was in the emergency room one day in the early '60s when two men had been brought in by the local police department; it seems they were involved in a jewel heist in the exclusive area of Hillsborough, California, near San Francisco. The perpetrators knew they were being sought, and they took quick measures to dispose of the jewelry. They each swallowed many of the precious stones, and the remainder were spread out on the floor and sucked up in a vacuum cleaner with hopes that they would return and get the jewels at a later date. Some sort of a chase ensued, and they came to Reno with two San Francisco detectives hot on their trail.

The culprits were brought to the emergency room at Washoe Medical Center where Fleet enemas were administered. They both admitted to swallowing the jewelry, and both were in extreme discomfort with abdominal pain. The thing that really tickled me was when I walked into the emergency cubical where they were being cared for, there were two San Francisco detectives each with a bed pan and a tongue depressor going through this fecal material picking out jewels. The emergency room personnel, in their usual sense of humor, named it, "The twenty four karat movement."

I recall vividly another emergency room admission because I happened to be there when the patient was brought in. A young man was working on a second floor ladder at a construction project on a motel south of Reno, when he fell off a scaffold and landed on a 3/4 inch rebar projecting from the foundation. The rebar penetrated under his right axilla and forced its way through his chest and out the left side of his neck. As he came in, he was bemoaning the fact that he was suppose to be married the following Monday. He was wondering if the injury would interrupt his plans. He was taken to the OR, where the rebar was removed, and by some miracle it hadn't damaged his lungs or heart. He was discharged three days later.

One evening while I was checking out to go home, the switch board operator told me that there was trouble in the delivery room. I took off down the hall and headed for the second south area where the delivery room was located. This was before husbands were allowed in the delivery room. There was always a lot of fuss about this, but the medical staff at Washoe thought it was not an appropriate place for a husband to be. At any rate on this particular afternoon, the husband of the patient had gone into the delivery room, while the staff had their heads turned, and he handcuffed himself to his wife's ankle. Her bag of water had broken, and she was in the early stages of delivery so there wasn't much to do but let him stand there handcuffed to his wife's ankle and watch the whole procedure. Characteristic of those days, any measure such as this always necessitated a call to the police department; they came and gave him a dressing down, and that was the end of it.

Sometime in 1962, I got a call from the operating room supervisor saying they had a problem in the operating rooms. The anesthesiologists reported that their patients were turning blue. They would turn off the wall oxygen line and turn on the tank supply, at which time the patient would pink up. The word soon spread and all the anesthesiologists were told not to use the wall supply. About this time, I was told that there were some strangers working on the manifold of the oxygen system which was located in the basement of the old south wing.

The hospital was supplied by Sierra Oxygen Company, which had its manufacturing plant on second street. After the oxygen was manufactured, it was piped directly to the hospital, through the manifold system, to the south wing and then on to the operating room or any other areas that were designed to take oxygen from a wall supply. I immediately went down to the basement and spoke to Mr. Carter, who was the assistant vice-president for Sierra Oxygen. He said he was there to find out the nature of the problem. As things turned out, it seems that the employees of the oxygen company would purge the system with carbon dioxide on a regular monthly basis. On this particular morning a valve had been switched, and instead of piping oxygen to Washoe Medical Center, they were piping carbon dioxide into the system.

Fortunately by this time, we had shut off all oxygen to the hospital and no one was the worse for it, but it could have been a first class disaster. The president of Sierra Oxygen was Tom Kean, a Nevada Assemblyman.

## Media coverage

During the years that I spent at Washoe Medical Center, we had repeated contact with reporters from the newspapers. The first reporter that I remember was Jim Hulse, who later went on to become a history professor at the University of Nevada, Reno. In fact, a few years back Jim wrote a very comprehensive book on Nevada history which is still good reading. The next reporter that I recall having contact with was Art Long, characterized by his green tinted glasses. Washoe Medical Center was considered part of his beat. I also had contact with Rollan Melton who was always fair and a good person to deal with. He was followed by Bob Nitsche. Bob made it a point to stop in to see me at least one morning during the week. There were times when there was breaking news at Washoe Medical Center that would be of a sensitive nature, and Bob would always cooperate with me in handling this in a very appropriate manner.

I don't recall the name of the reporter who I felt double-crossed me when he called on the telephone and asked if we had an abortion machine. This was before the United States Supreme Court made abortions a legal procedure. I told him, "No, we don't have an abortion machine. We have suction machines which are used to remove incomplete spontaneous abortions, as do all hospitals. In some cases the products of conception are left in the uterus after a miscarriage and have to be removed by suction." I told him that it had nothing to do with abortions.

The reporter asked me if he could have a picture of the machine. I said sure. He came down later that day with a photographer and took a picture of Ruth Hoffman standing next to a suction machine. The following morning the newspaper appeared with a picture on the front page of the second section, with a headline above it saying "abortion machine."

I will never forget Dr. Ernie Mack, chairman of the Board, walking into my office that morning. He was upset and angered, claiming it was my fault and I would lose my job as a result. After I had explained to him what had occurred, he settled down, accepted my story, and thereby ordered me to instruct the newspaper that if an apology wasn't forthcoming the hospital would initiate civil suit.

I so advised the newspaper, and the following day on page twelve, next to the classified section, buried as far back as it could be, was a statement to the effect that the administrator of Washoe Medical Center objected to the newspaper's description of a suction machine that is found in every surgery suite and their calling it an "abortion machine." It was no such thing as an apology, but at any rate that was the final chapter on that incident.

Over the years that I was administrator, we had an excellent relationship with the press. I found that there were always one or two reporters who were not muck-rakers but muck-makers. The likes of the one that took on the abortion machine. I felt that some of these guys, particularly those with the television stations, could be likened to the guys that come down out of the hills after the battle and shoot the wounded. More often than not their stories were not valid. They were particularly dangerous when handling statistics.

# A NEW DIRECTION, 1978-1998

A.P. SOHN

## Mr. Ogren Leaves Washoe Medical Center

In 1978 Mr. Ogren left Washoe Medical Center and the hospital leadership passed to Michael Newmarker who had been an assistant administrator. The best testimony to the part played by Carroll Ogren in the development of Washoe Medical Center is taken from an editorial in the *Nevada State Journal* published Saturday, November 11, 1978. It states:

> Ogren is one of a very small group of professionals and public officials in Washoe County who has left a nearly indelible imprint.
> He is a brilliant hospital administrator. And if Washoe Medical Center is a successful and solvent facility, it is due chiefly to Ogren's leadership.
> Ogren came to the hospital as an assistant administrator in 1957.

He was named acting administrator in 1963 and administrator the following year.

When he took over the hospital, it was a small county hospital, dependent to some extent on county revenues. It was having financial problems, and there was talk of closing it.

Ogren supervised its growth into a large regional hospital. He led the organization through several expansion projects, most notably the $21 million expansion that took place between 1959 and 1974.

He took the hospital off the public dole. Washoe Medical Center now is self supporting and requires no portion of the countywide property tax.

Ogren maintained a quality staff. The hospital has functioned smoothly through all its expansion traumas.

The hospital is now in fine shape financially. Bills are paid on time. Bond obligations are met. This is not characteristic of hospitals across the nation by any means. And in fact county hospitals have a reputation for being dismal warehouses, poorly financed and poorly staffed. That Washoe Medical Center breaks the stereotype is due largely to Ogren's leadership.

Ogren is a natural leader. He is smart and gets along well with people (and in an institution as diverse as a hospital, with a brilliant and sometimes temperamental staff, this is an accomplishment in itself).

## Years of Conflict—Establishing a Residency

Mr. Newmarker, Ogren's replacement, was immediately confronted by staff doctors who opposed University of Nevada School of Medicine residents being at Washoe Medical Center. While this controversy was dominating the Trustees' meetings, the other hospitals in Reno were maneuvering to gain an edge in competition, and the news media was waiting to resume the "baby war" which had started in 1976.

The medical school issue took front page publicity as the school looked to the hospital for teaching programs, while opposing doctors tried to subvert these efforts to train residents. In a separate but related action, the Washoe County Medical Society took a vote on a number of issues related to the medical school. Its members voted 101 no to 51 yes "that Nevada needs and can support a four year medical school." They also voted 96 yes to 48 no "that Nevada needs and can support a two year medical school." This resulted in a predictable reaction from politicians and the media, who stated that the doctors were trying to prevent competition and protect their income. To combat that argument, the opposing doctors contended that a small, poorly financed medical school could not produce excellent doctors who are competitive with doctors from more established medical schools.

In an attempt to mediate the controversy, the Board of Trustees opened their December 1978 meeting to the public. Chairman of the Board Robert Myles presided over a vitriolic meeting of the medical staff, the Board of Trustees, and leaders of the medical school, including Dean Tom Scully, and over 400 private citizens. There was heated debate between supporters of the medical school and the vocal opposition. Two days later the Trustees took control of the situation and voted to support the residency.

In an attempt to mollify the situation, Robert Cashell, Chairman of the Board of Regents of the University of Nevada, invited the leadership of the medical staff to his office at the Boomtown Casino to discuss the issues of conflict between the medical school and Washoe Medical Center's doctors. The dissidents were not part of the leadership of the medical staff and did not participate, but it is unlikely that they would have been swayed.

The Board of Trustees also tried to mediate the medical staff's concerns by forming a liaison committee to smooth over concerns about the medical school. A bright light at the end of the tunnel was the return in 1978 of three students from the University of Nevada School of Medicine who took their residencies at Washoe Medical Center—Dick Seher, Steve Parker, and Robert Platt who could and did compete successfully with residents of the more established schools.

After the smoke cleared, the hospital recognized the importance of medical education and paid part of the bill—$7,500 each—for the first residents at Washoe Medical Center. Even so, some members of the medical staff knew that the residents cost the hospital more than this figure and asked the administrator to estimate the indirect costs for medical education. After canvassing all of the hospital's departments, the administrator estimated that students and residents cost the hospital $150,000 a year for "in-kind services" such as sterile gloves, supplies, laundry services, and meals. Even before the Trustees' voted to support the residency program, the newborn intensive care nursery controversy was back on the table. Saint Mary's Hospital and Washoe Medical Center, once allies and good friends, were now fierce competitors.

## Years of Conflict—Good Friends Compete

It is difficult to say exactly when Washoe Medical Center and Saint Mary's Hospital parted ways and became fierce competitors, but it is safe to say that competition for patients was the wedge that drove them apart. Both hospitals competed for the Nursery, ICU, CICU, ER, and Care Flight (helicopter service).

Saint Mary's Hospital had always been a premier private hospital where care for the family was foremost. Its obstetrical unit said to be the finest in town. Washoe Medical Center, on the other hand, was the premier referral (tertiary) hospital that cared for patients with complicated illnesses, but it also served as a family hospital. For over a hundred years, it was the major indigent hospital for Washoe County. For certain, both hospitals cooperated and shared information and materials—a practice that never ceased. When price increases became necessary, they consulted and agreed on the percentage of increase. Although in today's competitive world this may seem like collusion, forty years ago it was an effort to control prices and keep increases to a minimum. The hospitals also cooperated in other ways.

On numerous occasions, supplies were shared between the hospitals. If a particular instrument or apparatus was needed in surgery and the other hospital had the only one in town, it was loaned across town. The hospitals also provided backup for equipment. Laboratory tests and blood inventories were shared. These are just a few of the areas where there was cooperation, and these continue today.

Even during the good times, there were minor disagreements. On occasion, Saint Mary's Hospital sent indigent patients unannounced to Washoe Medical Center's emergency room, but the major break came when Saint Mary's Hospital decided to open an emergency room in 1972 and compete for nonelective, emergency, and critically ill patients.[53] Even so, both hospitals, with a few exceptions, shared the same medical staff. In fact, some doctors played the hospitals against each other and moved back and forth between the hospitals if they didn't get the right surgery schedule or felt their patients weren't getting the proper care.

A shift in medical staff came in 1982, when all but one group of obstetricians moved their practices to Saint Mary's Hospital. There were several reasons for the exodus, but the most important reason was the escalating malpractice rate and threat of malpractice suits. Delivering poor, pregnant women without prenatal care who came unannounced to the emergency room at Washoe Medical Center significantly increased the chance of an unfavorable outcome with damage to the infant or mother. Furthermore, these women were more likely to sue a doctor they didn't know, and some lawyers put out the word, "If your baby has a birth defect, call us, it may be your doctor's fault."

After the turmoil, Washoe Medical Center's commitment to obstetrics was emphasized with a new unit in 1982 and the subsequent establishment of the Washoe Pregnancy Center.

## Years of Conflict—Neonatology

On June 23, 1978 Administrator Bud Reveley, of Saint Mary's Hospital, recommended the two Reno hospitals merge their obstetrical units and locate all deliveries at Saint Mary's Hospital. This made some sense because most of the deliveries in town were at Saint Mary's Hospital, but it failed to take into account the philosophical differences between the hospitals and the patients they serve, the necessity for an alternative to one hospital, and the number of indigent, high risk deliveries at Washoe Medical Center. This offer was another salvo in the "baby war."

Although the term "baby war" was coined by the *Nevada State Journal* on June 4, 1976, the conflict goes back to 1973 when Dr. Donald Pickering, the pioneer neonatologist in Reno, established the neonatal intensive care unit (NICU) at Washoe Medical Center and developed a ground and air transport system to bring stressed infants from other birthing centers. Our intensive care nursery was the first in northern Nevada and allowed specialists to give immediate emergency or surgical care to premature infants who were transported by plane or van to Washoe Medical Center. We had one unfortunate event when Dr. Ali Monibi was transporting in a small plane an infant to San Francisco. The plane crashed in the Sierra and the infant died as a result. Several others were injured in the crash, but survived.

By 1976, the unit was thriving, and Washoe Medical Center's Trustees "approved the purchase of two fetal monitors and made a commitment to establish a high risk maternity unit." This was a giant step forward in reducing newborn morbidity and mortality. Now, distressed and malformed infants could be delivered in an operating room where immediate surgery and life saving skills were available. Both neonatologists in Reno, Drs. Pickering and Missall, stated, "Washoe Medical Center is the only place that can properly care for a critical ill baby."[79] To further these efforts, in 1978, the Fleischmann Foundation gave $372,000 to Washoe Medical Center to expand its NICU.

After Reveley's recommendation in 1978, no further public statements were made until 1980, when Saint Mary's Hospital decided to add four NICU beds to their obstetrical unit. The State Health Division was quick to respond and stated they were considering legal action since the beds were not authorized, but the State was remarkably slow in taking action. Saint Mary's Hospital had built their unit without a CON and had let two contracts, each under $1 million. Also, Dr. Frank Mannino, Director of the Infant Special Care Center at the University of California recommended that Saint Mary's Hospital avoid the duplication as the community only needed one NICU. On December 18, 1981, Dr. Esmond S. Smith of the California Children Services inspected Saint Mary's Hospital and found that they did not meet California's standards for an intermediate NICU.

By 1982, Dr. Pickering had moved from the community leaving Dr. Steven Missal, who trained on the job with Dr. Pickering, as the only board certified neonatologist on Washoe Medical Center's staff, and he switched his allegiance to Saint Mary's Hospital. In order to obtain accreditation for its neonatology unit, the medical staff of Washoe

Medical Center had to recruit a neonatologist from outside of the state. Dr. Bonnie Lees was selected, but Senator Paul Laxalt's office had to intercede and obtain approval from the U.S. Department of Labor to get Dr. Lees, a Canadian citizen, certified to work in the United States. After Dr. Lees arrived, she was the only trained board certified neonatologist in northern Nevada.

After Dr. Lees arrival, Washoe Medical Center's NICU was certified as the regional NICU by the Nevada State Division of Health. The Director of Human Resources made an agreement with Saint Mary's Hospital that they could have their own unit, but they could not transport infants from other hospitals. However, the conflict was not over; three months later, a spokesman for Saint Mary's Hospital stated that they intended to ignore the agreement and they would transport infants. This action broke the armistice and once again, political pressure prevented the State from taking action. As the politicians procrastinated, Saint Mary's Hospital became more aggressive. In 1984, they hired a San Francisco attorney and threatened a federal suit claiming restraint of trade. Now, the fierce competitors became adversaries. Two years later, the hospitals agreed to join efforts and form a joint NICU.

Maybe the most telling aspect of the "baby war" was the state's inability to take a stand and eliminate expensive duplication when the experts and consultants agreed that one unit was indicated. Another interesting aspect of the two hospitals competing with each other was the media's ability to stir the embers into a conflagration and draw public attention. However, helicopter service soon became the main issue, and competition between the hospitals intensified.

## Years of Conflict—Helicopter Service

Washoe Medical Center's interest in a helicopter emergency service dates back to the early 1970s when Bill Lear financed a helicopter and Carroll Ogren used it to transport patients to Washoe Medical Center. At that time they found that it was too expensive to operate. By 1978, the concept of a trauma transport system built around a helicopter proved to save lives even though the economics were questionable. The efficiency of helicopter transport of trauma patients had been demonstrated in Vietnam. After the idea caught on, helicopter service to trauma units spread across the country, and most major metropolitan areas provided helicopter service to their designated trauma centers.

On August 25, 1980 the Trustees approved a helicopter transport system and agreed it should be in operation by the end of the year under the leadership of Mike Hoover. After much discussion, they decided against a joint venture with Saint Mary's Hospital and began an investigation to find a helicopter service. Trustees and emergency room doctors visited a similar transport system in Houston, Texas, where Dr. Red Duke had established a model system. When they found that billing patients and insurance companies using the transport system as an extension of the ER could make it pay, the Board voted to sign a two-year contract with Evergreen Helicopters. During this period, Saint Mary's Hospital became interested in leasing a helicopter., and when Washoe Medical Center chose Evergreen Helicopter Service, Saint Mary's Hospital was able to get a copy of Washoe's CON, and they used it to write their justification. According to Mike Hoover, many paragraphs were copied verbatim from Washoe Medical Center's CON. An orthopedic trauma surgeon from a group aligned with Saint Mary's Hospital was also able to turn the medical staff of Washoe Medical Center against its administration, and there was no medical staff support.

At the CON hearing, Administrator Mike Newmarker deviated from the organized presentation and Washoe Medical Center's expertise, including planner Carla Lauer, flight director Mike Hoover, and trauma surgeon Red Duke, was not presented. With much publicity in the press, Saint Mary's Hospital flew patients without certification while Washoe Medical Center waited for authorization before flying. After the facts were presented, It was up to the government to decide which hospital got the helicopter service, but politics and not medical expertise made the decision.

The GNSHA held a hearing and decided to award the helicopter service to Saint Mary's Hospital. Once again, politicians could not enforce a controversial decision, and it was left to the two hospitals to find a solution. In 1981, after ten months of negotiations, the hospitals agreed to a joint service with shared costs. However, two years later, both hospitals appeared to have lost when it was revealed that they were losing $1,371 on each care flight, but it was too late to reverse the decision—helicopters save lives!

One of the last chapters in the years of conflict was a natural outgrowth of the helicopter service. Who gets the trauma center designation?

## Years of Conflict—Trauma Service

The relationship of the helicopter service to a trauma center or an emergency room is a chicken and egg question. They go together, and neither comes first. Washoe Medical Center emergency room and trauma service dates back to at least 1941, when Mrs. Maida Pringle was the ER nurse and Dr. Dana Little was the house physician and in-charge of the emergency room. On July 21, 1986 Saint Mary's Hospital announced they were opening a trauma room in spite of the medical staff voting overwhelming against two ERs, and the gauntlet was once again thrown down.

In 1986 the Board of Trustees of Washoe Medical Center authorized a feasibility study by Donald Cook Associates to determine what preparations and changes were necessary to meet a Level II designation for a trauma center. The study found minor deficiencies and noted that the following nine conditions must be met: (1) a board certified trauma surgeon must be in-house and immediately available at all times; (2) a board certified emergency medicine specialist must be in-house and immediately available at all times; (3) a board certified neurosurgeon, orthopedist, and cardio-thoracic surgeon must be promptly available; (4) a board certified anesthesiologist must be immediately available and in the OR when the patient arrives; (5) in-house OR staff must be immediately available; (6) a radiology technician must be in-house and available; (7) a laboratory technologist must be in-house and available for blood gas determinations; (8) an educational program for the staff must be available; and (9) a public educational program must be ongoing.[54]

An inspector from the American College of Surgeons found the facilities were excellent, but the ICU was too crowded. The deficiencies were corrected, and Lawrence "Larry" P. Matheis of the Nevada Human Resources designated Washoe Medical Center the Trauma Center for northern Nevada. Saint Mary's Hospital objected, and a public hearing was scheduled. The ACS noted that Washoe Medical Center held the edge in trauma designation, but both hospitals had high standards and were a credit to the community. The ACS vote went to Washoe Medical Center because it had greater capacity to handle traumatized and seriously injured patients in their intensive care and emergency units. As a result, Saint Mary's Hospital dropped their bid for trauma center designation in November 1989 and Washoe Medical Center became the Level II Trauma Center. The decision was made by doctors outside of the community and not by politicians.

Even in the midst of these disputes, the hospitals provided good patient care. Characteristically, the news media focused on controversy and failed to point out that good patient care is provided by the hospitals, their doctors, and their nurses. In fact, the newspapers acknowledged as much in 1976, when they realized that their muckraking was not serving the public, and the *Nevada State Journal*, in the midst of the first round of the "baby war," published an article emphasizing that both hospitals were providing quality care. New services were also being developed as Washoe Medical Center and Saint Mary's Hospital continued in their roles as leaders providing patient care in the Reno-Tahoe area, and competition was a way of life.

## Laboratory Computer

Washoe Medical Center contracted for a new clinical laboratory computer system, funded by the Fleischmann Foundation in 1978, to link the clinical laboratory to all units and nursing stations, thereby giving doctors faster turn-around-time on laboratory test results. The computer system virtually eliminated lost laboratory results and provided more accurate billing information. A study before installation of the computer, performed by the department of pathology, revealed that fifteen percent of the bills were incorrect. Not fifteen percent overcharges, but equal amounts of over and undercharges, resulting in no overall change in revenue.

In 1980, Washoe Medical Center also acquired the pulmonary function equipment from the pathologists who had established the first complete pulmonary physiology laboratory in northern Nevada at the hospital in 1972. Larry Cody was the first pulmonary function technologist.

## Pediatric Intensive Care Unit

Pediatricians have always said that children are more than just little people; they are special and need special care. As a result the pediatric unit has always been an important ward in hospitals. In addition, the growing awareness of child abuse, coupled with child trauma, created a need for a special pediatric unit to care for severely injured and critically ill children. In 1981, Washoe Medical Center took the initiative and established the first pediatric intensive care unit in northern Nevada. Dr. Barry Frank, the first pediatric intensivist in northern Nevada, was appointed to direct and help design the unit.

## Another Grand Jury Investigation

Over the years, probably six or seven times dating back to 1869, whenever there was a substantial citizen complaint against the hospital, a grand jury investigation followed. Many times, the complaint was without substance, but the district attorney had the responsibility to investigate the allegation.

Late in 1981, District Attorney Cal Dunlap, in reaction to citizen complaints, began an investigation into the administration of Washoe Medical Center. He and the Grand Jury decided to investigate Mr. Newmarker's expenses at a Christmas party, hospital purchasing practices, contracts with various businesses and doctors, and the medical staff's recent no confidence vote. An editorial in the *Reno Evening Gazette* noted that several important assistant administrators had recently resigned and the public was losing confidence in the administrative operation. In addition, the medical staff was concerned about administrative practices, and a petition was circulated by Dr. Fred Fricke demanding changes. Following this action, members of the Board of Trustees and the Executive Committee of the medical staff met to discuss the leadership of the hospital and issues relevant to patient care. On November 2, 1982, Mr. Newmarker resigned and John Prout became Acting Administrator.

## The Second Reorganization

On June 13, 1983 a committee of the Board of Trustees and the medical staff completed their interview process and hired Mr. James Lamb to be the next administrator of Washoe Medical Center. The Board asked the medical staff to be involved in order for the medical staff to establish a better relationship with the new administrator and the Board. Not only did Mr. Lamb have a record of working harmoniously with doctors, but he had been through reorganization and had good knowledge of the legislative process..

After Mr. Lamb arrived, the Board authorized a "Feasibility Study of Corporate Reorganization" and made inquiries as to which Nevada statue needed to be changed to permit reorganization. The feasibility study took two years and weighed the pros and cons of reorganization.[55]

There were many advantages to reorganization: the hospital would (1) be able to diversify and compete by entering into joint ventures with providers, including physicians; (2) no longer be the target of an uninformed and occasionally biased press that casts the hospital in an unfavorable light; (3) find it easier to get future loans; (4) get more equitable treatment, compared to competitors, without open meeting laws that compromise strategy; (5) have increased ability to form relationships with other hospitals in northern California and Nevada; (6) have more stability in the Board makeup without countywide elections every four years; (7) have fewer federal and state legal regulations to meet; and (8) be able to enter into profit making ventures.

There were theoretical advantages for the hospital if reorganization did not occur: the hospital would (1) have more flexibility in labor relations than with reorganization; (2) be fully reimbursed for county indigents patients; (3) have limited tort immunity; (4) have more accountability to the public; (5) have right of eminent domain; and (6) have less disadvantages and restrictions in the regulatory area. After considering the feasibility study and noting that the advantages of reorganization far outweighed the disadvantages, the Board proceeded with restructuring and resolved that all employees receive fair treatment.

The Nevada Revised Statues (NRS) were amended to allow the

transfer of ownership of Washoe Medical Center from the county to a nonprofit, private holding corporation, and on October 28, 1985, the Board and County Commissioners transferred Washoe Medical Center's assets, patients, staff, employees, debts, etc. to a nonprofit corporation, Washoe Health System. Through the use of a $41 million bond issue, adequate capital was obtained to finance transfer and maintain employee benefits and purchase all capital assets. To consummate the transfer, the new corporation agreed to pay the county $1 million a year for twelve years and assume the hospital's debts. After the transfer, Washoe Medical Center immediately adjusted its strategy to take advantage of the available financial opportunities. Not everyone in the community was happy with the transfer. County Commissioner Rene Reid requested a Grand Jury investigation because she thought the $12 million was too low. The DA did not pursue the issue and no investigation was undertaken.

The new organization had a system wide board that oversaw the operation which included nonprofit Washoe Medical Center; joint ventures with doctors, including Sierra Nevada Laboratories; new profit making ventures, including a Health Maintenance Organization, Hospital Health Plan, and Western Medical Supply; an office building with numerous small businesses; and a state wide network of northern Nevada and northeastern California hospitals, including Sierra Valley Community Hospital, Eastern Plumas Hospital, Mayers Memorial Hospital, and Modoc Medical Center. Not all of these relationships would remain in the corporate plan, and the board eventually divested itself of Sierra Nevada Laboratories and the community hospitals.

## The Eleven-Story Tower Addition

After reorganization, the decisions was made to expand the campus to include a $30 million, eleven-story office building complex with doctors' offices, pharmacy, health workers' clothing store, heart Center, Remedee's Restaurant, delicatessen, Washoe Inn, a fitness center, patient resource center, and other patient services. The grand opening of the Washoe Professional Center occurred on April 22, 1989.

## The Cancer Center and Dialysis Unit

Previous to the eleven-story tower, a major expansion resulted in the 1987 Courtyard Center. The major benefactors were the Leon Nightengale Family and the Nell Redfield Foundation. The initial project, the Courtyard Center, included the dialysis unit and radiation therapy for cancer. When the new radiation therapy center opened in 1987, it included two linear accelerators—one with an electron simulator (model), forty times stronger and more accurate than the previous accelerator—and a CT-simulator. At the time, the new simulator was the only one west of Chicago and established Reno as a premier cancer treatment center. To understand the development of radiation therapy at Washoe Medical Center, one has to go back to 1961 when Dr. William Feltner joined Drs. Lee Sandars and Don Hlubucek in the practice of radiology at Washoe Medical Center.

In 1960 all radiologists were trained to do diagnostic and therapeutic radiology. The super specialist—the cancer radiation therapist who only treated cancer—was a new concept. The day of the generalist who knew a lot about everything was in the past. Then, Washoe Medical Center had an orthovoltage x-ray unit that was used to treat skin cancers and a few deep seated tumors. Unfortunately, the unit was not very powerful and the skin received the greatest dose; therefore, skin reactions were common and sometimes severe.

Also available to the radiotherapists were radioisotopes that could be injected into the blood to either circulate to diseased organs or treat blood conditions. In addition, radioactive needles were inserted into some superficial tumors where they could deliver a killing dose of radiation. These were the modalities used to treat cancer. What about the physical plant? According to Dr. Feltner, the first radiation therapy department at Washoe Medical Center treated three to eight patients per day and looked like "Abe Lincoln's cabin."

The next advance in the treatment of cancers came when radioactive cobalt units were developed. They produced greater penetration and had less skin reaction than the orthovoltage units. In 1969, because patients who needed cobalt therapy were sent to the Bay Area, and the hospital could not provide the $60,000 for a unit, the radiologists established a cobalt unit in their private office at 975 Ryland Street.

Within a few short years, the administration and the Trustees recognized the need for a modern radiation therapy department and approved the purchase of a 4 MEV linear accelerator with financial assistance from the Women's League and the Fleischmann Foundation. The new department was designed by Dr. Feltner, and when it opened in 1973, the radiologists hired Dr. Roger Miercort to head the unit and physicist Carl Chamberlain to assist in its operation.

In 1989 the new department had ample (25,000 square feet) space for physicians' offices, six examination rooms, a nursing station, treatment planning areas, conference rooms, cancer registry space, and an office for the Angel of Mercy Reno Cancer Council which supplies money to help patients over the massive financial hurdles encountered in contemporary cancer care. The current department's six radiotherapists—Gary Campbell, William Feltner, Robert Hume, Beth Hummer, Roger Miercort, and Jennifer Sutton—now treat sixty-five to eighty-five patients a day, and all tumors are treated, in contrast to the ten or twelve that were treated in the early days.[56]

Dr. John M. Davis recalled the genesis of the dialysis program: "In about 1966 Dr. Gilbert Lenz had a patient in kidney failure, and we had no dialysis equipment, so he bought one from Salt Lake City. It looked like a big wash tub and was called a Kolff dialyzer. Dr. Lenz's patient died before we could place it in use, but we used it later to dialyze patients who overdosed on barbiturates." Carroll Ogren remembers, "By the early 1970s, renal dialysis, using an artificial kidney, became common, and Washoe Medical Center transferred patients to the Bay Area who needed emergency treatment. Before the unit dialysis unit was established, patients bought their own dialysis machines for home use. In 1971 a patient, Doug Rimington who was treated at home, got a kidney transplant, and his family gave their dialysis machine to the Nevada Kidney Foundation. The foundation leased it to Washoe Medical Center for one dollar a year." This was the start of Washoe Medical Center's renal dialysis unit; Dr. David C. Johnson directed the unit, and Doug's mother, Claytha Rimington, was hired per diem as the first dialysis technician. In 1971 the dialysis unit consisted of one room, one bed, and one machine. Until 1975 only acute dialysis was performed at the hospital. Patients requiring chronic dialysis had to travel out of state for treatment or education for home dialysis.

In 1975 chronic dialysis was added to the hospital's program, Dr. Paul Clark joined Dr. Johnson, a second room was dedicated, outpatient services were provided, and Charlotte Matthews was the in-charge nurse. These were just a few of the changes as the program continued to expand. By the start of 1976, eleven patients were receiving outpatient dialysis.

Dr. Johnson relates the growth of the dialysis program, "As the program expanded and the community grew, the dialysis unit was moved to a room across from the ICU on the first floor where there was room for six outpatient stations and two acute stations. By 1980 a local home peritoneal dialysis training program had been established under the direction of Dr. Paul Clark and with the assistance of Georgianne Greene, R.N. In 1988 a twenty-four station unit, plus two isolation rooms, an area for home dialysis training and support, and an acute dialysis room with three stations were constructed in the Courtyard Center adjacent to the main hospital. The present supervisor, Aurora Wright, R.N., also supervised the unit during the 1988 construction. At the end of 1997, there were 165 chronic hemodialysis patients receiving outpatient treatment and 51 chronic home peritoneal dialysis patients. The unit also provides acute inpatient services to Saint Mary's Hospital and the Veterans Administration Hospital. In April 1997, Washoe Medical Center opened a satellite unit with seven stations for outpatients in Carson City ."

In 1997 the top two floors were added to the Courtyard Center. These two floors, above the dialysis and cancer centers, included patient care rooms and a free standing outpatient surgery center.

## The Parking Garage Addition

For over twenty-five years, inadequate parking was a chronic problem on the Washoe Medical Center campus. Mr. Ogren always said that parking was no problem. All we needed was 1,000 spaces next to the front door. The situation was alleviated in October 1996 when a $5 million, three-story parking garage was opened on Second Street adjacent to the eleven-story tower.

## Bone Marrow Transplantation

The latest in a long line of innovative programs at Washoe Medical Center was the establishment of a bone marrow transplantation program. The program was proposed by Dr. Stan Shane of the UNSOM to the Board of Trustees on January 22, 1990. At that time there were approximately 200 centers doing bone marrow transplants and over 10,000 transplants had been done worldwide. Start-up expenses for the four-bed isolation ward was estimated to be $436,934. The program opened on September 1, 1992, and nine patients received transplants during the first year. The program was steadily grown and fifteen to twenty patients per year are transplanted. The most common transplant uses autologous stem cells (using the patient's own normal cells) as treatment for breast cancer. Most of the patients are treated on an outpatient basis, but some are admitted when the blood count drops low and the patient requires intravenous antibiotics. Dr. Joao Ascensao of the UNSOM manages the patients at Washoe Medical Center and the laboratory located at the Veterans Hospital. G. Sloan Maes, RN is the clinical nurse specialist, Jo Anne Gould, RN is the manager, and Bonnie Holiday, RN is the bone marrow transplant coordinator.

## Into the Future

In April 1991, James Lamb resigned, and Robert Burn was appointed President and Chief Executive Officer (CEO) of Washoe Medical Center and Washoe Health Systems to lead them into the future. Mr. Burn has worked at Washoe Medical Center for twelve years, first as finance office and later as CEO. He had experience at Sunrise Hospital in Las Vegas and Reno Surgical Center.

1973 Tower dedication with Administrator Carroll Ogren (*left*), Dr. Ernie Mack, and Mr. Stuart Ogren (WMC photo)

Nurse Rose Costa (*right*), Dr. Larry Russell, and a social worker, circa 1960 (Louise Russell photo)

Nurses Bobbie (*left*), Dianne Savage, and Madeline Guisto (UNR cap), 1970s
(WMC photo)

Mrs. Geraldine
"Poison Lady"
Staples, 1988
(WMC photo)

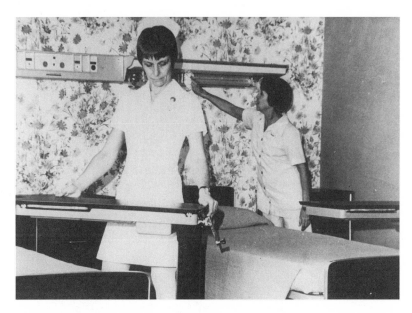

Nurse Jean Molde, 1973 Tower patient room (WMC photo)

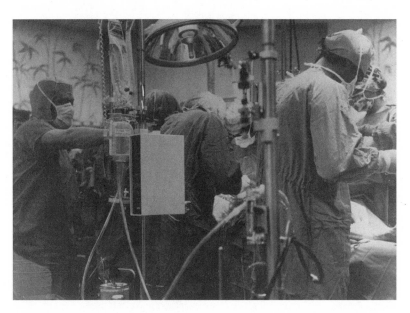

One of the first open heart surgeries, Drs. William Keeler (*right*), Robert
Nichols, and Robert Simon, and perfusionist Rick Russell, 1977 (WMC photo)

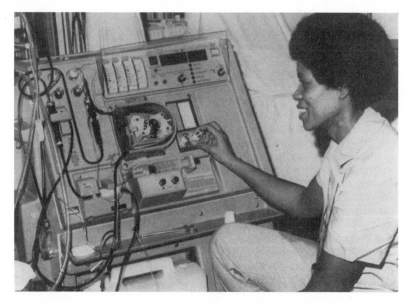

Head hemodialysis Nurse Charlotte Matthews, 1980 (WMC photo)

Chief of Staff Dr. Anton Sohn presenting certificate conferring honorary medical staff membership on Mrs. Maida Pringle, Dec. 1982 (WMC photo)

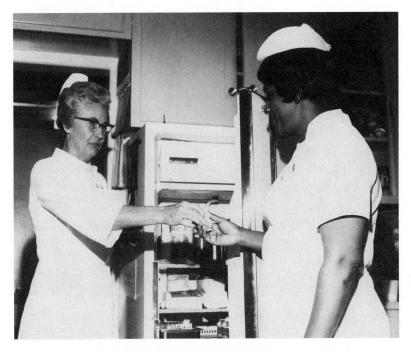

Nurses Vinette Blanchard (*left*) and Bernice Martin Mathews, December 1970
(WMC photo)

Bob Burn, Chief Executive
Officer, 1998 (Steve Young, WMC
photo)

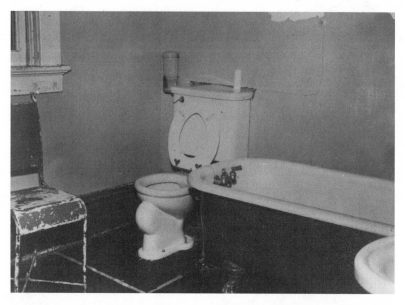

Patient room in 1906 building, $2 a day (Comp of Dr. Mack)

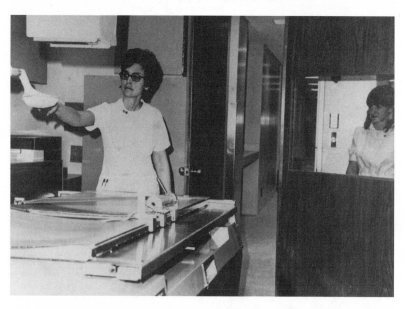

Radiology technician Judy Miller (*left*) and Student Tomi Argoitia in 1958 building (Gazette photo, Comp of Dr. Mack)

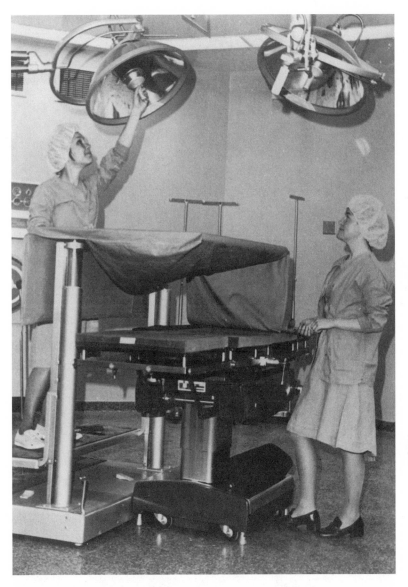

Operating room with ortho./neurosurg. table in 1973 addition (Gazette photo, Comp of Dr. Mack)

1961 building at the corner of Kirman (*left*) and Mill Streets (Comp of Dr. Mack)

1906 building in right background, 1953 building at left, Wyman Wing in center, starting construction of 1961 building (Comp of Dr. Mack)

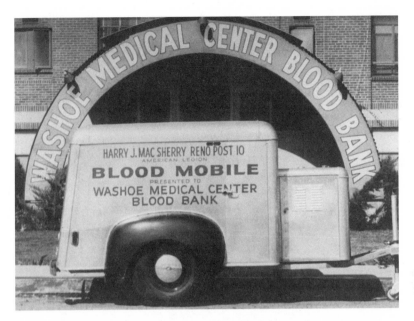

Washoe Medcial Center Blood Bank with bloodmobile, October 1955 (*Reno Evening Gazette*)

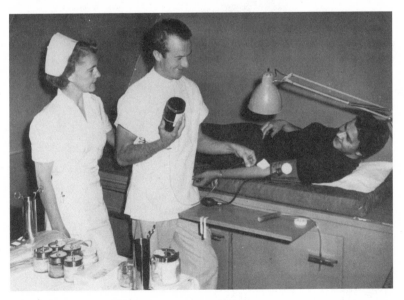

Nurse Evelyn Naeb, technolgist Charles Chester, and blood donor Toni Negri (Washoe Medical Center employee), October 1955 (*Reno Evening Gazette*)

Washoe Co. Hospital, Reno, Nev.

1906 Hospital (WMC photo)

Nurses Iva Haislip
(*left*) and Jean
Gans, April 1971
(WMC photo)

Washoe County Hospital circa 1907, Administrator Joseph Odett (*3rd from the right*), his wife Linda J. on his right, their daughter, Myrtle Meffley, sitting on the far right. (Comp. of Mrs. Billie Bennett)

Dr. Ernest Mack (*left*), Mrs. Maida Pringle and Administrator Carroll Ogren honoring Mrs. Pringle at the Sparks Nugget, mid 1980 (Comp of Mr. Ogren)

1959 LPN Graduates: Front row: unknown, unknown, Gladys Gaskins, unknown; 2nd row: Edna Bigrigg, Nancy Pleasants, Carol Little; 3rd row: Mr. Ross, Bernice Martin Mathews, Bertha Mack Mullins; 4th row: unknown, unknown; 5th row: Gertrude Powers; 6th row: Mrs. Pimentel, R.N. and Mrs. Clevenger, R.N. (Mr. E. D. Mack photo)

# NOTES

## 2. First Steps, 1862–1930

1. The facts presented in this chapter, and in the rest of the book, that are not in the endnotes are referenced in Appendix I.

2. From the County Commissioners (CC) records as researched by the County Planning Engineer in 1930 and recorded as the Board of Trustees' 1930 minutes. The author researched the CC minutes of the meeting and this item of business could not be found.

3. Pest is derived from pestilence, an infectious, epidemic disease likely to cause death.

5. Researched by the County Planning Engineer in 1930.

6. CC minutes April 8, 1863. Little is known about Dr. Weed other than he practiced in Washoe Valley from 1860 until 1867. This is not to say that he arrived in 1860 or left in 1867. Sohn, *The Healers of 19th-Century Nevada*, p. 144.

7. Myron Angel, ed., *History of Nevada....* p. 627. "It was not possible to determine the exact location of this original building, although sewer connections and foundations unearthed when the present Doctor's parking lot was installed indicate that it [the building] was situated along the Kirman Avenue side of the property." Carroll Ogren, *History of WMC.*

Dr. Henry Hardy Hogan, born in Virginia, graduated from the University of Virginia Medical College and came To Washoe Valley in 1864. He lived in Reno from 1870 until he died in 1902. Hogan was respected by his neighbors who elected him to the Nevada Assembly in 1871 and 1875. Sohn, *The Healers of 19th-Century Nevada*, p. 124.

8. Ogren, *History of WMC* and County Commissioners minutes.

9. In the nineteenth century, matrons were responsible for the laundry and other chores in the hospital.

10. County Planning Engineer.

11. Moris Walker, *A Life's Review and Notes on the Development of Medicine in Nevada....* Doctor Walker was born in Illinois in 1862. He graduated from the College of Physicians and Surgeons in San Francisco, an eclectic or botanical

medical college in 1901. Ross, *A Directory of Nevada Medical Practitioners Past and Present*, p. 149.

12. From an undated article in the REG that was given to the author by Mr. and Mrs. Odett's great great granddaughter, Billie Bennett. Little is known about Joseph Odett. He was born in 1845 and died in Reno in 1927. His family emigrated from France and entered the U. S. from eastern Canada. His wife, Linda, was born in 1848 and died in 1927.

13. County Planning Engineer.

14. Dr. Thoma was born in New York, trained at Albany Medical College, and came to Austin, Nevada, in 1867. In 1887 he moved to Reno where he became Superintendent of the State Hospital in 1891. He died in Reno in 1907.

Dr. Gibson, born in Missouri and graduated from Missouri Medical School in St. Louis, was superintendent of the State Hospital from 1905 until 1910. He died in Reno in 1919. Silas Ross, *A Directory of Nevada Medical Practitioners Past and Present*, pp. 143 and 52.

15. In 1930 the new addition was known as the West Wing, but by the time it was demolished in 1973, it functioned as the Administrative Wing.

16. See Appendix VIII.

17. James Scrugham, ed., *Nevada A Narrative of the Conquest...* p. 451. Also see Appendix VIII.

18. Sam Davis, ed., *History of Nevada*, p. 623.

19. Crosby, *American's Forgotten Pandemic*, p. 19.

20. A parallel between the treatment of a viral pneumonia and the treatment of a bacterial pneumonia is seen. Before the days of antibiotics, experts also could not decide if open windows and fresh air or closed windows were effective in treating a bacterial pneumonia. Anton Sohn, "Dr. Gerald J. Sylvain Oral History."

21. "The Nevada Flu Epidemic—1918" is published in *Greasewood Tablettes*, Spring 1991. The research of the newspaper sources on influenza was done by Phillip Earl of the Nevada Historical Society. The story of the identification of the 1918 virus is found in Jeffery Taubenberger, Science v. 275, pp 1793-1796.

22. This building was dedicated the Wyman Pavilion, after Dr. Rodney E. Wyman died in 1952. Born in Maine in 1893, Rodney graduated from Columbia University School of Medicine in New York in 1919. He came to Nevada in 1933 and was the only physician to serve three terms as Chief of Staff for the County Hospital. He was also the superintendent of the Nevada State Hospital from 1941 to 1945 and president of the Nevada State Medical Association (NSMA) in 1949. Dr. Wyman died June 22, 1952. Ross, *A Directory of Nevada Medical Practitioners Past and Present*, p. 159.

23. County Planning Engineer.

### 3. Coming of Age, 1930-1957

24. NRS, 1929, Chapter 169, Page 272.

25. Dr. John LaRue Robinson was born in 1872 and graduated from Keokuk Medical College, a proprietary medical school, in 1898. He moved to Nevada in 1904 and practiced as an Eye, Ear, Nose, and Throat specialist. Shortly after moving

to Reno, he organized the People's Hospital. He was also a president of the NSMA. Ross, A Directory of Nevada Medical Practitioners Past and Present, p. 122.

26. Ogren, *History of WMC.*

27. *Ibid.*

28. Earl Lamonte Creveling was born in New Jersey in 1886 and graduated from a homeopathic medical school in Philadelphia in 1912. He specialized in Eye, Ear, nose and Throat diseases and was a president of the Nevada State Board of Medical Examiners.

29. Alfred W. MacPherson graduated from the College of Medical Evangelists in California in 1929, and registered in Nevada in 1932. Ross, *A Directory of Nevada Medical Practitioners Past and Present*, p. 91.

30. Washoe County Hospital ledgers.

31. Thomas Wilbur Bath was born in Wales, Michigan, in 1865, and graduated from Adrian College before he attended St. Louis College of Physicians and Surgeons in 1892. After serving in the Spanish American War, he was licensed in Nevada in 1917. Then, World War I called and he served in the military before returning to Reno in 1921. Ross, *A Directory of Nevada Medical Practitioners Past and Present*, p. 7.

32. Alice Lillian Thompson was one of the first native-born Nevadans to come home to practice at the newly organized Washoe General Hospital. Born in 1876, she attended the College of Physicians and Surgeons in San Francisco, an eclectic medical school, and graduated in 1914 as an eclectic physician (botanical physician). In 1920, she returned to Nevada and for a short while directed the State Hygienic Laboratory (1921-1922). Ross, *A Directory of Nevada Medical Practitioners Past and Present*, p. 144.

33. These statistics are from the 1935 employee records.

34. Kevin Krajick, "Mining the scrap heap for treasure," *Smithsonian*, May 1997, p. 38.

35. *Ad valorem* tax is a percent of the assessed property tax that is allotted to the hospital.

36. Lawrence A. Russell was born in 1905 and graduated from Loyola University School of Medicine, Chicago, in 1931 and came to Eureka, Nevada, in 1949. In 1959 he moved to Reno and was the last county physician.

Vasco A. Salvadorini, born in California in 1915, graduated from McGill School of Medicine, Montreal, Canada, in 1940. After serving in the Navy during World War II, he practiced in Oakland for a short time before he came to Washoe Medical Center in 1951. Dr. Salvadorini has served as President of the WCMS, the NSMA, and for over twenty years was the only forensic pathologist in Reno.

Ernest Wood Mack was born in Reno in 1913 and attended the University of Nevada before graduating from the McGill School of Medicine, Montreal, Canada, in 1939. After serving as a neurosurgeon in the South Pacific during World War II, he returned to Reno in 1945. Dr. Mack was President of NSMA and Chairman of Board of Trustees at Washoe Medical Center for twenty years.

Leibert J. Sandars, born in Maryland in 1914, moved to Chicago where he attended high school, college, and graduated from University of Chicago-Rush Medical College in 1941. He interned in San Francisco and finished a radiology residency at UCSF in 1952 before coming to Reno. In Reno he was active in the American College of Radiology and in 1964 founded the Nevada Chapter. Dr. Sandars was president of the Washoe County Medical Society in 1964.

37. O'Brien and Associates. *Diagnosis and Treatment of the Acute Phase of Poliomyelitis and its Complications,* pp. 225–249.

38. "The Polio Epidemic of 1952-53" was published in *Greasewood Tablettes* summer 1995.

39. The Southwest Blood Bank is a nonprofit organization which draws and supplies blood components to many western communities.

40. The JCAH was a joint effort of the American College of Surgeons, American College of Physicians, and American Hospital Association to improve hospitals in this country by establishing standards for care.

## 4. Hospital Resident, 1957-1958

41. George Helmick Ross was born in Kansas in 1890 and graduated from Hahnemann Medical College, a homeopathic school in Kansas City, Missouri, in 1913. He served in World War I and came to Nevada in 1927. After practicing in Virginia City for sixteen years, he moved to Carson City.

42. These records were used to write this history and are high-lighted in the Appendix I.

## 5. Assistant Administrator, 1958-1964

43. The Quonset huts were World War II surplus buildings bought from the decommissioned Stead Air Base and moved to the hospital grounds in 1947.

44. John Charles Becker, born and educated in Reno, attended Northwestern Medical School where he graduated in 1941. He came to Reno in 1948 and practice orthopedics. He was Chairman of Board of Trustees of Washoe Medical Center.

45. Raymond Milton Brown was born in New York in 1915 and graduated from NYU School of Medicine in 1939. He came to Nevada in 1953 and practiced in Las Vegas before he moved to Reno.

46. Wyman Pavilion was named in memory of Dr. Rodney E. Wyman. Dr. Wyman, born in Maine in 1893, attended Columbia University School of Medicine and graduated in 1919. He moved to Nevada in 1933 and was superintendent of the Nevada State Hospital, 1941-1945. Dr. Wyman was president of the NSMA and chief of staff at Washoe Medcial Center for eleven years, the longest of any physician.

47. Letter from Senator William J. Raggio dated February 25, 1998.

48. Ibid.

## 6. Administrator, 1964-1978

49. The dedication and corner stone ceremonies were on Saturday, June 30 at 10:30 A.M. Past and present members of the Board were there. The Kerak Shrine presented the flag raising, and N. A. Tinkham conducted the Reno Municipal

Band. William F. Hill was the Chaplain for the Shrine, and Dr. Ernest Mack was the Master of Ceremonies. Dr. William O'Brien, a 33rd degree Mason, officiated.

50. Dr. George Furman related the story to Dr. A. P. Sohn.

## 7. People Make the Hospital (During Mr. Ogren's Tenure)

51. Carroll Ogren observed, "Washoe Medical Center never had a union. I think its clear to me why we never had any union problems. I felt that it was my job to anticipate the needs of the employees. Every chance I had to increase their benefit package or assure them they were going to get fair treatment, I did so. The same held true with health care insurance, vacation policy, holidays and the like. The Board and I made every effort to anticipate their needs. There was never a reason for a union. I will always look back on that with satisfaction."

52. Diener is the German word for servant, and in this country it designates one as an autopsy assistant.

53. Appointment of the county physician goes back to the beginnings of the Nevada hospitals in 1860. Each county had a paid county physician to care for the indigent. The county physician concept in Washoe County lasted exactly one hundred years.

## 9. A New Direction, 1978-1998

53. See Toll, *Commitment to Caring* (Reno: Nev. Acad. Press, 1983) p. 122.

54. Donald Cook Associates, Inc., *A Feasibility Study of Trauma Center Designation for Washoe Medical Center.*

55. Feasibility study of Corporate Reorganization, (Reno: Nov. 26, 1983.

56. Letter from Dr. William Feltner, February 27, 1998.

57. The history of radiation therapy was supplied by Dr. William Feltner.

## Appendix XIII

58. I spent some time discussing this whole business of being an identical twin because we went thirty years without ever being separated for a day. In grade school they had difficulty in telling us apart. Ironically in our kindergarten class there were five sets of identical twins. From the beginning the teachers in grammar school pinned a red cross button on me so we could be identified, who was Carroll and who was Stuart. I might add that this problem was with us throughout grammar school and all the way through high school. When we got into junior high school, our grades were so similar that we were separated because they felt there was probably a little cheating going on. The similarity of our grades continued on into high school. When we were in kindergarten, the University of Minnesota started a project studying twins, a project which continues on to this day. They have become quite expert in the study of twins. When we went into the Navy, the U.S. Government had a twin study program which we participated in until our discharge in 1954. They determined in high school and in college, that my brother and I had a correlation coefficient of 98

which is the same as any individual would have taking the same examination twice. It was always interesting to us that, particularly in college, if we took a final exam in accounting, we ended up with exactly the same grade but usually missed different questions.

59. Prepping consists of washing and shaving the area where the surgical incision is to be made.

60. Pediculosis is a condition of body lice infestation.

61. DTs or delirium tremens is a condition of altered mental and physical state that can occur when an alcoholic individual is withdrawn from alcohol.

62. In describing the *U.S.S Pittsburgh* losing its bow, I might go into a little detail about what happens. Naval ships have what is called watertight integrity which is what essentially that keeps them afloat. When you get underway in normal weather they establish what they call condition "Yoke" which means under those conditions certain watertight hatches must be closed and locked down. In heavy weather you go into another condition, "X-ray" where additional watertight hatches are shutdown adding to your watertight integrity. When you get into battle you go into another condition which shuts down practically every hatch in the ship and they can only be opened with specific authorization from the bridge. This means if a portion of the ship takes a torpedo, or in the case of the *U.S.S Pittsburgh* when it lost its bow it doesn't sink because you still have watertight integrity which is assured by all of those hatches behind the area of damage providing floatage. For this reason ships can suffer an awful lot of damage without sinking. In the case of the Okinawa typhoon, the *U.S.S Pittsburgh* lost all of her bow from behind the forward eight inch gun turret and still stayed afloat. The *U.S.S Quincy* was about to lose its bow but fortunately through expertise on the part of the captain, in turning the ship, they maintained their bow, but there was considerable leaking. For this reason the *U.S.S Quincy* put into San Francisco, into Pier 22, where I boarded her. We sat there for several weeks waiting to get into the Hunters Point Shipyard where several months were spent repairing that bow prior to putting the ship into mothballs.

63. A "sound" is a metal tube or rod. In this situation, it was used to dilate the urethra and break adhesions.

64. The "Wagensteen Alley" was a system of applying suction to a stomach tube.

# APPENDIX I
## Chronology of Reference Material

### 1863
April 8, CC: The commissioners authorized an ad in the *Washoe Times* requesting proposals to build a hosp.

Aug. 20, CC: Proposal for hosp. is rejected.

### 1864
Aug. 8, CC: Report from the committee on hospitals is accepted. Hospital fund to be used to purchase the printing building occupied by E. B. Wilson for $1,000.

### 1867
Feb. 4, CC: Dr. Joseph Ellis appt. the County Physician to care for the sick and indigent for one year at $1,000.

Aug. 6, CC: Authorized sale of hosp. property for $200 to D. R. Sturr.

Oct. 8, CC: Dr. Ellis released at his request and Bishop appt. the County Physician.

### 1868
March 3, CC: Dr. Bishop appt. the County Physician through 1869.

### 1873
April 4, CC: Dr. H. Hogan appt. the County Physician.

### 1876
April 10, CC: Authorized $5,000 to be placed in a hosp. fund to construct a county 0hosp. and establish a poor farm.

### 1885
June 2, CC: Dr. A. Dawson appt. the County Physician.

## 1889

March 11, CC: Authorized $250 to purchase a house in Wadsworth for the use of the citizens of said town as a hosp.

## 1893

March 13, CC: Authorized pay to Dr. Lewis $75, Dr. H. Bergstein $75, Dr. W. A. Phillips $64; and award of the contract to Dr. Phillips for care of the sick and to do autopsies as required by the county coroner.

March 14, CC: Awarded O. W. Ayers to be the superintendent of the county hosp. for one year. W. H. Joy to remain superintendent until May 1.

April 3, CC: Each of the two banks in Reno to equally hold insurance on the county hosp.

## 1895

March 7, CC: Mr. A. O. Ayers appt. the steward.

June 3, CC: County physician is John A. Lewis and the rules are:

(1) Indigents are admitted on an order signed by a commissioner;

(2) Inmates are discharged by the county physician;

(3) No inmate can leave the county farm unless given permission by the steward;

(4) All inmates are under the steward as directed by the county physician;

(5) No inmate is allowed on or in bed with his clothes on;

(6) Inmates are to do labor about the hospital or farm as directed by the county physician;

(7) County physician to visit the hosp. as emergencies demand;

(8) Hospital steward shall furnish nurses as required;

(9) The hospital shall be in good condition;

(10) Two meals are required, one of which shall be in the dining room if the patient's condition permits;

(11) Food is to be directed by the county physician; and

(12) Visitors only allowed between 10 A.M. and 4 P.M. Religious services can be held in the main ward on the Sabbath, if the county physician approves. All patient personal articles are deposited with the steward.

## 1898

July 5, CC: Indian from the reservation is in the County Hospital.

Dec. 5. CC: Hosp. Steward W. H. Joy authorized to make necessary improvements to the facility.

Sept. 19. CC: W. H. Joy's salary raised from $125 to $175 a month.

Dec. 31. CC: W. H. Joy died and on the 24th of Dec. Mr. Hull E. Joy appt. to manage the hosp. Mrs. (W. H.) Louise Joy to be the matron. The CC adopt. the following resolutions: (1) The hosp. and farm are under the full control of the matron and steward; (2) They can require the inmates to assist in the care of hosp. and the farm; (3) No inmate can leave the premises without written permit; (4) All transgressions are reported to the CC; and (5) Any inmate's complaint about mistreatment is to be in writing.

**1899**

Jan. 3, CC: $159.17 for building, 14 feet x 30 feet and one story high of wood. "Total cost of the building for six inmates."

**1901**

Feb. 5, CC: Joseph Odette to be steward on March 4. Drs. W. A. Phillips, P. T. Phillips, and Gibson to be County Phy. for six months; each will be the designee for two months.

Sept. 16, CC: Mr. G. E. Holsworth presented plans and specs for a new county hosp.

**1904**

April 18, CC: Drs. Gibson and Thoma requested instruments and tape for the hosp.

July 6, CC: Hosp. insured for $18,000; each of three banks to insure $6,000

Aug. 29, CC: Savage is are paid $100 to place a heating plant in the hosp.

Nov. 14, CC: Women's Relief Corps were given the SE 2nd floor room for old soldiers and others. Dr. S. K. Morrison to fill Dr. Gibson's term.

**1905**

May 5, CC: The hospital is insured for an additional $5,000.

Nov. 6, CC: A first class organ is placed in the hosp.

**1907**

Feb. 25, CC: Mr. J. Odette [sic] appointed steward.

**1908**

May 9, 1908, NSJ: The County Hosp. provides neat beds; neat ward, neat inmates and general air of good cheer under the direction of Mr. and Mrs. Odett.

**1917**

Jan. 5, CC: A. A. Burke and wife are appt. steward on Jan. 10. Drs. Morrison and Gibson appt. co phy.

**1920**

June 4, REG: The County Hospital is clean and orderly with sympathetic nurses. there are sixty-two inmates and eighty-five beds.

**1921**

Aug. 5, CC: Dr. A. R. DaCosta is appt. County Physician.

**1923**

Jan 8, CC: Eben Twaddle and Alice B. Twaddle are appt. superintendent and matron.

Feb. 19, CC: Operating rooms opened to all physicians after approval of CC.

**1924**

Jan. 5 CC: Dr. A. R. DaCosta resign. and Dr. A. F. Adams appt. the County Phy.

## 1927

Jan. 3. CC: Twaddle appt. super. and Dr. George L. Servoss is appt. County Phy.

## 1930

Nov. 5, BOT: The legislature of 1929 passed a bill that allows 30% of the taxpayers in a county over 10,000 inhabitants to establish a county hospital. "The petition presented, had the required number of taxpayers recorded, the question was submitted to the voters on November 4, 1930, and carried by a large majority almost two to one." The county commissioners appointed Mr. G. W. Nottingham, William McKnight, Mr. E. C. Mulcahy, Dr. Larue Robinson, and Mrs. Frank Ellis Humphrey to the Board of Trustees. At the first meeting of the Trustees, G. W. Nottingham is elected chairman and Mrs. Frank E. Humphrey secretary.

Dec. 27, BOT: Mr. Kenney is appointed the temporary manager of the Hospital. He is authorized to pay expenses up to $25 without Trustee approval.

## 1931

Feb. 1, BOT: The patient census is 178. Operating expense for January 1–24 is $3,802.31. Patients paid $610.

March 26, BOT: Fred DeLonchant is selected to be the architect for the new hospital.

BOT: Letter on April 4 to all doctors in the county inviting them to admit patients to the Hospital.

April 11, BOT: The name of the new Washoe County Public Hospital will be Washoe General Hospital.

July 25, BOT: Seven bids to build the hospital are received and three bidders were not qualified because they are not licensed in Nevada. J. C. Dillard is selected to build the Hospital for $198,997. Article by George I. James in the *Journal Weekly* stated that over one year after the vote of the people "Depression Makes Washoe Co. Hospital an Immediate Necessity." Also, maximum fee of $4 per day. Average of 111 patients, and only five or seven patients can make some payment. The daily cost per patient for the last year is reduced from $2.04 to $1.35. In the *Journal* November 14 an article states that the cost to the taxpayers of operating the hospital for ten months is $36,292. The total paid out was $46,376.16, but receipts were $10,083.19 The average number of patients was 112.

## 1932

Feb. 6, BOT: Dillard's selection as contractor is challenged in court. The Board cancels Dillard's contract after he agrees to the cancellation in court. The Board informs DeLonchant that the new hospital's cost is not to exceed $100,000.

Mar 16, BOT: Bids range from $93,166 (Wm. M. Kennedy) to $126,987 (Roush and Belz).

Mar 18, BOT: Kennedy is selected to be the contractor.

May 28, BOT: Bertha Wilkerson is the head nurse. The Board finds the complaint from Mrs. I McKay of Goldfield is unfounded.

July, BOT: Mrs. I. McKay of Goldfield sued the hospital for $25,000 for some eye problem incurred while she was in the hospital and treated by Dr. Earl Creveling. The Board discusses giving two weeks vacation with pay to all employees who have over one year service.

July 9, BOT: The grand jury investigated the hospital and reported: "highly commend this satisfactory management of Mr. Kenney."

Aug. 6, BOT: Approves bid to construct a maternity ward to handle patients that were being sent to maternity homes throughout the city.

Oct. 5, CC: Dr. A. W. MacPherson appt. asst. county physician for Sparks.

Oct. 29, BOT: Kennedy is given the bid for $31,352.80 to construct the maternity ward.

## 1933

Jan. 14, BOT: Mrs. Prudy is a member of the Board.

Jan. 16, BOT: Kennedy's bid to build the new hospital is rescinded—no money is available.

Dec. 29, BOT: Bylaws, Rules, and Regulations as passed by the Washoe County Medical Society are accepted for the hospital's medical staff.

## 1934

Feb. 26, BOT: Medical staff meeting at the Hospital: The applications from Dr. Parsons to be the pathologist and Drs. MacPherson and Piersall to be the radiologists are tabled. The medical staff requests a social services worker to be hired to help the medical staff determine the financial status of patients. Present at the meeting are Drs. Bath, Brown, Caples, DaCosta, A. Hood, D. Hood, W. Hood, Howell, Maclean, Miller, Morrison, Paradis, Reno, Robison, Samuels, Servoss, Shaw, Stadtherr, Sullivan, Thomsen, and Wyman.[107]

April 7, BOT: A reporter of the *Nevada State Journal* appears at the Board meeting and requests to enter the names of patients in the paper, but the Board decides that the patient's consent is necessary.

May 3, BOT: Dr. Bath requests to use the basement of the hospital for a clinic. The Board agrees this is important. No pathologist is hired because funds are too low.

May 25, BOT: Dr. MacPherson is hired to be the superintendent for $250 per month. In addition, he will take care of indigents, give anesthetics to indigents, and do x-rays and pharmacy work.

Aug. 4, BOT: State Hygienic Laboratory will do all bacteriology and chemistry without cost if the hospital pays $50 per month for supplies.

Aug. 17, BOT: The Board dispenses with Mr. Kenney's services because of disloyalty to the Board.

Sept. 28, BOT: Approved—Dr. Alice Thompson is to be employed as the pathologist for $200 per month, and Dr. Larry Parsons is to be a consulting pathologist for $100 a month.

## 1935

Jan 7, BOT: Mr. J. J. Kernan, H. C. Brown, Maud F. Dimmick are the elected members, Mr. Nottingham is appointed, and E. C. Mulcahy is the chairman.

Jan. 12, BOT: John J. Kenney is to be employed as business manager of the hospital.

All employees are asked to hand in their resignations at the start of the year; fifty-seven employees resigned and seventeen did not respond.

Feb. 23, BOT: Mr. Kenney is the superintendent, Wilkerson is superintendent of nurses, and Dr. MacPherson is the resident physician.

March 9, BOT: Discounts—No charge for regular duty nurses and doctors. 30% for doctor's families.

May 11, BOT: MacPherson resigns and sometime thereafter Kenney is appointed superintendent. Dr. Frank Samuels is to take charge of anesthesia.

Sept. 6, BOT: Board authorizes the Hospital to purchase a car, not to exceed $700.

## 1936

Jan. 12, BOT: Board members are Chairman Mulcahy, Secretary Dimmick, Nottingham, Kernan, and Harry C. Brown.

March 25, BOT: The Board appoints Mr. J. J. Kenney in charge of both hospitals: Washoe County Hospital (old) and Washoe County Public Hospital (new).

May 10, BOT: Bids will be taken for equipment to form a first-class laboratory. Bids to be discussed at the July 11 meeting. (No minutes are found for that meeting, if it was held.)

## 1937

Jan 5, BOT: Board members are Dr. Donald Maclean, B. A. Reed, Dimmick, and John I. Hickey.

Jan. 7, BOT: Parsons' salary is terminated, and he will be paid $10 for autopsies and $5 for examination of surgical specimens for indigents. He will bill for private patients.

Aug. 27, BOT: The Board orders that employees will not receive pay during sick leave.

Sept. 10, BOT: Mrs. K. Kakoris (Rose Silva) appears before the board and discusses the reasons for her dismissal from the laundry. Board will investigate. (She was reinstated.)

Dec. 7, BOT: Dr. Maclean requests that the four-room cottage at the rear of the North Wing to be used for a venereal disease clinic. His request is approved by the Board.

## 1938

April 7, BOT: Dr. Maclean will contact Mr. Noble Getchell regarding establishing a laboratory in the hospital.

Oct. 7, BOT: Mr. Kenney is asked to resign and Longfield appointed the temporary manager of the Hospital.

## 1939

Jan. 3, BOT: Mr. Kenney reinstated as manager.

Jan. 5, CC: DR. George A. Cann appt. county physician.

Jan. 27, BOT: Dr. Geo. A. Cann is the county physician.

April 24, BOT: A special meeting for "The meetings purpose is to get funds to operate the hospital."

July 31, BOT: Longfield is appointed the superintendent.

Nov. 3, BOT: Requests an emergency loan of $50,000 to pay debts.

Dec. 8, BOT: Several employees are dismissed because of cut backs.

## 1940

Feb. 12, BOT: Doctors of the staff appear before the Board and request a parking lot, improved food services, a head of the medical staff to be appointed, and reduced noise in the hospital.

April 6, BOT: The Board authorizes free hospitalization for the medical staff because of the hospital's better financial condition and your "splendid cooperation during our financial distress." Also authorizes free hospitalization for all hospital employees.

May 10, BOT: Edward S. Parsons is appointed as the hospital's architect.

June 10, BOT: Drs. D. Hood and Wyman, on behalf of the medical staff, request formation of a laboratory.

## 1941

Feb. 14, BOT: Board considers proposal to establish a children's orthopedic clinic in the hospital. Dr. Parsons is in charge of the laboratory.

April 10, BOT: Asks for emergency loan of $50,000 to complete Wing "B."

June 12, BOT: Dr. Thorpe is the hospital radiologist.

June 25, BOT: Nurses can administer first aid before the doctor arrives in the ER. Two doctors to be on call for ER.

Aug. 11, BOT: Problem in the nursery with rashes and infections. The medical staff takes steps to rectify the situation—wash diapers, sterile techniques, etc.

Aug. 27. Dr. Dana D. Little is appointed the house physician.

Oct. 23, (REG): Hospital decided not to request a bond issue.

Dec. 11, BOT: Blackouts arranged for the hospital as a result of World War II [The Pearl Harbor attack occurred on December 7].

Dec. 27, BOT: All of the pigs are in good condition for slaughter. All pigs to be sold to eliminate the bother of caring for them.

## 1942

Newspaper article: Auditor Lawrence J. Semenza report of Jan 1, 1938 to Dec. 31, 1941 recommends that the two hospitals merge. He also recommends that a more careful budget be made.

Jan. 10, BOT: D. D. Stingley is appointed the acting superintendent. Elks Club asks to sponsor the Crippled Children's ward.

Jan 22, BOT: The Board authorizes the purchase of four cows.

Feb. 10, BOT: Agrees to sell a filly for $4,000.

May 20, CC: Dr. Belknap asst. to sparks.

June 20, NSJ: Crippled Children Clinic now functioning. It has been in operation since Jan. 1 and has two wards.

Aug. 11, BOT: Bids are received on seven calves in the hospital dairy.

Aug. 20, CC: Dr. Lynn Gerow, Sr. appt. County Physician.

Aug. 25, BOT: Dr. Dana Little resigns as the emergency room doctor.

Sept. 10, BOT: The board donates the brass plaque with commissioners' names at the entrance to be donated to the war effort.

Sept. 23, BOT: Special meeting to consider nursing situation; many leaving for the war. They are given meals, laundry, and 15% pay raise. The Board asks for Mr. Stingley's and Mrs. Cauble's resignations, to be effective Nov. 1. Mrs. Olive B. Mason is made the "Head Supervisor" for nursing.

## 1943

BOT: Board members for 1943 are Chairman John I. Hickey, Dr. O. C. Moulton, Secretary Clarence H. Patten, A. E. Landers, Dr. Leo F. Corvino, and Peter L. Ferguson.

Feb. 15, BOT: Employees get hospitalization insurance for their families at 65¢ a month for spouses and 50¢ for children.

April 12, BOT: Extended free services to the medical staff and families.

May 10, BOT: Washoe County General Hospital to cooperate with the U. S. Public Health Service for their patients. Letter from the Surgeon General requesting the Hospital provide emergency service for civilian casualties in case of war coming to the U. S. Suggests forming an allegiance with St. Mary's Hospital to provide the service. Army Air Force Cadet Training Detachment at Univ. of Nev. to use WMC when cadets are injured.

June 29, BOT: The Government authorizes the establishment of a blood bank at WMC.

Aug. 6, BOT: Hospital agrees to take children of military personnel if they need hospitalization.

## 1944

BOT: Dr. L. B. Gerow resigns as county physician and Dr. G. O. Bradley is appointed to the position effective April 1.

March 20, 44. Lynn Gerow resign. as County Phy. and G. O. Bradley is appointed to replace him.

April 10, BOT: Architect Douglas Dacre Stone of San Francisco attends and presents preliminary plans for a postwar building.

June 10, BOT: Board to request $750,000 bond for new building, to go to voters in special election.

July 10, BOT: Payroll is $17,795.88 for June.

## 1945

BOT: C. V. Isbell Paving contributes paving for the parking lot.

Feb. 5, CC: Dr. G. O. Bradley resigned as County Physician.

June 19, BOT: All discounts stopped.

Aug. 4, BOT: Hospital's tuberculosis program is discussed.

Oct. 19, BOT: Architect Stone recommends the board consider three building options: Block A—Indigents and administration $780,000; Block B—Boiler room and laundry 143,000; and Block C— TB and isolation 245,000.

Oct. 26, BOT: Mrs. Pringle is appointed Supt. of Nurses.

Nov. 3, BOT: The Board directs the architect to draw plans for blocks A and B.

## 1946

March 5, CC: Harold E. Lohlien resign. Dr. Estrin appt. Co. Phy.

April 19, BOT: Employees get six straight-time holidays per year. If the employee works during the holiday they get double time.

June 4, BOT: Letter from chairman of the trustees stating that the 1945 legislature authorizes $100,000 transfer of money to the Hospital Building Fund. The Trustees request $750,000 bonds from County Commissioners.

July 3, BOT: Mr. Wallace is leaving because he is unhappy with the building process and with the doctors and their uncompleted medical charts.

July 11, BOT: Trustee A. E. Cauble is made temporary superintendent of the Hospital.

Oct. 4, BOT: Vlad F. Ratay is made the superintendent of the Hospital for a six months probationary period.

Oct. 21, CC: Raymond Yerg temp. appt. Co. Phy.

Nov. 4, BOT: J. Z. Estrin, W. P. Kelley, H. A. Strasser, H. W. Bischoff, E. A. Copeland, E. H. Gillespie, Arthur Holstein, E. G. Tainter, C. C. Wolfe, L. S. Sannella, and W. B. Leftwich applications are read, but bylaws require three readings. Board requested $750,000 in bonds. At end of Oct. there were 240 patients in the hospital.

Dec. 19, BOT: Hospital to serve meals to the jail inmates. Nov. 26. Dr. Parsons directed to discard frozen plasma stored since the War.

## 1947

BOT: Board members are Angus E. Cauble, L. Curtis Farr, Dr. O. C. Moulton, Dr. W. W. Hall, Bruce M. Thomas, and County Commissioners are Carl Shelly, Ernest J. Kleppe, and James Peckham.

Jan. 3, BOT: New building to cost $1,637,500.

Jan. 17, BOT: Moulton suggests that the Hospital needs a "Ladies Auxiliary" to help in getting publicity. The Board requests the Naval District transfer twelve Homoja Huts to the Hospital. Staff appointments require Nevada State Medical Association, Washoe County Medical Society, and Credentials Committee approval.

Jan. 31, BOT: Threat of a union in the laundry department. Dr. Parsons agrees to supervise the blood bank. Nurse anesthetist is working in the hospital. Sen. Pat McCarran, on Feb. 7, sent letter to the Hospital stating that the Homoja huts will be transferred.

Feb. 20, BOT: For the twelve Homoja Huts of corrugated steel the Navy will charge $275 each.

April 4, BOT: The huts are in place on the hospital grounds. Board agrees to rent one half of a hut to two employees for $30 a month per person.

Feb. 5. 47. Wm. B. Leftwich appt. the Co. Phy.

June 5, BOT: Twenty-four RNs meet with the Board and discuss salary, etc.

June 24, BOT: Board requests emergency loan of $150,000 from the county.

July 2, BOT: Medical staff applications for Frank A. Russell (assoc.), Sidney J. Tillim (State Hospital), Chas. Robt. Locke (assoc.), Geo. H. Ross (courtesy), Jesse Wm. Smith (courtesy in radiology), Wm. E. Winikow (courtesy at the VA), Francis Kernan (assoc.).

Sept. 8, BOT: Recommendations are approved for therapeutic abortions.

Sept. 9, BOT: Letter informing staff that unfinished charts must be brought up to date by Aug. 31, or they will be denied admitting privileges.

Sept. 20, CC: Dr. Wm. B. Leftwich resigned from County Physician and Dr. Hans Strasser is the temp. County Phy.

Dec. 20, CC: Dr. H. J. Valenta appt. the County Physician.

## 1948

March 4, BOT: Votes to join American Association of Blood Banks.

March 24, BOT: Hut #5 to be used for rheumatic heart patients, and pediatric ward to accommodate nine patients at $6.50 per person per day.

BOT: 1947 Annual Report—average of 238 patients in Hospital during the year. Births up 15% to 618 from 535 the previous year. Growth in services increased 66% to 85% over 1942. During 1947 Hospital spent $500,000 for groceries and supplies. Payroll up 179% to $883,477 from 1942. In 1947 there were 318 employees, up 53.5% from 1942. Nine huts installed for housing employees and three used for hospital services. Services improved during 1947 are as follows: installed blood bank, improved laboratory and maternity facilities, installed rheumatic heart ward and removed patients from the basement, installed county clinic in Hospital, and established a new medical library.

May 9, 1948, NSJ: First construction since 1932 now underway. $400,000 project includes laundry, dining room, power house and boiler room,

## 1949

BOT: Chair Bruce Thomas, L. C. Farr, Dr. E. W. Mack, Dr. O. C. Moulton, Dr. George W. Burke, and county commissioners are Carl Shelly, Ernest J. Kleppe, James Peckham.

Jan. 20, 49 H. J. Valenta re-appt.

Newspaper article: WMC bought two dorms that were used by Southern Pacific RR for employees not able to find local housing accommodations from the Public Housing Administration.

March 17, BOT: Reporters from the *Gazette* and the *Journal* attend. Tax allocation to the Hospital cut from 55¢ to 35¢ by the county commissioners, $160,000 less than the previous year.

March 23, BOT: letter, incomplete charts at all time high.

April 15, BOT: Report from Ratay on April 14 recommends that Hospital operations terminate on Sept. 30. Ratay's services terminated by the Board effective June 1.

May 16, BOT: Job to be offered to Mr. Fox.

June 7, BOT: Mrs. Pringle and Mr. H. Chester English, pharmacist, are functioning as superintendents. Southern Pacific RR dormitory is closing and hospital is interested in the buildings.

July 25, BOT: Mr. Armstrong of the *Evening Gazette* attends some of the meeting. Name changed to Washoe Medical Center upon recommendation of the Medical and Surgical Authority Committee.

Aug. 15, BOT: The entire rheumatic fever program is moved to the Hospital. It is not financially feasible to have a social services program in the Hospital.

Oct. 10, BOT: Pediatrics to be opened on Oct. 24.

Nov. 7, BOT: Mr. Henley of the *Gazette* attends. Southern Pacific dormitories are purchased.

Nov. 11, CC: Approved moving two dormitories.

Nov. 21, CC: County physician position is to be abolished.

Dec. 20, CC: Bob Beeks received the bid to move and relocate two dorms for $9,806.14.

Newspaper article: County physician position to be abolished on Dec. 31, and the newly appointed Dr. L. Russell will be the County Clinic Director. He will start on Dec. 15.

## 1950

Feb. 20, BOT: The Jan. county hospital bill is $31,254 and no funds are available to make the payment.

March 31, BOT: Special meeting to request emergency loan of $100,000 from the county.

May 15, BOT: Women's Auxiliary is organized, and meetings were held at the residences of Mrs. Robert Ziemer Hawkins and Mrs. John McLaughlin. Funds raising events are a style show in June, a concession at the Rodeo in July, and a dinner in October.

June 20, BOT: Dr. Lawrence Russell is appointed to the staff as director of the clinic and the county doctor.

July 17, BOT: Women Aux. has made $1,000 from the style show.

Aug. 22, BOT: There are 263 employees in the Hospital.

Sept. 22, BOT: Approves plans to have a Physical Therapy Department.

Sept. 26, BOT: Votes to have full-time hospital pathologist.

Oct. 16, BOT: Agreement with St. Mary's Hospital to have the same room rates.

BOT: Letter to Board from Fox: All employees get two meals per day plus salary. To start cafe and charge for meals on Dec. 1.

Nov. 20, BOT: All Employees meeting on Nov. 16 and make pay demands. Board decides to pay each employee $20 instead of meals. Wallie Warren and Fred Shields attend for the newspapers. Fox's letter to the Board stating that they do not have the money to effect a five-day work week or give pay increases.

Dec. 18, BOT: Dr. Salvadorini given contract to start Jan. 2, 1951. Dr. Gilbert doesn't have written contract for radiology services.

Dec. 24, BOT: Board cancels Gilbert's verbal contract on Feb. 21 because he doesn't want to be based exclusively at the Hospital.

## 1951

BOT: Moulton, Farr, L. B. Gerow, Mack, and John Belford are the elected Trustees; E. J. Kleppe, Ray Peterson, and Raymond Capurro are the county commissioners on the Board.

Jan 22, BOT: Medical records are three months behind in completion.

BOT: Physical Therapy to be established in February.

March 29, BOT: Hospital is showing a profit.

BOT: Letter dated March 14 from Mr. Fox: Newspapers called the Hospital a fire trap. Fire department inspector estimates it will cost $60,560 to correct the defects. (Hospital now has 247 Beds)

April 16, BOT: Requests $200,000 bonds to build two new wings.

May 21, BOT: Dr. Abrums is the radiologist.

Aug. 20, BOT: Dr. Locke feels he should get paid for TB work at the hospital.

Aug. 30, BOT: Votes for Dr. Locke to get paid for taking care of TB patients in the Hospital (the vote of the medical staff is forty for Dr. Locke getting paid and fourteen against).

Sept. 24, BOT: $5,000 gift from Ladies Aux. to remodel lab.

Oct. 8, BOT: Votes to have Mr. Fox seek legislation to permit the hospital to be leased to a nonprofit corporation. Fox states he suggested the name change to Washoe Medical Center.

Nov. 19, BOT: The Grand Jury investigates Redwood Pavilion and suggests it is inadequate for the number of old people that need to be housed there.

## 1952

BOT: Belford resigns and John Spann replaces him in April. Mack given the contract for doing EEGs in the Hospital. He brought his equipment from his office to the Hospital for the procedures.

Feb. 18, BOT: Dr. Estrin is the new radiologist.

March 5, Newspaper article: Harolds Club and employees give $4,500 iron lung to WMC.

March 17, BOT: Nurses are prohibited from smoking on duty.

April 21, BOT: Extensive discount policy passed.

May 18, Newspaper article: Second anniversary of Auxiliary.

June 16, BOT: Letter from Mr. Fox to Fleischmann Foundation asking for help establishing a school of nursing. Reply from Chairman Lester D. Summerfield that there is no money available at present. Mrs. Fleischmann is still alive and the foundation is not active.

Aug. 25, BOT: Hospital has no malpractice insurance.

Sept. 29, BOT: Drs. Leibert J. Sandars and Moreton J. Thorpe are the radiologists.

BOT: Bond issue for new addition passes in Nov. 4 election.

Dec. 9, NSJ: Fifteen Washoe County polio cases in November in addition to ten brought in from other counties and twenty-one Washoe County cases in Oct.

Dec. 15, BOT: Stone and Mulloy from San Francisco to be the architects.

BOT: Letter from Fox to Charles W. Mapes raising concerns about rumors of the polio drive in 1953. Forty-seven cases of polio at WMC and only fifteen applied for aid.

Dec. 21, Newspaper article: More than 100 polio cases brought to WMC this year. The youngest patient is seven week-old David Whitlock from Yerington. More than fifty cases from Washoe and over a 100 in the state. All are treated at WMC.

## 1953

BOT: Dr. Mack, Mr. Farr, and William Sieber are on the Board. Dr. Moulton was a member and resigned in Jan. John Spann replaced him. Dr. Gerow resigned in Sept. Questa replaced him in Nov. County commissioners are Peterson, Kleppe, and Capurro.

Jan. 7, BOT: Two week payroll is $31,528.05. Approved moving Hut #6 to near the emergency room to be used as the blood bank.

Jan 11, NSJ: Nevada in 1952 had 156 polio cases and 138 were treated at WMC.

Jan. 18, Newspaper article: Percentage wise Nevada has nation's worst polio epidemic.

Jan. 30, Newspaper article: Air above the Mapes being tested for polio by Dr. Edward C. Rosenow, Prof. Emeritus at the Mayo Clinic.

Feb. 16, BOT: Annual meeting of the Board. Pringle is the Asst. Adm., Laurine Sheppard is the Chief Nursing Supervisor. League raised $36,000 in 1952. There are 290 employees. Only hospital in the area with emergency services.

April 20, BOT: Three or four polio patients are in the hospital. The National Foundation for Infantile Paralysis owes the Hospital $18,000 and they have financial problems. Incomplete charts are a problem.

June 15, BOT: Two Quonset huts to be used for TB inpatients.

June 28, Newspaper article: Polio outnumbers all other infectious diseases in Washoe County.

July 20, BOT: Bill Gillis of *Gazette* is present. Four polio cases admitted during the first three weeks of July.

July 24, Newspaper article: Only hospital to have a radioactive isotope lab for treatment of tumors.

Aug. 17, BOT: Portable iron lung donated by the Veterans of Foreign Wars, Portola, California. The Hospital will go to five-day work week and room rates are increased to be comparable to St. Mary's Hospital.

Sept. 12, REG: WMC is flying blood to outlying hospitals. Everett Warren, the chief tech, takes the blood in his plane to Fallon.

BOT: Letter Oct. 24 from JCAH recommends recovery room for surgery. Letter from The Most Reverend Robert J. Dwyer expressing disapproval of WMC's policy on *Rules for Sterilization* and threatens to register public disapproval.

BOT: Letter from the Board to the medical staff stating that sterilization is only for medical conditions.

## 1954

BOT: Dr. Mack, Mr. Questa, Mr. John Spann, Mr. C. Farr, and William Sieber are on the Board. County commissioner members are Peterson, Kleppe, and Capurro.

Feb. 15, BOT: The new building is 60% complete. Discussion on establishing a Nursing School.

March 29, BOT: Annual meeting. Bernice Chadwick is Supervisor of nursing. Pringle is the Director of Nurses and Asst. Adm. Wallie Warren from the *Nev. State News* and Bryn Armstrong from the *Gazette* attend. Women's League has 435 members. In 1953, patients paid $1,057,968, County tax paid $350,343.

June 28, BOT: Requests bond of $600,000 to be paid in twenty years. The county commissioners will discuss the request.

Sept. 16, BOT: The county commissioners request the Board to reduce the request for a bond to $300,000, to be paid out of 35¢ tax rate.

## 1955

BOT: Mack, Questa, Farr, Siebert, and Rhodes are the elected Trustees. Ray Peterson, Ernest J. Kleppe, and Raymond Capurro are the county commissioners on the Board.

Jan. 15, BOT: Jim Hulse is present at the meeting for the press. Bills owed by the Hospital are three months in arrears. Income from physiotherapy dropped between 1953 and '54 because of polio epidemic in 1953.

Feb. 21, BOT: The Trustees make the Board term four year. They oppose salaries for Board members; AB 214 permits payment for Board members.

March 19, BOT: Surgical suite design awarded to architect firm of (David) Vhay and (DeWitt) Grow. Income over expense for February was $3,721 and $3,114 for March. Genevieve Young is appointed personnel director and Elaine Wangsness the housekeeping director.

May 2, BOT: Women's League constitution and by-laws passed.

May 16. Maternity is losing $20,000 annually. Eighty doctors are on the medical staff.

June 28, BOT: The Board approves a school of practical nursing to be based in the Hospital.

Aug. 5, BOT: Approves issuance of $300,000 in General Obligation Bonds for enlargement, repair and reconstruction of WMC.

Sept. 13, BOT: Siebert resigns to return to school. Mrs. Ben (Beatrice M.) Edwards will finish his term.

Dec. 5, BOT: There are 190 hospital beds available for patient use. American College of Surgeons approved Hospital's plan for a cancer center. The grand jury foreman attended and approved of the way the hospital did business.

## 1956

BOT: Board members are Edwards (elected), Dr. Mack (elected), C. Farr (elected), Capurro, Kleppe, Rhodes (elected), Questa (elected), and Peterson.

Feb. 27, BOT: Payroll is $43,000 for two weeks.

April 16, BOT: During the year of 1956-57 the Hospital will receive $366,000 from taxes.

June 17, BOT: Hospital to get liability insurance of $100,000/ $300,000.

July 18, BOT: Agrees to open a full OB service for a six months trial.

BOT: On Sept. 18 the Southwest Blood Bank will take over the blood bank and it will be located in the laboratory.

Sept. 20, BOT: Hospital owes suppliers over $100,000 and can expect only $50,000 from the county.

BOT: Letter Aug. 28 from Nevada State Board of Vocational Education agreeing to help establish a school of practical nursing with Reno High School Adult Education Division and WMC.

Oct. 24, BOT: Carl D'Gino of the *Gazette* attends the meeting. Proposed program for treatment and evaluation of retarded children. The Board agrees to use a Quonset hut for the program.

Nov. 28, BOT: School of Practical Nursing to start on Jan 14.

## 1957

Jan 23, BOT: Members of the Board are Dr. Mack (elected), Farr (elected), Rhodes (elected), Questa (elected), Mrs. Edwards (elected), and Peterson and Capurro who are county commissioners. Fox and Kotter are present in the meeting.

Hospital owes its suppliers $150,000. County owes hospital $69,729 and it is increasing $30,000 per month. Payroll is $100,000 per month.

Feb. 18, BOT: Present are Kleppe, Capurro, Tom Kean, Neil Humphrey (taxpayers assoc.), Kafoury, Howard McKissick, Fred Hill (Assemblyman), Mrs. Young, Pringle, and Mrs. Swope attend meeting.

April 8, BOT: Special meeting to meet with Jt. Bd. of Hosp Accred. team. [Maida] Pringle (Asst. Adm.), [Daphne] Green (Chief Nursing Supervisor), [Ed] Sontag (Direct of Maintenance), Mrs. Young (Bus. Manager), Mrs. O'Boyle (Dir. of Personnel), English (Chief Pharm. and Purchasing Agent), [Glen] Whiting (Dir. of Housekeeping), Mrs. [Helen] Nichols (Chief Record Librarian), Miss Joan Lewis (Chief Physical Therapist), and Bankofier (Dietetics). Full discounts for doctors and families, employees, Washoe County employees. Ten percent discount for nurses, pharmacists, non-resident doctors, morticians, doctors' staff, SW Blood Bank employees, and volunteers. Administrator is authorized to grant special discounts.

Sept. 26, BOT: Averaging 235 patients in the hospital.

Oct. 17, NSJ: Washoe Western School of Practical Nursing is sponsored by Nev. State Depart. of Vocational Education, Washoe Co. School District, and WMC. First class will graduate in Dec. Mrs. Geraldine Melady is the coordinator-instructor and Miss Lois Hartland is clinic instructor.

Nov. 4, BOT: Room rates $17 for two bed wards and $16 for four bed wards. New toxicology laboratory will add $600 per month to income.

## 1958

Jan 6, BOT: Hospital is the only Washoe County entity that gives pensions to employees. Hospital was going to close in 1949 and the commissioners asked the legislature that they be given representation on the Board in order to save the hospital. Fox mentioned that a University of Nevada SOM would be a great addition to the state. In 1956-57 the Hospital got $278,716 for county taxes; in 1952-53 it received $296,804.

April 14, BOT: Authorized installation of TVs in the rooms.

May 4, Art Long, NSJ: Tomorrow a new wing for $750,000 will open. Designed by Vhay and Grow and built by Macomber-Brunzell Construction Company. It includes twelve new X-ray units at total of $80,000. statistics show that 1,256 patients per month are seen in the emergency room. Cost of the new unit is supported by: $40,000 bonds, $100,000 state funds, $10,000 from the league, $210,000 federal funds, and $80,000 from the county.

May 25, NSJ: WMC Laboratory has toxicology capabilities and does tests on 6,500 patients a month.

June 23, BOT: Requested issuance of County Bonds for $1 million to build addition.

Sept. 29, BOT: Agreement with Orvis School of Nursing at the University of Nevada for their students and faculty to be covered by hospital insurance for hospital related accidents.

## 1959

BOT: Members of the Board are Dr. E. Mack, L. Curtis Farr, Mrs. Ben Edwards,

Bryce Rhodes, E. F. Questa, Ray Peterson, Benjamin F. Winn, J. C. McKenzie, C. Fox, Mrs. Dyer (staff Sec.). Insurance for employees raised 50¢ to $7.09. Hospital beds are filled. Two beds are in the hall. Approved bingo party for the league to raise money. Problem with physicians who have greater than five incomplete patient charts over thirty days old.

March 2, BOT: Private room charges went from $24 to $28. The Board requests $150,000 bond issue to the legislature for nursing home. A convalescent home of twenty-six beds is to be built.

March 23, BOT: Vhay is selected as architect for Convalescent home.

May 8, BOT: Jack Mathews, the Deputy District Attorney for the Hospital, attends. Mrs. C. Bohall is the new secretary. Nevada Heart Association is given rent free space at the hospital

May 27, BOT: Emergency loan of $200,000 from the County.

June 22, BOT: Ed Griffin, *Sparks Tribune* and Art Long, *Nevada State Journal* are present in the meeting. Fox resigned affective June 12. He has ten years service and has raised over $200,000 in donations, a first for the hospital. He also started the Women's League and it now has five hundred members.

June 24, BOT: Hospital property given for detention home. Special meeting with the Probation Board.

Aug. BOT: Present are Ogren. Mrs. Smith and Pringle. There are sixty applicants for administrator; Eight are interviewed. Kenneth Knapp of Oregon unable to reach an agreement on salary. Earl Horton agreed to $12,000 per year.

Sept. 8, BOT: Earl Horton is the new administrator. New policy for the Hospital requires two signatures on checks.

## 1960

Jan. 7, BOT: Board members are Mack, Questa, Rhodes, Edwards, Farr, Ben Winn, J. McKenzie, and Ray Peterson. Horton. Pringle, Bohall, and John Shaw Field attend the meeting.

March 28, BOT: Plans for future expansion of WMC to include a Geriatric Unit for $300,000.

Aug. 11, BOT: Special meeting to approve issuance of a bond for $2 million to enlarge the Hospital.

## 1961

Jan. 5, BOT: Board members are Dr. Pete Rowe, Richard L. Streeter, Dr. Jack C. Becker, and Michael A. Mirabelli. Horton, Ogren, Jacqueline Hollar (Staff Sec.), and Harry K. Brown (county clerk) attended. Wyman Wing increased from twenty-nine to thirty-nine beds. Other hospital beds number 120–140.

Oct. BOT: Report on Emergency Room by Ogren. In two months 2,264 cases treated in the emergency room; 43% are non-emergency. Dr. Larry A. Russell needs help with Public Assistance Medical Old Age Program.

## 1962

May 31, BOT: Patricia Keough is the new Adm. Secretary.

July 23, BOT: ICU rates raised from $45 to $50; Private rooms went from $30 to $35; Department heads are [LuAnn] Kamprath (Personnel), [Clyde] Smart

(Business Office), [Howard] Epling (Purchasing), [Edward] Sontag (Engineer), [Roy] Hogan (Laundry), [Juanita] Skaggs (Medical Records), [Glen] Whiting (Housekeeping), Miss Kit Soo (Physical Therapy), [Eldon] Phillips (X-ray), and [Jeanette] Bankofier (Dietary).

Aug. 29, BOT: Hill-Burton funds from Congress to give $275,000 ($37,000 more than expected). A consideration to hire four or five MDs for the emergency room to be taken to the med. staff.

Nov. 26, BOT: Stead military doctors to discontinue coverage of the Emergency Room on order from the base commander. WMC will need to hire five or six MDs to replace them.

## 1963

Feb. 25, BOT: Contract to build the new addition given to Walker Boudwin for $1,499,173.

May 27, BOT: JCAH inspected and approved the Hospital for three years.

Sept. 30, BOT: Horton resigns after four years as Administrator. Ogren is appointed the Acting Administrator.

Dec. 23, BOT: Request from the medical staff to start a two-year residency in general practice. A grant request for the program is sent to Fleischmann Foundation. Stop order is requested by the union on the new addition because the Hospital is using non-union personnel on the addition. Bill Hadley, Assistant DISTRICT ATTORNEY, is assigned to be the hospital attorney.

Independent 1963 Hospital survey by the Reno Area Health Study Group— WMC has 415 beds [census 250; 80% occupancy] and 874 births; SMH has 235 beds [census 174; 74% occupancy] and 1,549 births.

## 1964

March 23, BOT: Dr. Becker asked about the possibility of buying a cobalt machine ($60,000) for treating cancer patients.

April 27, BOT: Approved Ogren to be Administrator effective May 1, 1964.

May 25, BOT: Lengthy discussion on general practice residency.

Sept. 2, BOT: Announcement of dedication of the Henry Kohl Memorial Chapel, donated by Louise Kohl Smith, to be September 5.

Sept. 28, BOT: Edward W. Sontag is ill with leukemia, and Ogren recommends that he be continued in employment.

Oct. 26, BOT: New clinic in operation this morning.

## 1965

Feb. 22, BOT: Newly elected Benjamin Drummer raises the issue of pay for Board members. Becker questions if the members could prove they put in an eight hour day. Drummer say he won't abide by majority rule on compensation. His request is tabled.

March 29, BOT: Doctors Geo. Smith, Salvadorini, Sandars, and Anderson attend and want to start a Laboratory of Environmental Pathophysiology which will be sponsored by the Fleischmann Foundation. Hospital to pay utilities, housekeeping, secretary, telephone, and other incidentals. Equipment will cost $323,574. Laboratory is be housed in the Quonset huts.

May 24, BOT: Hadley's opinion is that if a member submits a voucher for pay the Board must act.

July 26, BOT: Drummer's voucher for pay didn't get a second.

Sept. 27, BOT: Dr. Geo. Smith recommended that a Cardiac ICU be established. American Hospital Association (AHA) recommended that Blue Cross be the Medicare intermediary.

Oct. 25, BOT: Letter by Rev. James P. Shaw of the Trinity Episcopal Church regarding a chaplain based at WMC. This was also discussed one year ago. Rev. Engeseth to be appointed the hospital chaplain.

Dec. 1, BOT: Drummer doesn't want to submit a voucher. His attorney attends the meeting. No action is taken.

## 1966

Jan. 28, BOT: Board members are Rhodes, McKissick, Becker, Cunningham, Sauer, Drummer, and Edwards. Administration officers are Ogren, Pringle, Asst. Adm Phil Smith, Sthultz, and Keough. Ogren noted that hospital based MDs requested to do their own billing. The Hospital asks the residency committee to put in writing their proposal to hire a consultant.

Feb. 28, BOT: Bond issue is approved for $14 million.

March 24, BOT: Architects presented their credentials for consideration. (William Morgan, Eric Chamberlin, and Leon King. Ferris-Erskine and Hellman, Welton Beckett and Associates, and Victor Gruen. The Board approved $100 to be spent for a residency consultant.

April 12, BOT: Special meeting to consider Title XIX (Medicare) problems. Robert Nitsche of the *Reno Evening Gazette* and the county manager, C. B. Kinnison, attended. The board approved participation in Title XIX or Medicare.

June 26, BOT: Thomas C. Wilson advertising firm is hired. Establishing a cobalt unit is considered. Postpones decision on hospital based MDs doing their own billing.

Sept. 26, BOT: Architectural firm of Welton Beckett and Roger Simpson are interviewed.

Nov. 10, BOT: Architects Simpson and Beckett are selected for the building project.

Nov. 30, BOT: Mention is made of a bench at Kirman and Mill with Walton's Funeral Home advertisement. It is inappropriate to be next to the hospital.

## 1967

Jan 9, BOT: Dr. Roy M. Peters on the Board.

Jan. 16, BOT: Members of the Pathophysiology Laboratory presented ideas on a proposed school of medicine (SOM). There is a long discussion of two-year SOM in Reno. Present are Drs. Salvadorini, Smith, and Licata. Charles Armstrong (President of the University of Nevada), N. Edd Miller (Chancellor), Anderson (Regent), Lombardi (Regent), Wendell Mordy (VP, Univ. of Nevada). Dr. Anderson stated the state pays $45,000 a year for students to go to SOMs out of state. Mordy stated the research unit at WMC may be vital to keep the SOM in Reno.

Jan. 30, BOT: Motion carries to appropriate $300,000 for the research facility.

March 21, BOT: Meeting with the architects. Mack thought the federal government would put in $5 million for the new building if the SOM was part of the hospital.

April 27, BOT: Joint meeting of Univ. of Nevada Board of Regents (Miller, Anderson, P. Hug, Jr., Harold Jacobson, Albert Seelinger, and Humphrey) and Hospital Trustees (Mack, Cunnngham, Edwards, Sauer, McKissick, Peters, and Drummer). Also present are Ogren, Pringle, Jerry Hall, Keough, Architects (Jack Beardwood, Dick McGee, Roger Simpson, and Bud Putnam). Perry Burnett, Asst. DA, and Daniel Walsh, Dep. Attn. Gen. There is much discussion on the relationship between the SOM and the county hospital. There are questions concerning hiring a dean, the time students spend in the hospital, and the number of students. (Anderson says twenty-four to thirty-two students). It will take one year to get a dean.

May 2, BOT: Hires Dr. Stafford Warren, former dean of UCLA to consult on the SOM complex.

May 29, BOT: Hospital lost three year accreditation; it is reduced to one year— many of the recommendations are directed at the medical staff.

June 29, BOT: William T. Rundio, the new assistant administrator, to arrive next month.

Aug. 1, BOT: Meeting with the architects. If a SOM is included in the new hospital the building will cost an additional $9 million. Schematics of the new hospital presented to the Board by the architects.

Aug. 8, BOT: Plan to go ahead without the SOM.

Aug. 28, BOT: Meeting with N. Edd Miller, George Smith, and Humphrey regarding plans to include the SOM.

Sept. 25, BOT: Commitment of $300,000 to the SOM still stands, but the Hospital is going ahead with the building program because the school needs time to get support. The SOM needs to get: (1) legislature support, (2) a fully committed teaching staff, (3) a full time dean, and (4) 5 years financing.

## 1968

Jan. 8, BOT: Members of the Board are Chairman Dr. Mack, Vice Ch. Cunningham, Sec. Edwards, Dr. Becker, Peters, Sauer, Drummer and McKissick. The board withdrew the $300,000 offer to help establish a SOM.

Jan. 26, REG: League has 706 members.

Aug. 26, BOT: Ogren complemented on the history of WMC that he researched and wrote. Recommended that it be placed in the cornerstone of the new building. A copy of this history can be found in the medical library at Washoe Medical Center.

## 1969

Jan. 7, BOT: Board members are Dr. Mack (chairman), Cunningham (vice chairman), McKissick, Dr. Becker, Sauer, Peters, Dr. Drummer (podiatrist), and Edwards. C. S. "Jerry" Hall project coordinator attended the meeting.

Jan. 27, BOT: Dr. Mark Raymond attends as a member.

Feb. 7, BOT: Special meeting. Dr. Tom Scully attends as an applicant for Director of Medical Education.

March 31, BOT: Dr. Scully offered the job of Director of Medical Education.

April 8, BOT: Special meeting with architect to review final plans.

April 22, REG: Dr. Wm. J. Bryan is guilty of four cases of sexual molestation of female patients. Convicted of furnishing liquor to a minor in Sparks in 1961 and surrendered license to practice medicine in Nev. Bryan is convicted by a Washoe County District Court. Placed on probation by Calif. BME.

May 14, REG: Clyde Fox died.

Nov. 12, REG: County commissioners agree to borrow $2M to fund the new addition.

Nov. 13, BOT: Approved request for emergency loan from the county of $2,125,000.

Nov. 20, NSJ: Bid by Jacobson is $17,660,000, $2,125,018 over the amount available.

Nov. 27, REG: WMC: the largest employer will embark on the largest building program in the state. WMC presently employs 890 and has an average of 420 patients. At present, patients needing cobalt therapy are sent to the Bay Area. The new unit will have a cobalt unit and a linear accelerator. The Hospital will have the only cancer treatment in the northern Nevada. Hospital will have renal dialysis in the new building.

### 1970

Jan. 5, BOT: Board members are Dr. Mack (chairman), Cunningham (vice chairman), McKissick, Dr. Becker, Dr. Peters, Sauer, Dr. Raymond, and Edwards. All discounts are removed and any discounts are to be at the discretion of the administrator.

May 16, Newspaper article: Dr. V. A. Salvadorini marks tenth anniversary of the WMC Poison Center. RNs Helen Steele and Helen Smith and secretary Judy Allingham staff the center.

July 7, BOT: Building committee meeting. Mrs. Pringle is the Acting Administrator, Dr. Scully is the Assistant Administrator. Bomb scare at both hospitals (WMC and SMH) over the weekend.

July 28, BOT: Harold S. Gorman attends the meeting to finish Edwards' term.

Aug. 11, BOT: Dr. Raymond is appointed secretary to fill Edwards' term.

### 1971

Jan. 4, BOT: Roy Pagni, Dr. Mack (Chairman), Dr. Becker, Dr. Raymond (Secretary), Harold S. Gorman, Dr. Peters (Vice Chairman), Dwight A. Nelson, and Howard McKissick are Board members. Change orders for the new hospital take most of the time,

Jan. 25, BOT: The amount tied up in incomplete charts is $420,000; the hospital is unable to collect from insurance companies and Medicare until the chart is complete.

Feb. 22, BOT: Cost of hospital malpractice is $100,000.

March 29, BOT: Made mandatory retirement for employees at sixty-five years. the amount tied up in incomplete charts is down to $8,000.

June 29, BOT: Approved linear accelerator mark VI for $156,000.

July 29, BOT: Motion passed to ask Senate Financing Committee for $3 million interim financing for the new building.

BOT: Sept. Letter of resignation from Kris Kakoris who is retiring after forty-one years of service.

August: First class of thirty-two students enter two-year medical school at the University of Nevada.

Oct. 28, NSJ: Renal dialysis machine given to Nevada Kidney Foundation by family of Doug Rimington who got a transplant and no longer needs the machine. WMC gets $1 a year lease from Nevada Kidney Foundation.

Dec. 1, NSJ: The League starts drive to raise $150,000 for the linear accelerator.

Dec. 12, NSJ: Linear accelerator day at WMC.

## 1972

Jan 3, BOT: Dr. Becker states his concern about the development of Surgi-Centers in Reno and competition with WMC.

Feb. 7, BOT: Two months payroll for the hospital is $285,000. Women's League had profit for 1971 of $119,000.

Feb. 7, NSJ: First class of medical students gets first exposure to patients.

April 3, BOT: Votes to purchase renal dialysis machine.

April 5, REG: Hospital gets second kidney dialysis machine.

April 24, BOT: All discounts discontinued except for hardship cases.

May 8, NSJ: SMH to open emergency room with the intent of increasing admissions.

Sept. 22, BOT: Special meeting to discuss the lack of progress on the building.

Dec. 21, NSJ: $5,000 raised by Fernley citizens for an artificial kidney, but James W. Minola died before the kidney arrived. The unit is donated to WMC.

Dec. 22, NSJ: WMC 's gardener, Caesar Lombardi, retiring. He started Sept. 22, 1942 as a milker at the hospital farm.

## 1973

Jan. 29, BOT: Richard N. Scott replaces McKissick on the Board. Board agrees to abide by Supreme court decision about abortions—woman can have an abortion in the first trimester.

March 14, NSJ: Workman unload $150,000 Linear accelerator at the new building.

March 14, REG: Linear accelerator funded by the Fleischmann Foundation ($36,945) and League ($150,000).

April 5, ST: WMC adds 160 beds.

April 21, REG: Rev. Richard W. Engeseth joined WMC in 1966.

May 7, BOT: Board set dedication date for new addition on June 30.

May: First school of medicine awards and granting of certificate of completion ceremony in Mack Auditorium at Washoe Medical Center. Physicians who were recognized at the ceremony are V. A. Salvadorini, W. W. Hall, William O'Brien, Lee Sandars, Fred Anderson, and Ken Maclean.

May 26, REG: Copies of the pen and ink drawing by artist Tom Summers of 1904 building to be sold to raise money for League.

June 30, NSJ: Pringle Way named after Mrs. Pringle. Corner stone ceremonies of the new building are on June 30.

Aug. 8, REG: WMC pulmonary function laboratory started in 1972 with Western Clinical Laboratories' equipment and Technologist Larry Cody.

Aug. 29, Newspaper article: Lions club Ex-President, Gary Bullis, formed the steering committee to start the eye bank at WMC.

Aug. 27, NSJ: Warren H. "Shorty" Holcomb dies at age 71.

Sept. 29, REG: The Washoe Western School of Practical Nursing est. in 1957 moves to Western Nev. Community College. Instructors are M. Esther Chalmers and Edith Rogers.

Nov. 15, NSJ: Price controls on hospitals signed by governor to go into effect.

Nov. 23, REG: First graduate, Karen Olsen from Wales, has completed the two year work program for Dietetians at WMC, the only such program in the state. Two women enter the dietetian training—Mary Colligan and Stephanie Risser. The program is approved by the ADA (Amer. Dietetics Assoc.)

Dec. BOT: Pringle retires to run for the Board of Trustees.

## 1974

Jan. 3, ST: Twenty-five new licensed practical nurses (LPNS) graduates receive their certificates.

Jan. 4, REG: Eye bank dedication attended by Gov. O'Callaghan.

Jan. 9, NSJ: Nurse Alma Johnson retires after thirty years.

Jan. 16, NA: New ground and air transport system for infants is initiated.

Jan. 28, BOT: Letter from obstetricians requesting that the two hospitals combine their delivery units.

Jan. 30, NA: New pulmonary lab gets diffusing equipment for $30,000

March 6, NSJ: For the first time, husbands are allowed in birthing room. Pat Peer is the OB head nurse.

March 17, NSJ: 2,000 poisonings last year reported to the Poison Center.

March 26, NSJ: Nurse Jeffress wears pantsuit. Nurses do away with traditional dresses.

May 20, NSJ: The second class, forty-five two year students, including forty-one Nevadans got Cert. of Completion from the SOM.

July 8, BOT: Board votes to hire a physiatrist.

July 29, BOT: Building progress at a standstill because of strike.

Oct. 24, BOT: Dispute with architect settled without going to arbitration.

Dec. 7, NSJ: Kris Kakoris died at 81 on the 5th.

Dec. 17, NSJ: Helicopter service started on the 16th.

## 1975

Jan. 27, BOT: Newly elected members of the Board are Dr. R. K. Myles, M. J. Pringle, Robert F. Rusk, and Kenneth L. Gaunt. Board votes to name auditorium after Dr. E. W. Mack.

Feb. 11, BOT: Annual budget for the hospital is now $30 million.

March 21, NSJ: Malpractice crisis, premiums go up 300%. Politicians say that is no reason to raise doctor's charges.

June 17, NSJ: Hospital to purchase brain scanner for $427,000.

Aug. 28, BOT: Two week payroll is $500,000.

## 1976

Feb. 22, NA: WMC to have first cancer intensive care unit and cancer ward in northern Nevada.

June 4, NSJ: "Baby War in Town" In 1975 SMH transported twenty-one babies to WMC. 1,350 were delivered at SMH. Ogren says that doctors have to decide where the NICU is located. Trustees "approved the purchase of two fetal monitors and commitment to establish a high risk maternity unit." Dr. Mohler requested the high risk unit and said it would five years before SMH could have one. WMC has the only infant intensive care unit. J. L. Reveley says SMH has an intermediate unit for infants.

June 5, NSJ: High risk babies should be brought to WMC —Pickering. SMH should not duplicate the infant ICU. Missall— "WMC is the only place that can properly care for a critical ill baby."

June 12, NSJ: Both Reno Hospitals offer quality care.

June 28, BOT: Moved to purchase body scanner for $175,000.

July 9, NSJ: Hospital to lease $400,000 scanner.

Oct. 7, BOT: Mrs. Pringle replaces Dr. Becker as Board Chairman.

## 1977

Jan. 3, BOT: Mr. Rusk resigns and the county commissioners appoint W. "Bill" Farr to take his place. Josephine Powell is a new elected member.

Jan 14, NA: Heart catheterization now available at WMC. Completion of the $425,000 facility to do heart catheterizations.

April 12, NSJ: Dale Hart, age 65, on Valentines Day became WMC's first open heart surgery patient. Dr. Robert Nichols was the surgeon.

April 14: Legislature approves four-year medical school.

May 31, BOT: Ogren is absent. Payroll for one half a month is now $600,000. The Board approved Trustee compensation.

June: New clinical chairs for the medical school arrive in Reno.

June 7, NSJ. Ogren on sick leave for one month. Norman Peterson is the acting adm. Ogren was sick in a similar manner two years ago.

June 27, BOT: Norman E. Peterson attends as the acting administrator. In personnel session, Ogren is reinstated as the administrator of the Hospital.

July 27, NSJ: Scanner upgrade approved, to cost $480,000.

August: thirty-six junior medical students begin their clerkships at WMC, VAH and in doctor's offices.

Aug. 29, BOT: Letter dated Aug. 24 from Dr. V. A. Salvadorini stating that he is retiring.

Aug. 30, REG: Hospital Board considers SOM affiliation.

Oct. 1, BOT: SOM requests: 1) Access for faculty, etc., 2) Office space for full time faculty; 3) Access for staff, students, etc. to the library and other hospital facilities; 4) Joint sponsorship for family practice residence.

Sept. 26, BOT: Dr. Smith speaks about the necessity of SOM affiliation with the hospital.

Sept. 27, NA: Dr. Salvadorini retiring on Oct. 1.

October: Dean Smith resigns, and Dr. Scully is appointed Dean.

Nov. 2, BOT: Gerald Bartley requests permission to move data processing from the Quonset hut to a Plumb Lane location; it is approved.

Nov. 14, NSJ: Gerald Bartley to increase computer service.

Dec. 12, NSJ: State Human Resource Director Mike Melner approves WMC getting a new scanner.

## 1978

Jan. 3, BOT: Draft #4 of affiliation agreement with the school reviewed.

Jan. 25, BOT: Revenue per budget for next year is $48 million.

March 27, BOT: Steven R. Brown is the new member of the Board.

May 1, BOT: Affiliation Agreement with the SOM is approved.

May 2, REG: Dean Scully says agreement between Hospital and SOM is signed.

May 21, NA: Top quality care available for infants established at WMC in 1976.

June 23, REG: Bud Reveley wants the two hospitals to merge their OB units and move to SMH.

Sept. 18, NSJ: Max C. Fleischmann Foundation gives ($1.2 million) grant to the Hospital to expand intensive care nursery ($372,000), boiler plant, lab computer ($545,000), metabolic and Cardio-pulmonary monitors ($102,000).

Oct. 2, REG: Daphne Green is retiring after 25 years at WMC. Mrs. J. Molde is appointed the Acting Director of Nurses.

Nov. 3, BOT: Ogren terminated by the Board. Mrs. Pringle resigns to avoid conflict of interest when her grandson, Mike Newmarker, is considered for administrator. Vice Chairman Raymond has the Board reaffirm its action on November 1 appointing Newmarker administrator.

Nov. 14, REG: GNHSA representative Dr. Bernard Feldman, neonatologist at Las Vegas Sunrise Hospital, said only one neonatology unit is needed in Reno.

Dec. 7, NSJ; Washoe County Medical Society after polling its membership says that SOM should cut back to two years. It went to four years in Aug.

Dec. 8, NSJ: Dean of the SOM Scully states the school has $900,000 from HEW and $600,000 from private parties to support the school's residents.

Dec. 11, BOT: Dr. David C. Johnson is present as Board member; he was runner up to Mrs. Pringle and is serving the remainder of her term. After meeting there was a general public meeting about the SOM and there is vocal, but not a majority, objection from the medical staff of the hospital. The Board appoints a liaison committee for the hospital to work with the SOM to implement the Affiliation Agreement.

Dec. 12, REG: Four hundred people jam the Trustees meeting to discuss the residency. Chief of Staff Dr. M. Christian suggests a study by the WCMS to determine if school should revert to a two-year program.

Dec. 15, NA: Trustees voted to support the residency program on the 14th.

## 1979

Jan. 10, BOT: Mrs. Pringle is back on the Board as a result of last fall's election. James Underwood, the new member, is excused from the meeting.

Jan. 11, REG: Trustees angry at SOM. Letter sent to Dean Tom Scully that the hospital was left out of the selection process for residents.

April 2, BOT: University officials attend and the first residents are approved— eight in Family Practice includes Judy Hilbish, Mary Sourwein, and Mike Stouder, two pediatric residents, and six Internal Medicine residents, including Steve Parker, Robert Platt, and Dick Seher. The named students are University of Nevada SOM graduates from the two-year school.

May 1, NSJ: Georganne Greene to be the asst. adm. for nursing; she will start May 14.

June 25, BOT: Hospital terminated DA's representative for the hospital.

July 5, REG: Seventeen residents selected: Family Practice—Stouder, Hillbish, Olmsted, Sourwein, Outcalt, Harn, Frinfrock, Dambro; Peds—Heath,

Neddenriep; Internal Medicine—Arger, Doeden Platt, Seher, Parker, Walters, Guttman.

Aug. 27, BOT: The Board funded up to nine residents at $7,500 each for one year.

October: Dean Sully resigns and Dr. Mazzaferri, chairman of internal medicine, is appointed Acting Dean.

## 1980

Jan. 28, BOT: Votes to acquire pulmonary function equipment from the pathologists who provided the first pulmonary function laboratory at the hospital and have been providing that service for the past several years. SOM business is a regular Board agenda.

Feb. 23, REG: Infant care flight from Reno (WMC) to San Francisco crashes and baby dies.

Feb. 20, ST: Occupational therapy underway at WMC.

March 20, BOT: Board resolves: (1) need for air transport for mothers and infants; (2) to support application for funding from Fleischmann; (3) to support effort to get state or federal funding for the counties; and (4) that if there is no funding the counties should recognize their moral and legal responsibilities to provide funds.

March 31, BOT: Receive funding from the Fleischmann Foundation to purchase a laboratory computer.

May 14, TDT: 'Baby War' flares. SMH decides to add four newborn ICU beds and GNHSA may challenge the legality of the action. Dr. Frank Mannino, Director of Infant Special Care Center at University of California at San Francisco (UCSF), recommends that SMH avoid the duplication as the community only needs one newborn ICU.

May 16: The SOM graduates thirty-six in the first class of MDs.

June 30, BOT: Cost to the hospital for the residents is one hundred and fifty thousand dollars "in-kind services" for year ending June 30, 1980.

July 26, REG: WMC has 564 beds.

August 25, BOT: Votes to approve concept of helicopter transport system.

Aug. 26, REG: WMC to get helicopter by Christmas, approved at Monday meeting of the Trustees.

Sept. 11, BOT: Votes not to enter in a joint venture for the helicopter with St. Mary's Hospital.

Oct. 27, NA: WMC applied in Aug. to HSA for the helicopter service.

Nov. TPR: Helicopter show in the park, GNHSA invited. WMC TV 3 on the air and in-house TV. Went on air July 1.108

Nov. 6, BOT: Votes to contract with Evergreen Helicopters for a two-year period. Establishes a Helicopter Advisory Board.

Nov. 24, BOT: SOM business: Dr. Robert Daugherty is coming to be the next dean of the SOM.

Dec. TPR: First health planner for WMC is Carla Lauer. ER Helicopter service center to be named after Bill Lear. Mr. and Mrs. "Clean," Roy and Lucille Hogan, say good-bye on Sept. 12 after over twenty years.

Dec. 29, REG: Board in dissent over sole source contracts.

## 1981

Jan. 7, BOT: Dr. Lynn Gerow and Robert Moore are on the Board with Dr. Raymond, Steve Brown, Maida Pringle, Dr. Myles, Bill Farr, Mr. Underwood, Dr. Peters, and Mrs. Powell.

BOT: GNHSA has hearing on helicopter.

Jan. 26, BOT: Board members are as follows: Chairman Brown, Vice chairman Myles, Secretary Pringle, Peters, Farr, Underwood, Gerow, and Moore.

Jan. TPR: League donates $121,000. Geraldine Staples, the "Poison Lady," retires from Poison Center after ten years.

Feb. TPR: First open heart surgery on April 5, 1977. Three hour surgery. Robert Nichols, the surgeon. New non-invasive lab, Stephen H. Milstein is the medical director, and John McCartney is the technologist.

March TPR: Men welcomed into the League for the first time. Jim McNeil, director of the Continental Lodge is the first member.

April TPR: First Health fair in the region opened on April 13 by Kathy List. Roberta Prutzman is the volunteer district coordinator. Seven hundred people turned out.

June 15, REG: Two asst. adm. resigned. Nitz and Sohn have "No comment," on the lack of confidence vote by the medical staff. Medical staff is also upset that it was not consulted on the helicopter service.

June 22, BOT: Special meeting with the medical staff to consider competency of the hospital administrator.

June 28, NA: Hospitals agree to have joint helicopter service after ten months of "haggling."

July TPR: Medical Explorers Post 117 at WMC under Dr. Robert Myles and Jim Holdridge wins top award in Reno with exhibit that depicts auto injuries.

Aug. 13, REG: Lakeside Community Hospital to open on Monday with twenty-eight rooms.

Sept. TPR: Care flight in operation at WMC and SMH. Co-medical directors are Drs. Willard Bross (WMC) and William Michelson (SMH). Life Line in operation is the first in Nevada. Pediatric ICU to be in operation in Dec. Barry Frank is the first Board certified pediatric intensive care specialist in the area and is the co-director.

Sept. 28, BOT: Votes to enter into negotiations with MedLab for a laboratory computer. Fleischmann Foundation is providing $545,000. The bid is over this amount, but the Hospital has the money. Year to date daily census is 406.7 patients; daily emergency room visits are 143.2, and the daily surgical case load is 27.36.

Oct. 1, NSJ: Dunlap and the Grand Jury are looking deeper than party expenses at Christmas party. They are looking at WMC's bidding process and the medical staff's no confidence vote.

Nov. TPR: Mrs. Linda Hoover steps down on Dec. 20 after one and half years as Director of Nursing.

## 1982

Feb. 22, BOT: ICN site visit went well.

March 4, Editorial in the REG: Linda Hoover, RN resigned in Nov. 1981 as assistant administrator for nursing. Public is loosing confidence in WMC administrative operation. Also in Nov. 1981 the PR director, Dick Rhyno, left abruptly. "Hospital and county officials must clean up the administration—or someone else should do it for them."

March 4, REG: DA still investigating hospital's purchasing practices that violated state law. Investigation was on-hold during the Priscilla Ford murder trial.

REG: WMC is certified to be the hospital for the Crippled Children's Services.

March 29, BOT: Recommendation to hire Dr. Bonnie Lees, neonatologist, to run the neonatal intensive care unit after Dr. Missall leaves to go to Saint Mary's Hospital.

March 30, Newspaper article: WMC approved as Regional Neonatology Unit if neonatologist is hired within six months..

Sept. TPR: Dialysis unit opened in Jan 1, 1975. 109 patients in the first five years. Neonatal ICU certified by the Nevada Bureau of Children's Health Services and Crippled Children's Service. Dr. Richard C. Bentinck is the bureau chief. This is the eighth year it functioned as a regional unit. Dr. Bonnie J. Lees is the director.

Oct. 20, REG: Dr. Robert G. Proctor, chief of OB at Washoe Medical Center, says SMH doesn't take its share of indigent patients.

Oct. 21, Newspaper article: Acel Martelle, Director of Human Resources, states SMH is operating a neonatology unit that may "exceed its legal authorization."

Oct. 31, REG: Nine years ago WMC started a neonatology unit. SMH expanded their unit in 1979.

Nov. 2, BOT: Special personnel meeting. The Board votes to accept Michael Newmarker's resignation. John Prout is named the acting administrator. Mr. Newmarker is appointed a special consultant through Aug. 1983.

Nov. 10, NA: Grand Jury and DA Cal Dunlap are investigating Hospital's reimbursement of Newmarker $1,016 for a Christmas party. Newmarker resigned on Nov. 2.

Nov. 10, REG: SMH not abiding by the neonatology agreement. SMH spokesman, Dr. Michael Pokroy states that they intend to go around the agreement that they only treat infants born in that hospital.

Nov. 12, Reporter Helen Manning for the REG: The Board vote to release Hadley from the attorney-client privilege is 3:3. Pringle, Myles, and Gerow voted to not waive the privilege. Moore, Brown, and Underwood voted to waive.

Nov. 14, REG: Hadley refused to answer questions and Dunlap asks the board to waiver attorney-client privilege. Board refuses.

Nov. 16, BOT: Special meeting to consider District Attorney Calvin Dunlap and the Washoe Grand Jury's request that WMC waiver attorney-client privileges while investigating Hospital and administrator.

Nov. 29, REG: WMC has new OB unit.

## 1983

Jan. 10, BOT: Board Members are Chairman Robert Myles, Dr. Lynn Gerow, Bob Moore, Dr. Arrah Curry, Vivian Freeman, and County Commissioners Gene McDowell, James Lillard, and Belie Williams.

Jan. TPR: Dr. Salvadorini says Pringle is the "mother hen to all the doctors at Washoe Med." Chief of Staff Sohn says "She has the ability to be decisive and look right into the heart of the problem." Dr. Mack states, "Mrs. Pringle understood the personality of the doctors and they felt her devotion to the patients and their families was the same as theirs." Keough states, "She always maintained a firm control, no matter what the situation was." Jeanne Bohall adds, "A lot of her most popular comments were unique only to Maida's vocabulary. No one could ever copy her style and humor." At the fifty-first medical staff meeting she became a honorary lifetime member of the medical staff.

March TPR: Same day surgery initiated, and it will reduce some patient bills by 50%. The cost of cataract surgery is cut from $2,800 to $1,800.

June 13, BOT: Votes to hire James Lamb as the Administrator.

Aug. 22, BOT: In executive session the director of cardiology is discussed, and the Board votes to replace him.

Oct. 4, BOT: Moves to have a Joint Board Liaison Committee with St. Mary's Hospital, to promote better communications and investigate how costs can be reduced.

Nov. 16, NSJ: WMC seeking approval for $15 million regional cancer and dialysis center. WMC now has twenty-seven cancer beds.

Nov. 28, BOT: Motion to develop a policy to require all medial staff members to have malpractice insurance.

Dec. NSJ: Hospitals may ground care flight. They are loosing $1,371 per flight.

Dec. 19, RG-J: Ronald McDonald House to be built one block from WMC at 323 Maine Street in 1984 as a result of the work of WMC's planner Carla Lauer.

## 1984

Jan. 23, BOT: Votes to compensate the Chief of Staff.

Feb. 27, BOT: Approves mandatory malpractice for practitioners in the hospital to be $500,000.

March 15, BOT: Walther, Key, Maupin, etc. selected to be the hospital attorney.

March 26, BOT: Barbara Lindh, admitting officer for twenty-four years, is retiring.

May 11, RG-J: New ultrasound scanner at WMC, the only one in northern Nevada.

June 24, RG-J: "Reno baby war flares"—Saint Mary's hires a San Francisco attorney to plead case before Bart Jacka, Director of Nevada Human Resources. SMH threatens to file federal suite.

July 23, BOT: WMC market share in the Reno area is 54.6%.

Nov. 26, 1984, WMC "Feasibility Study of Corporate Reorganization" advantages for reorganization are: 1) In order to diversity the Hospital must enter into joint ventures with providers, including physicians. The present organization doesn't permit joint ventures; 2) Now WMC is the only hospital in Reno open to public scrutiny; therefore, it is target of uninformed and occasional biased press; 3) easier to get future loans; 4) equitable treatment, compared to competitors, under open meeting laws; 5) increased ability to form relationships with other hosp; 6) more stability in the Board makeup; 7) tax dollars are decreasing, but the Hosp. doesn't get any at present; 8) fewer legal regulations; 9) can enter into profit making adventures; and 10) accountability to the public can be achieved through a board based corp. membership. Advantages for remaining the same are: 1) more flexibility in labor relations with the present organization; 2) fully reimbursed for indigents; 3) limited tort immunity; 4) less accountability to the public; 5) right of eminent domain; and 6) disadvantages and restrictions in the regulatory area.

## 1985

April 10, ST: WMC wins a CON from GNHSA for expansion of dialysis and radiation therapy.

April 22, BOT: Resolves that employee fair treatment continue if corporate restructuring occurs.

May 28, BOT: Cost of restructuring to be $250,000.

June 17, BOT: Complaint filed by SMH against WMC's rural efforts is refuted by the District Attorney.

Sept. *TPR*: Ronald McDonald House to open in spring 1986.

Oct. 28, BOT: The Board and County Commissioners adopt the transfer of WMC's assets, patients, staff, employees, debts, etc. to a nonprofit corporation, Washoe Health System (WHS), Hospital becomes private not for profit under WHS.

Nov. 3, RG-J: County to receive $12 million for WMC.

Nov. 25, BOT: Votes to proceed with Office Building Project at a cost of $22 million. Bonds not to exceed $18.7 million.

Dec. *Nev. Business Outlook*: New Corp. will assume $25 million debt and the county will receive $1 million per year for 12 years.

## 1986

BOT: Board of Governors of the new corporation, WMC, Inc. is Curry, Lamb, Ganchan, Lillard, McDowell, Moore, Myles, and Williams.

Feb. 14, RG-J: Bob Hope to appear at MGM benefit of WMC's Children's Miracle Television Network.

May 6, BOT: Dr. Anton Sohn attended as the first voting Board member to represent the medical staff.

May 27, BOT: Board set the ground breaking for the new office building to be June 10.

May 29, RG-J: Hospitals end baby war and agree to joint program for NICU. Agreement stems from Nev. Human Resources director's decision to designate both hospital as regional units.

June 7, RG-J: WMC to break ground for new eleven-story office building.

June 23, BOT: Assistant Administrator John Prout is a Board member.

June 28, RG-J: Gov. Byrant signed law to go into effect on July 1 that cuts back hospitals' charges.

July 20, RG-J: Baby war on new turf. Both Hospitals to have birthing centers.

July 21, EDFP: SMH to open trauma room this week.

Oct. 23, BOT: League bylaws to be rewritten to provide increased auxiliary service to the hospital.

Dec. 1, BOT: Washoe Health System Network comprises Sierra Valley Community Hospital, Eastern Plumas Hospital, Mayers Memorial Hospital, Modoc Medical Center, Great Basin Medical Clinic, and Washoe Health Network, Inc.

## 1987

Jan. 12, BOT: Curry, Freeman, Ganchan, Lamb, Moore, Chairman Myles, and Prout attended.

Jan. 19, BOT: Dr. Frank Lewis from the ACS visited on Jan. 15 and noted that the ICU is too crowded, but the facilities are excellent.

Feb. 23, BOT: Curry, Ganchan, Hollingsworth, Lamb, McDowell, Mullins, Murphy, Chairman Myles, Prout, Robbins, and Sohn.

Feb. BOT: *A Feasibility Study of Trauma Center Designation for Washoe Medical Center* by Donald Cook Associates, Inc. found minor deficiencies, and to get a Level II designation the following conditions must be met: (1) board cert. trauma surgeon must be in-house and immediately available at all times; (2) board cert. emergency medicine specialist must be in-house and immediately available at all times; (3) board cert. neurosurgeon, orthopedist, and cardio-thoracic surgeon must be promptly available; (4). board cert. anesthesiologist must be immediately available and in the OR when the patient arrives; (5) in-house OR staff must be immediately available; (6) radiology technician must be in-house and available; (7) lab technologist must be in-house and available for blood gas determinations; (8) educational program for the staff must be available; and (9) public educational program must be ongoing.

April 9, RG-J: Resource Center opens at WMC.

April 28, EDFP: Rawson introduces plan to reduce hospitals' profits.

May 5, NA: Seventy-five laid off at WMC by early retirement and attrition to lower costs.

June 8, RG-J: Health cost containment bill goes to governor.

Oct. 21, RG-J: SMH admits sending indigent patients in a taxi to WMC, but they were not in critical condition. New law allows hospital to seek triple damages for indigent patients who have been dumped.

Oct. 27, RG-J: WMC intends to file charges against SMH and Sparks Family Hospital (SFH) for allegedly dumping indigent patients. WMC accused SMH and three rural hospitals controlled by SMH for sending fifty-one indigent patients. SFH sent nine indigent patients. SMH denies the accusation, saying doctors requested the referrals. SMH says the cases involved psychiatric patients and SMH has no psychiatry unit.

## 1988

Jan 2, BOT: Chairman Myles, Burn, Coward, Dr. Curry, Erickson, Higgins, Lamb, McDowell, Mulllins, Murphy, Robbins, and Dr. Sohn. Dr. Cafferata is appointed Med. Director of Trauma.

Aug. 22, BOT: Recommended establishing a committee with the SOM to set educational goals for WMC. SFH has requested permission to enter the open heart market.

Sept. 17, RG-J: WMC designated Trauma level II unit earlier this year by Director Larry Matheis, Nevada Human Resources.

Sept. 26, BOT: Dr. Myron Gomez appointed Director of Trauma. SFH asks to have OB unit. It and trauma were prohibited in the CON when the hospital was built.

Oct. 16, RG-J: Two poison-control centers (WMC and SMH) serve the community.

Nov. 30, RG-J: WMC's new cancer center will treat 1,500 Nevadans per year. $13 million cancer center will have radiation therapy. Has a new stimulator that is only one west of Chicago. It is forty times stronger and more accurate than the old linear accelerator.

Nov. 8, RG-J: WMC and SMH spar over SMH's plans to have an open heart program. WMC has had one for eleven years. Myron Gomez is the new director of the trauma unit.

Nov. 22, DST: Trauma center designation will have a new public hearing to decide on WMC or SMH.

Nov. 28, BOT: Proposal to establish a cardiovascular institute at WMC.

Dec. 1, RG-J: The ACS notes that WMC holds the edge in trauma designation, but both hospitals have high standards and are a credit to the community. WMC has greater capacity to handle trauma and more capacity to handle seriously injured patients in their intensive care and emergency units.

Dec. 26, RG-J: WMC to go smokeless on Jan 1.

## 1989

Feb. 19, RG-J: WMC dialysis unit to open on Wed. The center has twenty-four machines and can treat 100 patient per day.

March 12. Regional Dialysis Center held grand opening on Feb. 22.

April 19, RG-J: Grand opening of the Washoe Professional Center on April 22.

June 1989: Dr. Liebert Sandars, radiologist, retires.

July 2, RG-J: WMC sues city of Reno for selling land to them that was contaminated with toxic waste.

July 19, REMSA: Intoxicated individuals don't belong in the ER.

Aug. 28, Child Care Center is licensed for seventy-seven children. Business plan of the center is approved.

Nov. 2, RG-J: SMH drops bid for trauma center after hearing they failed to meet ACS standards. WMC notified that they met all of the qualifications. SMH spent $1 million a year to keep trauma surgeons on duty around the clock.

Dec. Annual report for Pathology: A kidney Biopsy program, the first new pathology service in several years, has been started.

Dec. 31. Dr. R. K. Myles retired from the Board after fifteen years of service, seven years as chairman.

## 1990

Jan. 22, BOT: Patrick Coward is the new chairman of the Board. Dr. Shane of the SOM proposes a bone marrow transplant program.

March 26, BOT: Dr. Ted Berndt, Bob Burn, Dr. Bill Carlson, Pat Coward, Bill Farr, Jerry Higgins, Dr. Dick Inskip, Jim Lamb, Gene McDowell, Bertha Mullins, Judy Murphy, Roy Powers, Dr. Roger Ritzlin, Roy Robbins, and Ronald Bath are the members of the Board.

May 29, BOT: approved that WMC become a teaching hospital and approved support for the residency program. $220,000 is approved for residency.

June 25, BOT: Art of Living Institute (ALI) at WMC treats patients diagnosed with substance abuse.

## 1991

April 8, BOT: Robert B. Burn is appointed the Acting President and CEO.

April 9, BOT: Search started for a new CEO.

April 22, BOT: Joint board meeting of WMC and Washoe Health Systems made Burn President and CEO.

## 1992

Report to BOT: Bone marrow (BM) transplant program started thirty years ago. There are 200 centers and over 10,000 transplants have been done worldwide. Start up expenses for WMC would be $436,934 for a four bed ward.

Jan. 27, BOT: Approved four bed BM transplant unit.

Report to BOT: Reno Cardiac Medical Group, Inc. sold to WMC during the second quarter 1991.

Members of the Board of Governors are Bob Burn, Dr. Bill Carlson, Pat Coward, Bill Farr, Jerry Higgins, Dr. Phil Landis, Gene McDowell, Bertha Mullins, Judy Murphy, Andy Pearl, Roy Powers, Dr. Roger Ritzlin, and Roy Robbins.

April 27, BOT: Pat Keough retiring on May 29 after thirty years of service to WMC. BM unit bid given to C & S Construction for $229,675.

May 26, BOT: The new trauma ICU is to be dedicated to the flight crew that perished in the helicopter accident in Nov. 1991.

Aug. 24, BOT: Motion carried to require UNSOM to provide $1 million for malpractice insurance for their residents.

## 1993

March 23, BOT: SNL sale to be completed in two to three weeks.

BM transplant opened on Sept. 1, 1992. Nine patients were transplanted in the first year.

## 1994

Feb. 2, BOT: Approved a motion awarding the garage construction contract to Krump Construction.

March 24, BOT: Dr. Bill Carlson is the new chairman. The new garage is to be done in Aug. or Sept.

April 18, BOT: Members of the Board are Dr. Carlson, Dr. Arger, Burn, Coward, Farr, Dr. W. Hall, Dr. Landis, Miller, McDowell, Mullins, Murphy, Powers, Robbins, and Leo Seevers.

## 1995

Jan 23. No change in governors. Feasibility study to share computer information on patient tests with St. Mary's.

Feb. 21. Approved lab computer for $950,000.

March 20. Bone marrow transplant program report. Income for the first two years was $600,000, and the hospital's investment was recouped in 13.3 months. Overall survival rate is 80% similar to other units in the U.S.

## 1996

Dec. 19. Bill Farr's term on the Board expired.

March 18. Agreed to send a letter of intent to pursue joint ventures in Gardnerville / Minden with Barton Hosp. at South Lake Tahoe .

April 22. Approved $750,000 to support Truckee Meadows Tomorrow. Approved $250,000 to Public Health Foundation. Approved $2.1 M to UNSOM for BM and residency program. Approved $250,000 for UNSOM to est. collaborative clinics.

May 20. Carson-Tahoe and Barton Memorial Hospitals have no interest in joint venture in Gardnerville.

June 17. Michael G. Alonso is a new appointed member of the Board.

May 20. Candace Evart is a new appointed member of the Board.

Oct. 28. Protocol and policies approved for Nurse Midwives to work in the hospital.

## 1997

Feb. 18. Motion to allow physician assistants to work in the hospital does not carry.

Aug. 18. Agreed to pay reading fees to physicians in various departments for work done on indigents. They will receive the average rate of the six big hospitals in Nevada.

# APPENDIX II
## Medical Staff Members
### (January 16, 1958 when Mr. Ogren was a resident)

| NAME | CATEGORY | PRIVILEGES |
|---|---|---|
| Applewhite, N. | Sr. Active | Otolaryngology |
| Anderson, F. | Active | General Surgery |
| | | Orthopedics |
| | | Gynecology |
| Arbonies, W. | Active | Radiology |
| Becker, J. | Active | Orthopedics |
| Berger, E. | Active | Pediatrics |
| Bibb, C. | Honorary | Otolaryngology |
| Biglin, R. | Active | |
| Brigman, L. | Honorary | Pediatrics |
| Bryan, W. | Temp—App Pend | |
| Brown, R. | Provisional | |
| Broadbent, R. | Active | |
| Cann, G. | Active | Internal Med |
| Cantlon, E. | Active | General Surgery |
| | | Orthopedics |
| | | Gynecology |
| Cantlon, V. | Active | General Surgery |
| | | Orthopedics |
| | | Gynecology |
| Clarke, S. | Active | Ophthalmology |
| Coddington, F. | Temp—App Pend | |
| Callister, J. | Temp—App Pend | |
| Corvino, L. | Courtesy | |
| Creveling, E. | Honorary | Otolaryngology |
| Crosby, R. | Active | Anesthesia |
| Duxbury, M. | Active | Internal Med |
| DeTar, J. | Temp—App Pend | |

| NAME | CATEGORY | PRIVILEGES |
|---|---|---|
| DaCosta, A. | Honorary | Public Health |
| Elliott, F. | Active | Internal Med |
| Falk, M. | Active | Dermatology |
| Farrell, G. | Provisional | |
| Fuller, J. | Honorary | Ophthalmology |
| | | Otolaryngology |
| Gerow, L. | Active | |
| Gilbert, H. | Active | Radiology |
| Gould, L. | Provisional | |
| Greear, J. | Active | Ophthalmology |
| Hall, W. | Active | General Surgery |
| | | Orthopedics |
| | | Gyn/Ob |
| Hand, E. | Courtesy | |
| Harper, C. | Active | General Surgery |
| | | Orthopedics |
| Herz, J. | Active | Orthopedics |
| Hillstrom, E. | Active | General Surgery |
| | | Orthopedics |
| | | Gynecology |
| Hood, A.J. | Honorary | General Surgery |
| Hood, D. | Honorary | Internal Med |
| Hansen, E. | Provisional | |
| Kelley, W. | Active | |
| Kernan, F. | Active | Internal Med |
| Kipanidze, O. | Active | Pediatrics |
| Lambird, D. | Active | |
| Landers, A. | Honorary | |
| Little, D. | Active | |
| Little M. | Active | Gynecology |
| Locke, R. | Active | Tuberculosis |
| Lombardi, L. | Active | General Surgery |
| | | Gynecology |
| Kapo, P. | Provisional | |
| Mack, E. | Active | Neuro-Surgery |
| Maclean, K. | Active | General Surgery |
| | | Orthopedics |
| | | Gynecology |
| Magee, G. | Active | Ophthalmology |
| McCarran, S. | Active | |
| McCormick, W. | Provisional | |
| Mohler, D. | Provisional | |
| McNitt, C. | Active | Dermatology |
| Meng, F. | Senior Active | |

| NAME | CATEGORY | PRIVILEGES |
|------|----------|------------|
| Moulton, O. | Active | Ophthalmology |
|  |  | Otolaryngology |
| Muller, V. | Honorary | General Surgery |
|  |  | Gynecology |
| Mullis, T. | Active | Gyn/Ob |
| Nannini, L. | Active | General Surgery |
|  |  | Orthopedics |
|  |  | Gyn/Ob |
| O'Brien, W. | Active | Anesthesia |
| Palmer, L. | Active | Pediatrics |
| Parsons, L. | Honorary | Pathology |
| Pasutti, W. | Active | Pediatrics |
| Peterson, L. | Active | General Surgery |
|  |  | Orthopedics |
|  |  | Gynecology |
| Petty, R. | Courtesy |  |
| Phelan, S. | Active | Internal Med |
| Reno, E. | Senior Active |  |
| Roche, A. | Active |  |
| Roberts, C. | Active | Ophthalmology |
| Ross, S. | Active | Obstetrics |
| Ross, G. | Courtesy |  |
| Rowe, P. | Active | Internal Med |
| Rudisill, E. | Provisional |  |
| Russell, F. | Active | General Surgery |
|  |  | Orthopedics |
|  |  | Gyn/Ob |
| Russell, L. | Active |  |
| Salvadorini, V. | Active | Pathology |
| Samuels, F. | Active | Obstetrics |
| Sandars, L. | Active | Radiology |
| Scott, J. | Active | Pediatrics |
| Scott, A. | Active | Anesthesia |
| Sheretz, R. | Active |  |
| Shaw, D. | Honorary | Otolaryngology |
|  |  | Ophthalmology |
| Sondregger, M. | Temp—App Pend |  |
| Simpson, W. | Active | Anesthesia |
| Smernoff, N. | Active |  |
| Stahr, R. | Active | Pediatrics |
| Stadtherr, A. | Courtesy |  |
| Tappan, W. | Active | General Surgery |
|  |  | Gynecology |

| NAME | CATEGORY | PRIVILEGES |
|---|---|---|
| Thom, J. | Courtesy | |
| Thompson, D. | Active | Internal Med |
| Taylor, H. | Active | Internal Med |
| Tillman, S. | Courtesy | |
| Trinkle, A. | Active | Urology |
| Tuttle, J.P. | Honorary | General Surgery |
| | | Urology |
| Valenta, H. | Active | |
| Wiig, P. | Active | Gyn/Ob |
| Wolf, C. | Active | Gyn/Ob |
| Winnikow, W. | Courtesy | |

# APPENDIX III
## Department Heads Under Mr. Ogren, 1967

| NAME | TITLE |
|------|-------|
| Carroll W. Ogren | Administrator |
| Maida J. Pringle, R.N. | Ass't Administrator |
| W. J. Sthultz | Controller |
| Howard Epling | Pharmacy / Purchasing |
| Barbara Lindh | Admit / Out-Patient |
| Jeanette Bankofier | Dietary |
| Leon Garrett, M.T. | Laboratory, Chief Tech |
| Eldon Phillips | X-ray, Chief Tech |
| Roy P. Sampson | Personnel |
| Catherine Supple | Executive Housekeeper |
| John MacLeod | Maintenance |
| Leonard "Roy" L. Hogan | Laundry |
| Lawrence P. Mooney, P.T. | Chef Physical Therapist |
| Ida Vivian McCulley | Med. Record Librarian |
| Lawrence Russell, M.D. | Clinic Director |
| Daphne Green, R.N. | Chief of Nursing |
| Ruth Hoffman, R.N. | Surgery |
| Delbert McConnell | Inhalation Therapy Chief |
| Sari Nash | EKG |
| Claendel Talbot | EEG |

# APPENDIX IV
## Medical Staff: Dates of Arrival

1864 (CO. PHY.)
Weed, A. Gideon

1867 (CO. PHY.)
Bishop, Simeon
Ellis, Joseph

1873 (CO. PHY.)
Hogan, Henry H.

1885 (CO. PHY.)
Dawson, Alson

1893 (CO. PHY.)
Bergstein, Henry
Lewis, John A.
Phillips, William A.

1901 (CO. PHY.)
Phillips, Percy T.
Gibson, Samuel C.

1903 (CO. PHY.)
Thoma, George H.

1904 (CO. PHY.)
Morrison, Sidney K.

1906 (CO. PHY.)
Asher, John A.

1921 (CO. PHY.)
DaCosta, Albert R.

1924 (CO. PHY.)
Adams, Albert F.

1927 (CO. PHY.)
Servoss, George L.

1932 (CO. PHYS.)
Creveling, Earl L.
Gerow, James W.

CLASS OF 1933
Bath, Thomas W.
Brown, Horace J.
Caples, Bryon H.
DaCosta, Albert R.
Hood, Arthur J.
Hood, Dwight L.
Hood, Wm. H.
Howell, Wm. L.
Maclean, Donald
MacPherson, A. W.
Miller, Dr.
Morrison, Sidney K.
Paradis, Henry A.
Parson, Lawrence
Reno, Elwood F.
Robison, Martin A.

Samuels, Wm. Lee
Servoss, George L.
Shaw, David L.
Stadtherr, A. L.
Sullivan, John J.
Thompson, Alice
Thomsen, Dr.
Wyman, Rodney E.

CLASS OF 1934
Adams, Albert F.
Bice, Barrett D.
Fuller, John Andre
Hund, Erwin John
Kingsbury, Wm. N.
Landers, Aurthur E.
Larson, Dr.
Lombardi, Louis E.
Piersall, Claude E.
Samuels, Frank W.
Shaw, William A.
Thom, James

CLASS OF 1935
Brown, Horace J.
Coblentz, Alex.
Harper, T. Clair
Kipanidze, Olga
LaRay, Dr.
Muller, Vinton A.
Thorpe, Moreton J.
Tuttle, Joseph P.
West, Claudius W.

CLASS OF 1936
Moulton, Olin C.

CLASS OF 1938
Brigman, Lemuel R.
Fightlin, Harry E.
Goodyear, Arthur
Lang. John R. A.
Roche, Alan J.

CLASS OF 1939
Anderson, Frederick

Bibb, Clyde J.
Cann, George A.
Nannini, Leo
Stahr, Roland W.

CLASS OF 1940
Belnap, H. Earl
Hemminger, Geo.
Little, Morris
Menke, Blaine H.

CLASS OF 1941
Hensel, George C.
Little, Dana D.

CLASS OF 1942
Applewhite, N. E.
Wiig, Paul O.

CLASS OF 1943
Clarke, Samuel T.

CLASS OF 1944
Bibb, John D.
Brabec, Paul F.
Bradley, Grover O.
Hall, Wesley W. Sr.

CLASS OF 1945
Plamer, John E.

CLASS OF 1946
Bischoff, H. W.
Cantlon, Edwin L.
Copeland, Edgar
Estrin, Joseph Z.
Gillespie, Elmer
Holstein, Arthur
Kelley, Wayne P.
Leftwich, Wm. B.
Lohlein, Harold E.
Sannella, Lee S.
Strasser, Hans A.
Tainter, Eugene G.
Wolfe, Clare C.
Yerg, Raymond

CLASS OF 1947
Gerow, Lynn B., Sr.
Locke, C. Robert
Kernan, Francis
Maclean, Ken. F.
McGee, George
Ross, George H.
Russell, Frank A.
Smith, Jesse W.
Tillim, Sidney J.
Valenta, Henry J.
Winikow, Wm. E.

CLASS OF 1948
Becker, John C.
Berger, Emanuel
Elliott, Frederick
Gilbert, Harry B.
Harrell, Voss
Mack, Ernest W.
Melarkey, D, DDS
Moore, Walter H.
O'Brien, William
Pasutti, William
Rea, Stanley L.
Ross, Silas E.
Rowe, Peter
Scott, Arthur E.
Scott, John G.
Smith, P. W.

CLASS OF 1949
Crosby, Robert C.
Elia, Joseph C.
Russell, Lawrence
Sweeley, Merle E.
Taylor, Horace

CLASS OF 1951
Abrums, George
Greear, James N.
Herz, James R.
Hillstrom, Earl N.
Mullis, Tom N.
Salvadorini, V. A.
Simpson, Wm. E.

CLASS OF 1952
Falk, Mortimer S.
Groomes, Charles
Sanders, Liebert J.
Tappan, Wm. M.

CLASS OF 1953
Broadbent, Robert
Brown, Raymond M.
Fien, Irving
Peterson, Lowell J.
Phalen, Joseph S.
Smernoff, Noah
Trinkle, Albert J.

CLASS OF 1954
Duxbury, Millard
Hanson, Elmer F.
Gould, Leslie H.
McCormick, Willard
Mohler, Donald I.
Sheretz, Richard
Thompson, David S

CLASS OF 1955
Callister, John W.
Coddington, F. L.
DeTar John H.
Quinn, Walter F.
Sonderegger, M.

CLASS OF 1956
Fleming, Chas. E.
Landis, S. N.
Lenz, Gilbert G.
Peters, Roy M.

CLASS OF 1957
Bryan, William J.
Farrell, George R.
Guisto, Donald F.
Kapo, Peter J.
Rudisill, Eibert, M.
Sargent, Jack P.
Williams, David E.

CLASS OF 1958
Belcourt, Claude M.
Edmiston, John M.
Ervin, John R.
Hlubucek, Donald
McCuskey, Chas  Sr
Miles, Hoyt B.
Myles, Robert K.
Rosenauer, Adolf
Sage, Roderick D.
Sande, John P.
Stewart, Robert L.
Stokes, Frank C.
Teipner, William
Watson, John M.

CLASS OF 1959
Champion, Wm. J.
Davis, John M.
Magee, George F.

CLASS OF 1960
Roberts, Frank E.

CLASS OF 1961
Decker, James
Feltner, William R.
Glenn, Gerard E.
Raymond, Mark B.
Rueckl, Frank V.
Sauls, Carl L.

CLASS OF 1962
Curry, Arrah C.

CLASS OF 1963
Bynum, William L., Jr.
Hall, Thomas E.
Halvorson, Harold
Roberts, David L.

CLASS OF 1964
Flanary, Jack
Furman, George J.
Kavanagh, Thom.
MacLellan, Warren
McCuskey, Chas. Jr.

Pickering, Donald E.
Soli, Donald
Stapleton, John J.

CLASS OF 1965
Barnet, Robert
Botsford, James
Dane, Lear
Dow, Stephen
Kaiser, Richard
Kelly, John C.
Magnette, Jules
Mannix, Francine
Montgomery, E.
Mousel, Donald K.
Peterman, Albert F.
Prentice, Edwin
Schieve, Donald R.
Shonnard, C.

CLASS OF 1966
Coppola, Ralph
Cudek, Ronald P.
Dales, Gerald Jr.
Lieb, Fredrick
Loudon, Don Ross
Malmquist, Ken. W.
Nelson, Laurence D.
Schultz, Robert P.
Smith, George T.

CLASS OF 1967
Boyden, Fred
Gilmore, Richard C.
Gretchen, Edward A.
Inskip, Richard C.
Morelli, Robert
Talsma, Jack E.

CLASS OF 1968
Avery, M. Ronald
Barnstein, Norman
Carlson, A. Wm.
Felder, Gerald B.
Filippini, Charles
Higgs, William T.
Johnson, David C.

Nitz, Gordon L.
Proctor, Robert
Reinkemeyer, Joseph
Sohn, Anton P.
Stone, Ray
White, Paul

CLASS OF 1969
Beye, Richard D.
Billharz, David
Bolstad, Owen
Bruce, Robert
Cavell, Richard J.
Day, Donald W.
Iliescu, John
Jones, H. Douglas
Keeler, William
Learey, K. Lynn
Postman, Marshall
Scully, Thomas
Simon, Robert C.
Tenney, James N.
Thompson, Newton
White, Paul

CLASS OF 1970
Brady, Thomas W.
Christian, Maynard
Clift, Robert C.
Ehrlich, Edward
Emery, Clyde
Evans, Joseph
Hendrick, Harry
Huneycutt, Harry
Jonasz, Henry
Kelly, Betty L.
Laubscher, Fred
Moore, Richard
Noehren, Walter
Pemberton, Penelope
Watson, David S.
Wichman, John W.

CLASS OF 1971
Blake, David F.
Bodensteiner, Thomas
Bryant, John A.

Dorostkar, Massoud
Jorgenson, Richard
Gainey, Michael O.
Hall, Wesley W., Jr.
Kraft, John W.
Mann, Raymond J.
Miercort, Roger
Olson, Donald R.
Prutzman, Geo. W.
Standlee, Thomas

CLASS OF 1972
Atcheson, James B.
Bennett, Darrell
Cafferata, Treat
Clark, Peter F.
Colgan, James R.
Dapra, David J.
Hamilton, R. Darrell
Lashier, Harvey
Llewellyn, Gene A.
Marshall, Angus
Pelter, William M.
Sellyei, Louis F.
Stapleton, Thomas
Zebrack, Jerry N.

CLASS OF 1973
Berberian, Joseph
Guerin, Bernard
Haislip, Donald B.
Missall, Stephen R.
Nichols, Robert T.
Rasul Mujahid
Schonder, Adolph
Wigmore, Wm. L.

CLASS OF 1974
Buntain, William L.
Fischer, John R.
Forsythe, James W.
Gregory, Paul J.
Kotnik, Anthony J.
Levy, Louis A.
Maher, Alfred J.
Mahoney, Jerome J.
Mast, Jeffrey W.

McCleish, Laurence
Milliman, James C.
Moore, Kent A.
Riley, Patrick W.
Rothstein, Ronald
Shapiro, Leonard
Truchard, Anthony

CLASS OF 1975
Campbell, John
Clark, Larry
Clark, Paul
Cunningham, A.
Davis, Philip R.
Dawson, William
Edwards, David
Gerow, Jr. Lynn B.
Greenberg, George
Lindner, Luther
Manalo, Pacita E.
Massaro, Joseph
Phillips, Wayne
Smalley, Jo B.
Strand, Gareth
Strong, Janet
West, Bud

CLASS OF 1976
Admirand, Wm. H.
Ahmad, Imdad
Berndt, Theodore B.
Diedrichsen, David
Diedrichsen, Jame
Disiere, John
Feinberg, Jonathan
Fricke, Frederick J.
Fricke, Johanna S.
Ganchan, Richard
Gansert, Gary G.
Glick, Eugene
Lindner, Luther E.
Madoff, Lawrence
Mazo, George N.
Moore, Bolivar B.
Nielsen, Charles
Pokroy, Michael
Porras, Mario E.

Saeger, Kenneth
Savran, Stephen
Treanor, Walter J.
Van Buren, Wm.

CLASS OF 1977
Anderson, Grant
Burgess, John
Cecchi, Geoffrey
Cresanta, Daniel
Cunningham, Steve
Dooley, John
Douglas, John
Elliott, Vernon
Farmer, Rodney
Ford, William R.
Gardner, Larry
Greenwald, Ed.
Hardy, Thomas
Hastings, Chris.
Karrasch, Charles
Lieberstein, Loth
Lurie, Arthur J.
McNeil, Daniel
Monibi, Ali
Newmark, Michael
Petit, Alan
Rankin, Thomas
Ritchie, Kenneth
Shields, John
Taylor, Neill
Tetzlaff, Thomas
Tucker, Scott
Weiss, Malcolm
Wood, William A.
Walker, Joseph R.

CLASS OF 1978
Apicella, Michael
Bacchus, Malcolm
Balvin, Gregory
Barelli, Anthony
Bierman, Kerry C.
Boyd, Rise
Brady, Bernard
Bruce, Merle
Bullias, Bruce

Cameron, John
Conklin, Thomas
Conran, William
Cryer, Henry
Dietz, Patrick
Dudding, Burton
Fenwick, Peter
Feinberg, Jonathan
Fulton, Robert
Gauthier, Joseph
Grace, Stephen
Hansen, Daniels
Henning, Gay
Horgan, John
Horowitz, Jay
Hume, Horace
Johnson, Michael
Kurtz, Kenneth
LaLonde, John C.
Landis, Phillip
Lemieux, John
Martin, Robert L.
Mazzaferri, Ernest
Miller, Frank
Nunez, Juan
O'Neill, Thomas
Payton, Charles
Pauly, Ira
Quaglieri, Charles
Ralston, Robert
Ramos, Susan
Ramos, William
Rayner, Abi
Scott, John J.
Sewell, Glen
Shields, John
Stafford, Edward
Stevland, Nelson
Stoloff, Stuart
Terry, William T.
Thompson, Alfred
Torman, Howard
Towle, Thomas
Voyevidka, Ihor
Wallace, Bruce
Wheeler, Jaime K.

CLASS OF 1979
Abrass, Gary
Altrocchi, John
Atcheson, Steven
Black, Franklin
Bloomfield, S.
Blurton, Richard
Bonar, Robert
Brady, Stephen
Buchwald, Susan
Calvanese, Jerry
Chambers, Joseph
Davis, P.R.
Delionbach, Louis
Desmarteau, John
Edwards, David
Glick, Eugene
Gutride, Martin
Hall, Stephen
Harrison, William
Heffner, Richard
Held, Charles
Horgan, Edwin
Kotnik, Anthony
Mackey, Dennis
Madoff, Lawrence
Mammen, Robert
McElreath, Ricky
McMullen, Joseph
Merchant, Robert
Milstein, Stephen
Neilson, Richard
Penrod, Dallas
Priest, Richard
Reagan, Brian
Reddy, Atigadda
Segall, Michael
Schiff, Steven
Snatic, John
Spohr, Mark
Stitt, Robert
Sutherland, T.
Tappan, Ross
Thompson, Stanley
Torch, William
Trigueiro, Craig
Walker, Alan

Whipple, Gerald
Williamson, John

CLASS OF 1980
Brown, Dennis J.
Buckley, Conor P.
Campbell, Bruce D.
Chamberlain, Jay
Christenson, Steve
Coughlin, Timothy
Dankworth, Gary
Davis, John S.
DePalma, Ralph G.
Dieringer, Paul E.
Erickson, John M.
Fenwick, Peter
Fredericks, Robert
Fuller, Colin
Glover, John
Handke, Darrel D.
Heinle, Donna L.
Howatt, James
Karpilow, Craig
Kenton, Robert
Maddux, Bill
Mishler, Alan J.
Mishler, William
Neal, Miron W
Noble, Larry M.
Parker, Lexey S.
Peacock, John H.
Peters, Doug
Phillips, Paul W.
Phillips, Wayne R.
Pollock, Hilton R.
Pomeranz, Gary
Prupas, Malin
Rich, Phillip
Ritzlin, Roger S.
Rosenquist, Robert
Schnaser, Allen
Seligman, Karl
Shankel, Stewart
Smith, Ronald L.
Walker, William
White, Robin
Wong, Alan L.

CLASS OF 1981
Andrews, John
Bajo, Stephen
Berry, David
Bigley, George
Blakey, Richard
Bomberger, Richard
Brenner, William
Charney, Phillip
Clark, Kenneth
Clark, Odette
Clemmensen, Chas.
Diamond, John
Drake, Terrance
Ferrel, Nancy
Foster, Randall
Frank, Barry
Glass, Michael
Hinton, Ladson
Humphrey, Steven
Krissoff, William
Mackintosh, Fred.
Malin, Jacob
Malone, Brian
McNamara, T.
Monagin, John
Naughton, Martin
Peters, Doug
Scherf, Christman
Stites, Deane
Swarts, Raymond
Thornton, William
Wark, John
Woodbridge, John
Young, Norman

CLASS OF 1982
Allred, James
Altman, Stewart
Artman, Henry
Betz, John
Bhoothalingom, E.
Blake, David
Bosis, Daniel
Cox, Richard
Class, Patrick
Crow, Howard

Daines, Michael
DeBardelaben, Gene
Dixon, Sherwood
Edwards, Michael
Hanke, Richard
Harn, Beverly
Havens, Carol
Henson, Hale
Hill, Haydon
Hutchinson, David
Idler, Randy
Johnson, Charles
Knight, Melvin
Kozar, Mark
Lees, Bonnie
Levenson, Barry
Moss, Steven
Parks, Samuel
Peterson, Daniel
Spring, Donald
Stouder, Michael
Tannenbaum, Bruce
Toth, Michael
Uhalde, Margaret
Uppal, Surinder
Walker, Kay

CLASS OF 1983
Class, Patrick L.
Colletfi, Patrick J.
Cox, Richard
Debardelaben, E.
Galloway, Patricia
Goodman, Philip
Hanke, Richard
Harn, Beverly
Herz, Patrick S.
Hicks, Henry C.
Hollen, Joe R.
Jackson, Michael V.
Johnson, Charles E.
Lardinois, Claude
Lombard, Joseph F.
Lynn, Edward J.
Maddox, Robert
Miller, Jade DDS
Millman, Jeffrey D.

O'Neill, William
Parlasca, Robert J.
Rinehart, Jess S.
Rueckel, Victor
Small, Elisabeth C.
Sobczak, Ronald
Simpson, Graham
Spogen, Daniel R.
Taylor, J. Karl
Thompson, Leonard
Trimmer, William
White, Robin S.

CLASS OF 1984
Allen, Stanton H.
Arger, Kosta M.
Carpenter, Charles
Draper, Edward M.
DuBrott, Robert
Edgcomb, John S.
Fountain, Todd B.
Irwin, Michael
Juell, Brian E.
Lamberts, Eric W.
Larson, Trudy A.
Lawrie, D. James
Maher, Patrick
McCormack, Brian
McLennan, James C.
Neilsen, Ronald
Parker, Steven W.
Quaglieri, Frank C.
Reddy, Moola P.
Rueckl, F. Victor
Ryan, John E.
Sieffert, George F.
Smith, Calvin S.
Sullivan, Rita

CLASS OF 1985
Andrews, John D.
Bertrando, Robert
Dipaolo, Chris.
Dyches, Timothy J.
English, Harry A.
Garcia, Ricardo A.
Ho, Lester

Jones, James DDS
Knutzen, Victor K.
McCalla, W (DDS)
McKee, Denise D.
Mock, David L.
O'Donnell, John N.
Pisani, G. DDS
Schumacher, Mark
Seher, Richard P.
Simpson, Lex A.
Wadia, Gurjeet
Zell, Steven C.

CLASS OF 1986
Amanatullah, Faisal
Bannister, R. Bruce
Brown, Cynthia  M.
Cole, Barry
Drummer, Eric M.
Evert, David
Ferguson, Rodger
Gray, John F.
Greenhouse, Arnold
Haley, Michael D.
Hannon, Lawrence
Johnson, David
Klose, Craig W.
Kroening, Richard
Manny, Brad T.
Mortensen, Eric J.
Rafael, Richard
Sachdev, Pratima
Wilkinson, Thomas
Zwerin, Marvin B.

CLASS OF 1987
Antone-Knoll, C.
Bayless, Joseph M.
Berman, Steven E.
Brickner, Kurt
CampBell, Gary E.
Carlson, Kurt
Cassidy, Donald T.
Chotiner, Harold
Clark, Donald
Conrath, F. Craig
Culhane, Daniel E.

Deweerd, John J.
Dilley, Thatcher
Eaton, John M.
Gilbert, Warren S.
Goring, Catherine
Grace, Stephen G.
Graves, Brad T.
Hilbish, Judy F.
Lawrence, Hannon
Keil, Martin K.
Klaich, Larry D.
Komadina, Thomas
Lloyd, William J.
Lombard, Timothy
Mar, David A.
Marshall, John J.
McCaskill, Terry L.
McCormack, Brian
Miller, Glenn G.
O'Gara, Thomas D
Plecha, Stanley L.
Reimer, Galen M.
Sanders, Thomas J.
Schenk, Sheldon J.
Smith, Leslie S.
Torok, James A.
Vandergon, Dirk D.
Vandyken, Donald
Vicks, Steven L.
Zweig, Richard

CLASS OF 1988
Baldo, Richard M.
Barakat, George H.
Barulich, Matthew
Bray, Timothy J.
Coughlin, Timothy
Crawford, Cynthia
Duxbury, G.
Gomez, Myron J.
Gunderson, Mark C.
Haller, John L.
Hess, George H.
Hills, John F.
Hope, Thomas J.
Hueftle, Mark G.
Johnson, Gary E.

Mailander, Paul M.
McGaw, Terrence G.
Mozen, Paul H.
Palosaari, David E.
Parker, Lexey S.
Povolny, William
Starr, E. Gary
Stites, Deane A.
Stutes, Damon L.
Tiffany, Frank J.
Yup, Gary L.

CLASS OF 1989
Allgood, Mark R.
Arnow, Jonathan E.
Basta, Robert D.
Becker, William
Black, Donald R.
Bonaldi, Louis A.
Chapman, Todd P.
Clark, Ellen G.
Clark, H. Donald
Cox, Charles G.
Davee, Thomas S.
Dietrich, John
Dinwiddie, Kevin
Fletcher, Dirk G.
Gansert, Guy G.
Griswald, James
Hahn, Mark E.
Hays, Thomas
Heaton, John W.
Horsley, Eugene .
Lee, Vivian E.
Linkus, Kevin A.
Martell, Algis
Maul, Mary M.
Meyer, Roger P.
Morgan, William
Morris, Colleen A.
Mullen, Bruce E.
Pixley, John S.
Rattray-Hahn, S.
Romick, Charles
Scott, Raymond H.
Shane, Stanley R.
Shields, Samuel S.

Simon, Edward M.
Swackhamer, Robt.
Vacca, Dante F.
Weiss, Lawrence J.
Young, Terrance S.
Zucker, David A.

CLASS OF 1990
Ardill, Richard H.
Bryant, Darla A.
Bryg, Robert J.
Durant, William J.
Garey-Sage, Jon.
Hershewe, Gerard
Hummphrey, Linda
Humphrey, Michael
Kelley, Francis P.
Kennedy, Steven R.
Lazalt, Kristin A.
Haydon, Curtis F.
McClintock, Paul
Rahe, Richard H.
Raven, Karen A.
Rembetske, Thomas
Rodriquez, Gomez
Russell, Pamela K.
Sande, Craig M.
Scully, Christopher
Smith, Dwight
Yamamoto, Dennis T.

CLASS OF 1991
Abelow, Stephen
Adams, Richard T.
Bittker, Thomas
Brandl, Joseph P.
Brown, Curtis W.
Bruce, Stephen
Bruno, Anthony J.
Cappiello, Wm.
Farringer, Bruce
Field, Anthony
Fisher, Robert D.
Fleming, Hilari
Heinz-Sader, Nancy
Hiss, Paul
Hutchens, Craig

Johns, Joseph
Kiener, Joseph
Konakis, Janie
Lafferty, Linda
Laine, Jonathan
Mullins, Richard
Oksenholt, Lorrie
Omellas, Pamela
Pollock, Hilton
Powell, Berkley R.
Rosen, Richard
Van Antwerp, Jas.
Vandelist, Craig
Williamson, Shane

CLASS OF 1992
Adams, Allyson
Ascensao, Joao
Campione, Ann-M.
Carrrea, Frank
Carter, Jan
Christopherson, K.
Delaplain, Tracey
Fiore, David
Glantz, Katheryne
Harrison, Clark
Harris, Reta
Hummer, Beth
Iturate, Eloy
Kanellos, Angelo
Kiser, Michele
Kressler, Michael
Lee, Richard
Lorenzen, Kirsten
Miller, Grant
Mirghani, Eltag
Oujevolk, America
Phillips, Steven
Rappaport, James
Recchia, Steven
Rhoades, Terrence
Shapiro, Robert
Sladek-Lawson, R.
Tjoa, Manuel DDS
Webster, Jeffery
Willcourt, Robin
Winder, Cheryl

Winder, James
Young, Perry

CLASS OF 1993
Abbott, Lisa
Berry, Robert
Boyden, Eric
Boyd, Phillis
Chryssos, Basil
Craner, James
Davis, Phillip
Davis, William
Dearmont, Karen
Endo, Cathy
Gay, Laurence
Gaetke, Mark
Hall, Claire
Hamor, Paul
Hartsell, Conrad
Hayes, William
Hinofosa, Tomas
Kalanges, Lauri
Kasprzak, Peter
Kip, Phelps
Koci, Timothy
Libert, Keith
Markin, Jay
Mathis, David
McNulty, Candace
Miller, Melissa
Miyazake, Wm.
Morgan, Jay
Oliver, Diane
Pappas, James
Passalacqua, Brian
Potter, Charles
Richeson, Robert
Romick, Charles
Stanko, Michael
Stratton, Richard
Sutton, Jennifer
Taylor, Steven

CLASS OF 1994
Aguiar, P. Abel
Altinsan, Saide
Benneth, Kath.

Bonnet, Gabriel
Caruso, Daniel
Chaffin, David
Cotter, Thomas
Cutler, Kenneth
Delos Santos, D.
Edney, Stephen
Graettinger, Wm.
Green, Tracey
Harris, Richard G.
Hayes, Anne
Johns, Diana
Johnson, L. Alan
Klein, Beth
Lasko, Kevin
Mathis, Chris
Mayer, Ralph
McCartan, James
McCartan, Julie
McDermott, Karen
Nielsen, Jarl
Palant, Carlos
Prothro, David
Riley, Robert
Quan, Richard
Schrage, Jon
Schwartz, Mindy
Scott, Carlos
Sobiek, James
Shapiro, Michael
Smith, Emily
Stumph, Paul
Sweeney, Edwin
Thomas, Dianna
Van Epps, Lee
Vanreken, Calvin
Waggoner, Perry
Wesely, Andrew
Zamboni, Anthony
Zimmet, Sidney

CLASS OF 1995
Bachman, Teresa R.
Byram, A. A.
Callister, T. Brian
Capra, Samuel W.
Clark, Peter S.

Eckert, Kathryn L.
Frishman, Richard
Gamboa, R. DDS
Howton, Marcia J.
Irish, Barbara A.
McVey, John E.
Meerschaert, C.
Mellum, Stacy E.
Miller, Denver J.
Morkin, Michael J.
Oki, Earle Y.
Preston, Digby M.
Rubin, Steven E.
Virden, Charles P.
Wilson, John W.
Hoberg, Matthew J.
Huene, Donald S.
Juarez, Kathleen B.
Lokshin, Boris M.
Piasecki, Melissa P.
Rowe, Dan E.
Watson, David W.
Weed, Andrea K.
Wyatt, Arthur J.

CLASS OF 1996
Anderson-Jenkins, J.
Arcomano, Todd R.
Aikin, Brent A.
Albright, Janet L.
Auld, Kathleen L.
Baft, Murray D.
Blackhart, Bret S.
Bailey, Robert M.
Bryan, Richard H.
Cullen, Mark T.
Cunningham, James
Daub, David J.
Eidel, James M.
Foulk, Russell A.
Harris, Ethan G.
Hasfurther, Daniel
Hicks, Ronald B.
Jacobs, Scott E.
Johnson, Joseph E.
Kiene, Kevin L.
Kietzky, Alan R.

Laird, Dania o.
Melvin, Susan Y.
Pitman, Kenneth
Platon, Pacita S.
Plecha, Edward J.
Shonnard, Paul Y.
Smith, David E.
Tatem, Stewart A.
Thienhau, Ole J.
Topham, Robert B.
Walls, Joseph P.
Wolff, Robert S.

CLASS OF 1997
Anders, D, DPM
Bonds, Christi L.
Daham. Philip
Daniels, Mark
Earle, Onna J.
Fyda, Thomas M.
Gardner, Geraldine
Gettelman, Thomas
Guyton, Douglas C.
Hald, David E.
Hald, Sherrie A.
Hardy, Christian
Hodge, Richard G.
Ichino, Jake H.
Iida, Calvin T.

Javaid, Farrukh
Johns, Diana C.
Jones, Christian
Fleming, Cynthia
Gingold, Jeffrey N.
Levin, Michael L.
Louie, Timothy J.
Matsumura, Jerry S.
Matsumura, G. F.
McGee, Donald L.
Miyagawa, Dean K.
Molina, L d L DMD
Nelson, Lisa A.
Osgood, Patrick J.
Peterson, Lyn C.
Picetti, Paul
Puglisi, Austin V.
Rasoumoff, Theo.
Schubacker, M.
Scott, Charles R.
Sims, D. W. DDS
Sundstrom, Steven
Tew, Joel
Watanabe, Henry
Williamson, Larry
Wiltse, Lisa R.
Witmer, Bruce
Yee, Elaine M.

# APPENDIX V
## Board of Trustees Chairmen*, 1930–1998

| | |
|---|---|
| G. W. Nottingham | Nov. 1930 to Jan. 1933 |
| William McKnight | Jan. 1933 to Jan. 1935 |
| E. C. Mulcahy | Jan. 1935 to Jan. 1937 |
| J. J. Keenan | Jan. 1937 to Jan. 1939 |
| B. A. Reed | Jan. 1939 to Aug. 1940 |
| John I. Hickey | Aug. 1940 to Jan. 1945 |
| Peter Ferguson | Jan. 1945 to Jan. 1946 |
| Angus E. Cauble | Jan. 1946 to Jan. 1949 |
| Bruce M. Thomas | Jan. 1949 to Jan. 1951 |
| Olin C. Moulton, M.D. | Jan. 1951 to Apr. 1952 |
| Ernest W. Mack, M.D. | Apr. 1952 to Jan. 1963 |
| Bryce Rhodes, Attorney | Jan. 1963 to Jan. 1967 |
| Ernest W. Mack, M.D. | Jan. 1967 to Jan. 1975 |
| John C. Becker, M.D. | Jan. 1975 to Oct. 1976 |
| Maida J. Pringle, R.N. | Oct. 1976 to Nov. 1978 |
| Mark B. Raymond, M.D. | Nov. 1978 to Jan. 1981 |
| Steven R. Brown, stock broker | Jan. 1981 to Jan. 1983 |
| Robert K. Myles, M.D. | Jan. 1983 to Jan. 1990 |
| Patrick Coward, telephone Exec. | Jan. 1990 to Mar. 1994 |
| William Carlson, M.D. | Mar. 1994 |

*Changed to board of Governors in 1985

# APPENDIX VI
## Administrators, 1893-1998

| | |
|---|---|
| W. H. Joy (Steward) | May 1893 |
| O. W. Ayers (Steward) | May 1893 |
| W. H. Joy (Steward) | Dec. 1898 |
| Hull E. Joy (Steward) | Dec. 1898 |
| Joseph Odett (Steward and Supt.) | Mar. 1901 |
| Burke, A. A. (Supt.) | Jan. 1917 |
| Twaddle, Eben (Supt.) | Jan. 1923 |
| John J. Kenney (Bus. Mgr.) | Dec. 1930 to May 1933 |
| Alfred W. MacPherson, M.D. (Supt.) | May 1933 to Feb. 1935 |
| John J. Kenney (Bus. Mgr./ Supt.) | Feb. 1935 to Oct. 1938 |
| A. L. Longfield (Temp. Mgr.) | Oct. 1938 to Jan. 1939 |
| John J. Kenney (Supt.) | Jan. 1939 to July 1939 |
| A. L. Longfield (Supt.) | July 1939 to Dec. 1941 |
| Mrs. Meta C. Shull (Act. Supt.) | Dec. 1941 to Jan. 1942 |
| D. D. Stingley (Act. Supt.) | Jan. 1942 to July 1942 |
| D. D. Stingley (Supt.) | July 1942 to Nov. 1942 |
| Henry Wallace (Supt.) | Dec. 1942 to July 1946 |
| Trustee Angus E. Cauble (Temp. Supt.) | July 1946 to Oct. 1946 |
| Vlad F. Ratay (Supt.) | Oct. 1946 to June 1949 |
| Maida J. Pringle ( Jt. Temp. Supt.) | June 1949 |
| H. Chester English (Jt. Temp. Supt.) | June 1949 |
| Clyde W. Fox (Supt.) | June 1949 to Aug. 1959 |
| Earl E. Horton (Adm.) | Sept. 1959 to Oct. 1963 |
| Carroll W. Ogren (Act. Adm.) | Oct. 1963 to May 1964 |

| | |
|---|---|
| Carroll W. Ogren (Adm.) | May 1964 to May 1977 |
| Norman E. Peterson (Act. Adm.) | May 1977 to June 1977 |
| Carroll W. Ogren (Adm.) | June 1977 to Nov. 1978 |
| Michael J. Newmarker (Adm.) | Nov. 1978 to Nov. 1982 |
| John Prout (Act. Adm.) | Nov. 1982 to June 1983 |
| James Lamb (CEO) | June 1983 to Apr. 1991 |
| Robert B. Burn (CEO) | Apr. 1991 to present |

# APPENDIX VII
## Chiefs of Staff, 1933-1998

Sidney K. Morrison, M.D. , 1933–1934

John A. Fuller, M.D., 1935–1936

Rodney E. Wyman, M.D., 1937–1942

A. J. Hood, M.D., 1943

Rodney E. Wyman, M.D., 1944–1946

Vernon Cantlon, M.D., 1947

Edwin Cantlon, M.D., 1948

George R. McGee, M.D., 1949

Rodney E. Wyman, M.D., 1950–1951

Ernest W. Mack, M.D., 1952

Frederick Anderson, M.D., 1953

Francis Kernan, M.D., 1954

Wesley W. Hall, Sr., M.D., 1955

Earl Hillstrom, M.D., 1956

William A. O'Brien, M.D., 1957–1958

Kenneth Maclean, M.D., 1959–1960

Walter F. Quinn, M.D., 1961

Horace Taylor, M.D., 1962

Lowell J. Peterson, M.D., 1963

William Tappan, M.D., 1964

John G. Scott, M.D., 1965

Donald I. Mohler, M.D., 1966–1967

J. Malcolm Edmiston, M.D., 1968

Carl L. Sauls, M.D., 1969–1970

Arthur E. Scott, M.D., 1971

Robert K. Myles, M.D., 1972–1973

Arrah C. Curry, M.D., 1974–1975

John P. Sande, M.D., 1976–1977

Maynard Christian, M.D., 1978–1979

Gordon Nitz, M.D., 1980–1981

Anton P. Sohn, M.D., 1982–1983

Charles F. McCuskey, M.D., 1984–1985

Richard Ganchan, M.D., 1986–1987

John M. Erickson, M.D., 1988–1989

Roger S. Ritzlin, M.D., 1990–1991

Phillip Landis, M.D., 1992–1993

Wesley W. Hall III, M.D., 1994–1995

William O'Neill, M.D., 1996–1997

John Gray, M.D., 1998–

# APPENDIX VIII
## Early Reno/Sparks Hospitals

*Adventist Hospital—1907*
  804 Ralston Street
  Dr. McCubben, proprietor
  Nathan S. Overton, Supt.
  Became El Reposos in 1912

*Allen Maternity Hospital—1919*
  544 N. Virginia Street
  Established by Mrs. Allen

*Bond Memorial Hospital—1946*
  829 N. Virginia Street
  Closed in 1952

*Florence Crittenden Home—1913*
  937 Forest Street
  Now 1000 Plumas Street
  Became Sam Platt residence

*Hudson Hospital—1942*
  43 California Avenue
  Closed in 1945

*Invalid's Hospital—1904*
  519 W. Sixth Street
  Cornelia J. Wentworth, Supt.
  Became *Wentworth Hospital*
  at 322 Chestnut

*Nevada Sanitarium—1923*
  South Arlington Avenue
  Dr. C.C. Galsgie, prop.
  Closed in 1924

*Nevada State Hosp—1881*
  Sparks, Nevada

*Nurses' Hospital—1908*
  Virginia St at Fourth St

*People's Hospital—1909*
  Virginia St at 4th 2nd fl
  Est. by Dr. J. L. Robinson
  Miss Cunningham, Supt.

*Red Cross Hospital—1908*
  Alice Hopkins, Supt.

*Reno General Hosp—1929*
  429 Eighth Street
  Closed in 1933

*Reno Hospital—1915*
  Alice Craven, Supt.

*Rigelhuth Maternity Hosp*
  Lake Street near 6th St
  Mrs. Rigelhuth, Supt.

*Manitou Sanitarium*
141 W. Fifth Street
Mr. Anderson, Supt.

*Mount Rose Hospital—1914*
429 Granite (Arlington Ave)
Dr. George McKenzie, prop.
Closed c. 1923

*Nevada Hospital—*
Photo at Nev. Hist. Soc.

*St. George Hospital—1904*
835 Mill Street
Mrs. Lisak, Supt.
Merged with Roosevelt Hospital

*St. Mary's Hospital—1908*
Walnut and Chestnut Streets

*Sierra Hospital—1905*
507 South Virginia Street
Pearl Mill and Mrs. Bell Byfers,
proprietors

*Southern Pacific Emergency Hosp*
1909, For railroad employees

*Swain Hospital—1906*
Clement C. Swain, Supt.

*Royal Hartung Hospital*
71 Ralston Street
Old People's Home
I.O.O.F./ Rebecca Lodge

*Roosevelt Hospital—1907*
550 Sierra Street
Frances O'Hara, Supt.
Merged with St. Geo Hosp
and located at 550 Mill

*University Hospital—1905*
University Campus
For students and faculty

*Veteran's Hospital —1939*
Locus Street
For veterans

*Wentworth Hospital—*
322 Chestnut Street
C. J. Wentworth, Supt.
see Invalid's Hospital

*Whitaker Hospital—1904*
507 W. Seventh Street
Drs. Fee & Rulefson
Mary E. Evans, Supt.

# APPENDIX IX
## Management Staff, 1998

| NAME | TITLE |
|---|---|
| Bob Burn | Chief Executive Officer |
| Jim Miller | Chief Financial Officer |
| Rod Callahan | Chief Operating Officer |
| Lynn Atcheson | Marketing |
| Dennis Miligan | Physical Services |
| Brian Moore | Human Resources |
| Rich Newman | Employee Relations |
| Eugene Spoon | Telecommunications/Security |
| Dianne Cornwall | Assistant to CEO |
| Jan Johnson | Patient/Guest Relations |
| Karen Massey | Medical Staff Services |
| Alden Hatch | Internal Audit |
| Adda Alexander | Vice President Nursing Admin. |
| Kathryn Wehrli | Vice President Finance |
| Patty Evans | Information Officer |
| Mary Ellen Wilkinson | Health Continuum Services |
| Gayle Hurd | Health Continuum Services |
| Gary Wescott | Imaging Center |
| Dawn Ahner | Accounting |
| Chris Bosse | Fincnce Provider Services |
| Elaine Sue Sutherland | Business Office/Admitting |
| Christine Thorne | Medical Records/Case Coord. |

| | |
|---|---|
| Steve Tapogna | Materials Management |
| Marie Hamway | Vice President Admin. |
| Dr. Murray Batt | Quality Services |
| Ron Stewart | Food Service |
| Joe Eidem | Food Production |
| Reta Harris | Lifeskills |
| Dean Schmaltz | Cardiopulmonary Services |
| Leigh Parker | Respiratory Care |
| Janice Beck | Surgical Services |
| Karen Meskimen | Special Care Units |
| Sadie Tate Crowder | Medical Nephrology |
| Gloria Swinney | Surgical Acute |
| Brenda Hardy | Neurology/Orthopedics |
| Barry O'Sullivan | Patient Escort/Traction |
| Kimberly Winters | Labor and Delivery |
| Christy Collins | Labor and Delivery |
| Becky Haase | Pediatrics |
| Keri Meranda | Beginnings Child Care |
| Linda Kendig | Postpartum |
| Sue Rich | NICU |
| Sharon Johansson | Lab Services |
| Vern Barnes | Core Lab |
| Ruth Ripsom | Nursing Operations |
| JoAnne Gould | Oncology |
| Aurora Wright | Dialysis |
| Diane Rolfs | ER |
| Deborah Dieter | Rehab Therapy Services |
| William Hess | Radiological Services |
| Jeff Monaghan | Pharmacy |
| Kurt Conkey | Storeroom/Patient Supply |
| Forest McMullen | Facilities Planning |
| Duane Telecky | Plant Services |
| Jane Tors | Communications |

# APPENDIX X
## Nursing Directors, 1932–1998

| | |
|---|---|
| Bertha Wilkerson (Supt. Nurses) | May 1932 to Jan 1934 |
| Teresa Hall (Supt. Nurses) | Jan 1934 to May 1934 |
| Bertha Wilkerson (Supt. Nurses) | 1934 to Feb 1937 |
| Laura Waugh (Supt. Nurses) | March 1937 to Sept 1938 |
| Mrs. Work (Act. Supervisor) | Sept 1938 to 1940? |
| Janet Cauble (Supt. Nurses) | March 1940 to Nov 1942 |
| Olive B. Mason (Head Supervisor) | Nov 1942 to Sept 1945 |
| Maida J. Pringle (Supt. Nurses) | Oct 1945 to 1953 |
| Maida J. Pringle (Asst. Adm.) | 1953 to 1957 |
| Daphne Green (Director) | 1957 to Sept 1971 |
| Sylvia Chism,Ph.D. (Director) | Sept 1971 to July 1973 |
| Daphne Green (Director) | July 1973 to Oct 1978 |
| Jean Molde (Act. Director) | Oct 1978 to April 1979 |
| Georganne Greene (Asst. Adm.) | May 1979 to April 1980 |
| Linda Hoover (Asst. Adm.) | May 1980 to Dec 1981 |
| Ardis Kinney (Co-Act. Director) | Dec 1981 to Spring 1982 |
| Greg Adams (Co-Act. Director) | Dec 1981 to Spring 1982 |
| Shirley Green (Asst. Adm.) | Spring 1982 to Dec 1986 |
| Ardis Kinney (Vice Pres.) | Dec 1986 to Oct 1997 |

[1]On Sept. 26, 1994, nursing supervising responsibilities were divided between two vice presidents

# APPENDIX XI
## Auxiliary Presidents Since 1950

Mrs. Charles W. Mapes, Sr., 1950–1952

Mrs. John McLaughlin, 1953

Bea Edwards Fariselli, 1954–1955

Mrs. David Vhay (Mel), 1956

Mrs. John Becker (Jane), 1957

Mrs. Douglas Cloud, 1958

Cornelia Rhodes, 1959

Louise Kohl Smith, 1960

Mrs. C. Robert Locke (Phyllis), 1962–1963

Mrs. Robert Mitchell, 1964–1965

Mrs. L. Curtis Farr, 1966–1967

Mrs. Gene Gastanaga, 1968–1969

Mrs. Everett Cohoon (Helen), 1970–1971

Vicki Crosby, 1972

Mrs. Laure Sheppard, 1973

Mrs. John Saibini (Jeanne), 1974–1975

Mrs. Silas Sellers (Linda), 1976

Mrs. Katrina Barger, 1977

Mrs. Francis Andrews (Betty), 1978

Mrs. Leland Churchyard (Maral), 1979

Mrs. Jess Jenkins (Jeanette ), 1980

Betty Stoddard Muncie, 1981-1982

Mrs. Thomas Harvey (Maxine), 1983-1984

Mrs. Adolf Rosenauer (Eva), 1985

Mrs. Roger McCormach (Norma), 1986
Mrs. Hudson Lee (Arlene), 1987
Mrs. Michael Cormier (Helen), 1988-1989
Mrs. Barbara Long, 1990-1991
Mrs. Peggy Pecetti, 1992-1993
Mrs. VictorWolfe (Harriet), 1995-1996
Mrs. L. Diane Kinkade, 1997-1998

# APPENDIX XII
## History of the Women's League

Washoe Medical Center's League was forty-eight years old on May 10, 1998 and was the brainchild of Administrator Clyde Fox and Chief of Staff Rodney Wyman. Inspired by the two year-old Auxiliary to the Washoe County Medical Society (AWCMS), it was originally called the Women's Auxiliary, but in order to avoid confusion with AWCMS, the name was changed to Women's League. Later, as men were included. "Women" was dropped from the name.

Mr. Fox's opening challenge to the League, "the only one of its kind in our state," in 1950 was: "This organization can go anyplace you ladies will take it. Money cannot be derived from hospital fees any more than a sufficient amount to operate the hospital; therefore, the Auxiliary can be of great help in obtaining much needed improvements and equipment." He could have just as easily stated that not enough money can be generated to operate the hospital, and we cannot count on the county tax. Mr. Fox informed the members that six committees could address the hospital's needs. These were public relations, grounds and gardens, maintenance and decorations, diagnostic facilities, personal relationships, and geriatrics.

The names of the founders of the organization sounded like a who's who of early Reno and supplied the impetus to its success. They were mesdames Robert Z. Hawkins, Charles W. Mapes, Sr., Norman Biltz, John McLaughlin, David Vhay, Frank Payne, Rodney E. Wyman, Roland Stahr, and James O. Greenan. Mr. Clyde Fox and Dr. Rodney E. Wyman were also founders. At the first meeting, Mrs. Mapes was elected president and three fund-raising events were scheduled. The next meeting was a general membership meeting and in Quonset Hut #6 at Washoe Medical Center.

The first event was a fashion show at the home of Mr. and Mrs. John McLaughlin. It was attended by 600 guests and raised $1,033 for the hospital. By the end of 1950, $5,434.71 had been raised, and the membership had grown to ninety-six. The following summer saw the inauguration of the popular TOMBOLA, the Basque word for fair, and sponsorship of the hospital gift shop. Other fundraisers included formal balls, teas, fashion shows, Easter and Christmas shopping fairs, and numerous special events. In his column for the Reno Gazette-Journal Rollan Melton stated, "They've conducted more drawings than Carter's got pills. They've peddled cakes and other goodies and sold souvenir programs. Auctions have yielded much income, selling items ranging from dining room sets to love seats."

To date, they have raised over $4 million, sponsored scholarships for educational programs at Washoe Medical Center, provided for expansion of hospital facilitates, brought equipment such as isotope counters, raised money for a linear accelerator, made available infant car seats for newborn infants, and bought furniture for the hospital. It would be impossible to list all of the good that the volunteers of the league have done for the hospital. And it all comes from the heart.

# APPENDIX XIII
## C. W. Ogren, Early Years

### My Childhood in Minnesota, 1927-1942

I was born March 22, 1927 in Minneapolis, Minnesota to Mabel (Wohleen) and Peter Ogren, both first generation Swedes whose parents were born and raised in Sweden. My grandparents came over in the late 1800s through Canada and settled in New London, Minnesota, a farming community in the southwestern part of the state. My parents left New London around 1925 and moved to Minneapolis, where my father went to work in the oil mills [refineries]. My twin brother, Stuart, and I were the last of four boys.[58] John is the oldest and Robert is next in line, followed by us.

Our childhood in Minneapolis was austere in 1939 at the end of the depression when there was no work. John enlisted in the U.S. Army Air Corps with the assurance that he would be assigned to aircraft duty. There was no Air Force at the time; all flying was assigned to U.S. Army Air Corps. In 1945 he was discharged and entered the University of Minnesota. In 1942 Robert enlisted and attended flight school. During World War II he flew B-24 and P-40 airplanes.

I went to public schools in Minneapolis: Corcoran Elementary School, Folwell Junior High School and Roosevelt High School. I graduated in 1945 when Stuart and I joined the navy. If a student stayed in school until the age of eighteen he was automatically drafted into the army, and we didn't want army service so we left early to join the navy.

### Minneapolis General Hospital, 1943-45

Before we joined the navy, my twin brother and I were orderlies at the "City Hospital" in Minneapolis. We started work at the age of fifteen, and worked in the hospital for thirteen years. We were forced to work because our family needed the money. My father was laid off from the oil mill and then worked as a street car motorman. As the Great Depression worsened, he was laid off from the street car company and forced to go on relief. There wasn't any work.

In our neighborhood, the only person who had work was a man who had a moving truck which afforded him a marginal living; then, one winter when it was about thirty-five degrees below zero he failed to drain the fluid from the block of the truck. The block froze and cracked, putting him and his family on veterans relief. He also had a disability pension from World War I. Now, our whole neighborhood was on relief.

By the winter of 1943, during the height of the War [World War II], jobs became plentiful. My father worked at an ammunitions defense plant, and the Ogren boys pitched in to help with family finances. Before that Christmas, a neighbor kid found an orderly job in the Minneapolis General Hospital, and he gave me Mr. Herliman's name, who was in charge of maintenance and outside services. He hired me on the spot and that was the beginning of a lifelong tenure in health care. It was by chance I started a career in the hospital industry because I didn't have any special interest; it was just a place to work.

Help was hard to find, and the hospital was willing to take almost anyone who could breath and handle a mop. As an orderly, I worked at a variety of tasks, from hauling ice to prepping patients for surgery to delivering diet trays to mopping floors.[59] Each night when I went to work, I didn't know what my job was going to be.

At the time my twin brother was working as a streetcar conductor. After a year, he joined me as an orderly at the hospital, which was a four hundred bed, charity hospital restricted for Minneapolis residents. Affiliated with the University of Minnesota School of Medicine, it had approximately twenty interns and fifteen residents. The hospital paid interns twenty-five dollars a month with room and board, and residents were paid $115 a month. It was interesting to note that there were few interns or residents who were married because they couldn't support a family. I had many interesting experiences with the interns and residents.

We had a tradition every Christmas; we filled a bath tub in the interns' quarters and one in the residents' quarters with ice where they put their drinks for celebrating Christmas and New Years. There were times when I wondered who was taking care of the patients.

It is interesting to note the evolution in patient care. In the early days at the general hospital, the staff administered electroshock therapy using a Ford electric coil. Patients essentially had their brains "blown up" because the doctors were unable to control the current. It was stopped until they perfected the technique. Some medical treatments in those days were primitive by today's standards.

Another example is the technique used to keep confused patients from climbing out of bed. We used side boards which were long pine boards twenty inches high that hooked to the metal beds, one on each side. The boards were tied to the bed with leather thongs, and it was often difficult to work on a patient while leaning over the side. The boards provided a bizarre sight because it looked like the patient was lying in a box.

Infant incubators made by the engineering staff were also primitive. They were large wooden boxes with lights on the exterior to provide heat. The incubators were not efficient because there wasn't a way to control the heat, but it did the job for our babies.

The hospital had wards with twenty-five beds and two rooms on each floor for critical or terminal patients. Privacy was provided by curtains on a frame that were rolled to the bedside. This practice was observed in most hospitals until the early 1960s when Medicare came into existence, and semiprivate and private rooms replaced the wards.

As an orderly, I worked in the emergency room off-and-on for eight years. There, we had two trauma rooms and two rooms used essentially for patients who had non-emergent illnesses. Also there were two cubicles for minor examinations, a women's ward of three beds, and a men's ward of four beds. In the men's ward there was a large bathroom, which was used essentially for decontamination purposes. The homeless and the Washington Avenue bums came in with pediculosis, scabies, maggots, and the like.[60] I guess over the period of eight years I cleaned up most of the skid row bums at one time or another. This was a job that I never relished. I think each time I went through this procedure, I scratched for two days.

On one occasion I called Cedric Adams, who was a leading newspaper columnist in Minneapolis, and asked him to come over and take a look at what I was doing. This was done with the approval of my supervisor, and it was well known that Mr. Adams was interested in local human interest stories. He was astounded to see the extent of the filth on this patient, and the hoards of lice crawling over him. He did a big article and description of the situation in his Minneapolis paper.

I also took care of Ben Benson, who was the King of the Hobos for the entire United States. On another occasion I undressed the president of Western Union who had suffered a seizure on a Minneapolis street, and was astounded when I took off his tailor-made, silk suit with a diamond stick pin in his tie. I found absolute filth from his waist down. He hadn't taken a bath in months.

The emergency room had four ambulances: two 1932 Ford ambulances and two 1939 Cadillacs. The Ford ambulances were essentially sick-call ambulances, used to pick up patients who were referred to us by physicians. We used the Cadillacs for emergency calls. The two emergency ambulances served the entire city of Minneapolis, something that would be inadequate now. I helped unload the ambulances. Since the general hospital was a charity hospital for inner-city residents, patients from outside the city were transferred to the University Hospital.

Besides unloading ambulances, my other jobs included prepping (washing and shaving) patients. These were primarily drunks. I also prepared the male patients for examination by the physicians. I watched over patients who were temporarily confined to beds in an observation ward. Many of these were patients with DTs or those who had suffered epileptic seizures and usually didn't need to be kept in the hospital for a long period of time.[61] My last duty before I went home was to sweep and mop the entire department.

Another of my experiences as the emergency orderly was that at the age of sixteen, I delivered my first baby. I took a lady out of the ambulance and was told to get her up to the OB Ward because her water had broken, and she was in labor. I headed for the elevator. It was after hours, so I had to operate the elevator in addition to taking care of the patient. Between the second and third floor she delivered. I think I was a good deal more scared than she, but somehow I managed. I took her to the OB ward where a nurse delivered the placenta.

I became somewhat of an expert in delivering babies. About three weeks later,

I was in the lobby of the Farmers' Mechanics Bank in Minneapolis when a women went into labor on a bench outside of the credit manager's office. I demonstrated my experience when I took her into the office and delivered a baby girl.

My salary at the hospital was eighty-nine dollars a month. I worked a six day week from four to midnight. I got out of high school at 3:15, hopped a street car, and went to work at 4:00. There was no overtime for work over eight hours. There were many times after emergencies such as fires, train wrecks, and the like, that I worked all night and well into the next day without any compensation. If I had school the next day, I would miss school, but I always had a good excuse. My brother and I worked at the hospital until March 1945, when we joined the Navy.

### Navy Enlistment, 1945-46

Because we had hospital experience, the Navy inducted us as second class hospital corpsman with the understanding that after boot camp they would shuttle us to the hospital corps school in San Diego, California. We spent seven weeks in boot camp and seven weeks at the hospital corps school; then, we went to the Corona Naval Hospital in Corona, California, which at that time was the hospital that served all American Pacific fleet patients who had rheumatic fever, tuberculosis, or chest disease. We took care of American Prisoners of War who got tuberculosis in Japanese prison camps. It was a miserable task because most of the time we were understaffed, working extremely long hours, and using poor contagion practices. As a result, a number of my fellow crewmen got tuberculosis. Fortunately, and happily I might add, after the first year the Navy transferred me and my brother to sea duty. We reported to a holding camp at Shoemaker, California, on the outskirts of San Francisco.

We were there for a couple of weeks before the Navy transferred us to the heavy cruiser *U.S.S. Quincy,* Which was in port for repairs. The *U.S.S. Quincy* was tied up at Pier 22 in San Francisco, where it remained for three months waiting to get into the shipyard at Hunters Point. The *U.S.S. Quincy* had been caught in the Okinawa typhoon and nearly lost its bow. The *U.S.S. Pittsburgh* which was a heavy cruiser accompanying the *U.S.S. Quincy* totally lost its bow.[62] There were several destroyers sunk in that typhoon.

We had a major problem raise its ugly head after being in San Francisco for a few weeks; the crew took advantage of the availability of liquor and women of all kinds producing a significant increase in venereal disease. Penicillin was still in short supply. We did have enough to take care of most of the patients in the acute stage, but a lot of them had advanced gonorrhea or syphilis. When penicillin ran out we treated gonorrhea with argerol. When the patients suffered urethral adhesions we passed sounds up the urethra, a nasty and painful job.[63]

In the more advanced stages of syphilis, we used Napharsen (naphthalene) and bismuth. We had so many luetic (syphilitic) patients on the ship that once a week we announced over the public address system for them to report to sick bay for their shots. It was always interesting to inject Napharsen into the vein. We did it slowly because the patient turned beet red and sweated profusely. We combined this with bismuth which was given intramuscularly in the buttocks. I became an expert at injecting bismuth because if not done correctly it would form an egg-sized, uncomfortable lump. In spite of our expertise, bismuth always crystallized and formed a mass in the buttocks that can be seen on x-ray.

We did not go to sea on the *U.S.S. Quincy* with the exception of taking it from San Francisco to Bremerton, Washington, where we put it into moth balls along with other capital ships such as the battleships *U.S.S. Wisconsin* and the *U.S.S. New Jersey*. Later, we received the battleship *U.S.S.* Missouri, the ship on which General MacArthur and the Japanese signed the Peace Treaty ending World War II in the Pacific.

After Bremerton we returned to Minneapolis for discharge in 1946. We were on military leave from the City Hospital, and upon returning, we returned to our jobs as orderlies. There were about twelve of us who had been working at the hospital prior to going into the service. We all got discharges at roughly the same time and returned to work and enrolled in college.

We were in the midst of a polio epidemic. I became an extraction orderly for Sister Elizabeth Kenny, who was hired by the hospital to take care of polio patients. Sister Kenney was quite a women: she was tall and had a booming voice that could be heard half a block away. She didn't have patience with anyone who didn't do as they were told. Minneapolis General Hospital was the only hospital in the United States that recognized her treatment. It was my job to put strips of woolen blankets into boiling water and extract the water. After extraction of the hot water, they were applied to the patients.

In 1951, I transferred from the emergency room to work as the night audit clerk in the main lobby of the hospital. From 11:00 P.M. to 7:00 A.M., I audited admissions, discharges, transfers of service, deaths, births, and so forth. In the morning I sent a report to all of the appropriate departments from the administrator down telling them the location of patients. It was also my morning job to sign-in the visiting doctors. These were the heads of departments from the University of Minnesota and included George Fahr, who was one of the fathers of the electrocardiograph machine (he brought the EKG machine to our hospital in 1922); Dr. Bucholtz, who was a famous neurosurgeon; and Dr. Owen Wagensteen, who was chief of surgery and made many important contributions to medicine including the Wagensteen Alley.[64] Dr. Wagensteen was known around the world for his contributions to medicine.

My first experience with Dr. George Fahr was not a good one. It was my job, with another orderly, to sweep and mop the entire main entrance that was made of a white marble. After we finished the job on this particular night, I sat on top of the mop bucket while my associate pushed me with the mop handle down the hall. He pushed me onto the elevator and the bucket tipped over. Unbeknown to us Dr. Farr who was always impeccably dressed and wore a homburg, was standing at the door way to the elevator on the floor below, and was soaked with dirty mop water. The following day I reported to the administrator's office where I was summarily read over for my indiscretion. I guess that must have been the time when I decided to be an administrator.

About this time we started dating nurses. It had been a rigid rule that the nursing students could not date orderlies. Orderlies were considered low brows and administration didn't want them associating with nursing students or nurses. We also had a large school for x-ray and laboratory technicians and dating was inevitable. It came to a head when we unionized and the union head took the problem to administration. They were forced to relent and agree to dating. We had some status because we were college students even though we were still working as orderlies. From that time on, there was no discouragement of the orderlies dating nurses.

## University of Minnesota and Navy Recall, 1946-55

We brothers were all back together again and enrolled in the University of Minnesota; however, John had enough of the University after one year and reenlisted in the Air Force where he stayed until he retired at twenty-five years. My twin brother and I majored in sociology because we both intended to pursue a career with the Minnesota Youth Opportunity Commission, a revolutionary program where a person under twenty-one guilty of a felony was not committed to prison, but was sent to the youth authority. It was a great opportunity to work with disturbed and disadvantaged young people. That was the reason we majored in sociology.

We finished two years of college when the Korean War broke out in 1950. To get a little more money during college, my twin brother and I had served in the Naval Reserve, drilling every Monday night and taking a two week cruise every summer. Therefore, we were recalled to the Navy. Once again all four of the Ogren boys were in the military: Stuart and I went to U.S. Naval Hospital at Great Lakes, Bob went to Korea where he flew as a spotter pilot in AT-6's over North Korean lines, and John was in the Air Force in March Field, California.

We were recalled in June 1950 to the Great Lakes Naval Station where we worked with the wounded who were flown from Fairfield/Suisun City near San Francisco. I think this was the first time that the wounded from all three branches of the services were put in a naval hospital for treatment. After four months, we were discharged because the Navy decided it would be best for them if we completed our college education and reentered the service as officers. If the Korean War was underway when we finished, we would be subject to recall. It was still in progress, so we were recalled and commissioned Ensigns. We reported for duty on board the carrier *Coral Sea* and served as gunnery and line watch officers from 1952 through the fall of 1954. We spent the bulk of the two years in the Mediterranean.

After discharge, we learned that there were openings in the social services department at the hospital. We applied and were accepted. We went from being orderlies before the navy to being medical social workers after discharge. This was not taken well by many of the old-time social workers who remembered when we were orderlies and felt that we were a cut below them.

One particular incident that will stick with me all of my life relates to when as a social worker I was the admitting officer in the emergency room. It was my job to determine eligibility of patients who needed inpatient care. On this one particular occasion, we had a patient come in with an avulsed finger from a farm machinery accident. After emergency care, he needed hospitalization, but because he lived outside the city, I called the University Hospital for authorization. They agreed to take him, after questioning me as to whether the doctors in the city hospital emergency room had given him adequate care. I assured them that they had. After I made the arrangements, we took him in an ambulance to the University Hospital.

A few days after that, the family felt that he had gotten less than the finest treatment because they felt he should have been admitted immediately to the city hospital. The press got the story and raised a big hullabaloo. It was on the front page of the *Minneapolis Star*. The day after the newspaper article I was told that Mayor Hubert Humphrey would like to see me. The following day I went over to his office at City Hall and was ushered in to explain my actions. Mayor Humphrey treated me cordially. He felt that I had done the best I could do under the circumstances, and that I had complied with the hospital's rules and regulations. He suggested that in the future I continue to use discretion in referring patients to the University Hospital.

My brother and I worked as medical social workers until 1955 when I came in contact with an administrative resident in the hospital who was serving his residency at the University of Minnesota. I was immediately interested in what he was doing and asked him to get me a catalog on course work in hospital administration. My brother and I looked at the catalog and immediately decided: this is for us.

## Washington Univ. Hosp. Admin. School, 1956-57

When we applied to the University of Minnesota School of Hospital Administration, James Hamilton directed the school. If you got past Hamilton's assistant in the interview process, you had it made and would be accepted into the school. We got past his assistant, but Hamilton said, "I will take one of you, but I won't take both. It's against my philosophy to admit twin brothers to hospital administration."

We learned from other graduates that his reasoning was that he wanted graduates all over the map because he ran a hospital consulting service. He felt that the more graduates he had in the industry, the more his consulting service benefited. At any rate, we shared expenses and wanted to be together. We decided to give another school a try.

We had an ex-orderly friend, Jim Bremseth, who was enrolled at the School of Hospital Administration at Washington University in St. Louis. He sent us the necessary information, and we applied in the spring. We were called a month later for an interview. Washington University accepted both of us for the fall 1956 semester. During that year we were encouraged by the faculty to examine files on past students who had served residencies throughout the United States. We were told to apply for interviews with several administrators and to make contact during the Christmas season.

Our residents were spread throughout the United States with various preceptors, and they submitted ninety-day reports on their experiences. I examined a host of files from western hospitals because I wanted to go west. There was a file on Washoe Medical Center where Clyde Fox was the administrator; two prior administrative residents from Washington University had also served there. There were also files on two Denver hospitals: Denver General and General Rose.

I was accepted for interviews by all three and scheduled Washoe Medical Center for my first interview during the second week of December 1956. I met with Mr. Fox, and he mentioned that there was a rule stating that no agreement could be made between a preceptor and prospective resident until after the first of the year. Mr. Fox and I talked this over, and he wanted to have me as a resident because of my past hospital experience. He suggested that we make a secret agreement and join forces.

I called the administrators at General Rose and Denver General and said that I had changed my mind; I would not be seeing them for an interview. On a handshake, Mr. Fox and I made an agreement that the following August, I would report to Washoe Medical Center.

# BIBLIOGRAPHY

Angel, Myron, ed. *History of Nevada with Illustrations and Biographical Sketches of its Prominent Men and Pioneers* (Oakland: Thompson and West, 1881) reissued by (Berkeley: Howell-North, 1958) Poulson, Helen J., *Index to Thompson and West's History of Nevada*, Bibliographical Series, no. 6 (Carson City: Univ. Nev. Press, 1966).

County Commissioners' Records.

Crosby, Alfred W., *America's Forgotten Pandemic: The Influenza of 1918* (Cambridge: Cambridge Univ. Press, 1989).

Davis, Sam P. ed. *The History of Nevada*, 2 Vols. (Reno: Elms Pub. Co., 1913).

Feasibility Study of Corporate Reorganization (Reno: Washoe Medical Center, 1984).

Independent 1963 Hospital survey by the Reno Area Health Study Group.

Krajick, Kevin, "Mining the Scrap Heap for Treasure," *Smithsonian*, May 1997, pp. 34-44.

Cushing, Harvey, Address at the opening ceremonies of the Neurological Institute at McGill University, September 27, 1934..

Office of the Washoe Co. Planning Engineer, "Historical Data of the County Hospital Taken From Washoe County Records," Unpublished.

O'Brien, William A. and Associates, *Diagnosis and Treatment of the Acute Phase of Poliomyelitis and its Complications* (Balto: Williams and Wilkins Co., 1954).

Ogren, Carroll, "History of Washoe Medical Center," Unpublished.

Oldham, Willa, *Carson–Tahoe Hospital: The Story of a Caring Community* (Genoa, Nevada: Desk Top Publishers, 1987),

Ross, Silas E. *A Directory of Nevada Medical Practitioners Past and Present* (Private printing: 1957).

Scrugham, James G., ed. *Nevada, A Narrative of the Conquest of a Frontier Land*, 3 v. (Chicago: Amer. Hist. Soc., 1935).

Smith, George T., and V. A. Salvardorini, "Pulmonary Embolism," *Rocky Mt. Med. J.*, V. 63, 1986, pp. 42–48.

Sohn, Anton Paul, "Dr. Gerald J. Sylvain Oral History," Reno, Nev. Path. Depart. Univ. Nev. School Med. 1991, Unpublished.

———, *The Healers of 19th Century Nevada: A Compendium of Medical Practitioners* (Reno: Greasewood Press, 1997).

———, "The Nevada flu Epidemic—1918," *Greasewood Tablettes*, v. 1, spring 1991.

———, "The Polio Epidemic of 1952-53." *Greasewood Tablettes*, v. 2, summer 1995.

Taubenberger, Jeffery K., Ann H. Reid, Amy E. Krafft, Karen E. Bijwaard, and Thomas G. Fanning, "Initial Genetic Characterization of the 1918 'Spanish' Influenza Virus" *Science* v. 275, March 21, 1997, pp. 1793-1796.

Toll, David W. *Commitment to Caring: A History of Saint Mary's Hospital* (Reno: Nev. Academic Press, 1983).

*TPR* (Temperature, Pulse, Respiration—Washoe Medical Center pub.) Jan. 81.

Walker, Moris Rollins, *A Life's Review and Notes on the Development of Medicine in Nevada: From 1900 to 1944* (Private Printing).

Walker, Moris Rollins, "Story of the Nevada State Medical Society and Nevada Medicine" (Private Printing; 1937).

Washoe Medical Center, Board of Trustee minutes, 1930-1998.

Washoe Medical Center, *Feasibility study of Corporate Reorganization*, Nov. 26, 1984.

Washoe Medical Center, Medical Staff records.

# INDEX

## I

1960 Olympics
   injuries, 48

## A

Abrums, Dr. George, 153
ACS, 156
   formation of JCAH, 103, 140
   trauma inspection, 127
Ad Valorem tax, 25, 39, 139
Adams, Cedric
   journalist, Minneapolis, 215
Adams, Dr. Albert
   co. phy., 145
Adams, Greg
   nursing direct., 208
Adventist Hosp., 11, 203
Affiliation Agreement
   SOM, 166
Ahner, Dawn
   accountant, 205
aircraft observation tower
   W. W. II, 23
Alexander, Alexander
   vp nursing admin., 205
Allen Maternity Hosp., 203
Allison, Helen
   Carson-Tahoe Hosp., 112

Alonso, Michael
   trustee, 175
Amer. Assoc. of Blood Banks
   WMC joins, 152
Amer. College of Phys.
   JCAH, 140
Amer. Dietetics Assoc.
   approves dietetic program, 164
Amer. Hosp. Assoc., 160
   JCAH, 140
Amer. Med. Assoc.
   radiologists and path. billing, 106
Anderson, Dr. Frederick, 109, 160, 163
   chief of staff, 201
   regent, Univ. Nev., 108
   research lab., 159
Anderson, Victor
   photographer, 71
Andrews, Mrs. Francis
   Women's League, 209
Angel of Mercy Reno Cancer
   Council, 133
Arger, Dr. Kosta, 174
   resident, 167
Armstrong, Bryn
   *Reno Gazette-J.*, 155
Armstrong, Charles
   pres. UNR, 108, 160
Armstrong, Louis
   patient, 64

Armstrong, Mr.
  *Reno Gazette-J.*, 152
Art of Living Institute, 173
Ascensao, Dr. Joao
  bone marrow transplant, 135
Assoc. of West. Hosp., 48
Atcheson, Lynn
  marketing, 205
Ayers, A. O.
  steward, 144
Ayers, O. W., 199
  supt., 144

## B

baby war
  with SMH, 120, 123, 125, 128, 164,
    167, 170, 171
Bailey, Mary, 70
Baker, Don
  Incline Village Hosp. study, 66
  Nev. Div. Hosp. Ser., 46
Ballard, Sandy, 70
Bankofier, Jeanette, 159, 181
  dietetics, 77, 157
Barger, Mrs. Katrina
  Women's League, 209
Barker, Jay, 93
Barker, Nurse Connie
  wife of Jay, 93
Barnes, Vern
  core lab., 206
Barnett, Clara
  Lyon Health Center, 113
Barr, Jerri, 70
Bartley, Gerald
  computer mgr., 79
Barton Memorial Hosp., 175
Bath, Dr. Thomas, 139, 147
  path. and x-ray ser., 20
Bath, Ronald
  trustee, 173
Batt, Dr. Murray
  qual. ser., 206
Bd. of Trustees
  records storage, 37

Beardwood, Jack
  architect, 161
Beck, Janice
  surg. ser., 206
Becker, Dr. Jack, 160, 161, 162, 163,
  165, 197
  ch. trustees, 140
  cobalt machine, 52, 159
  office bldg., 58
  trustee, 73, 158
Becker, Mrs. Jack
  Women's League, 209
Beeks, Bob, 153
  moved RR living quarters, 24
Behncke, Wm.
  bus. mgr., 61
Belford, John, 153
  resigns, 154
Belknap, Dr. H. Earl, 149
Bennet, Wm.
  No. Las Vegas Hosp., 113
Bennett, Mrs. Billie J.
  relative, Joseph Odett, 138
Benson, Ben.
  king, hobos, 215
Bentinck, Dr. Richard
  Nev. Children's Health Ser., 169
Bergin, Leo
  Fleischmann Foundation, 88
Bergstein, Dr. Henry, 144
Berndt, Dr. Ted
  1st heart cath., 65
  trustee, 173
Bible, Senator Alan, 90
Biltz, Mrs. Norman
  daughter of H. Auchincloss, 87
  Women's League, 211
Biltz, Norman
  WMC benefactor, 87
Bischoff, Dr. H. W., 151
Bishop, Dr.
  co. phy., 143
bismuth
  treat. for syphilis, 216
Black Death
  plague, 12

Blanchard, Vinette, 70
blood bank
  est., 150
Bohall, Carl
  bus. office, 78
Bohall, Jean, 170
  med. staff sec., 78, 97, 158
Bond Memorial Hosp., 203
bone marrow transplant
  UMSOM, 135
Boomtown Casino
  meet. with med. staff, 121
Bosse, Chris
  fin. provider ser., 205
Bradley, Dr. Grover, 150
Brady, Dr. Thomas, 35
Brandsness, Dave
  Elko Gen. Hosp., 112
Breen, Fran
  Fleischmann Foundation, 88
Bremerton, Wash., 217
Brooke Army Hosp.
  burn unit, 71
Bross, Dr. Willard
  Care Flight, 168
Brown, Dr. Horace, 147
Brown, Dr. Raymond, 51, 140
Brown, H. C.
  trustee, 147, 148
Brown, Harry
  co. clerk, 158
Brown, Steve, 168, 169, 197
  trustee, 166
Bryan, Dr. Wm., 161
  med. staff outlaw, 100, 101
Bucholtz, Dr.
  Minneapolis neurosurg., 217
Bullis, Gary
  Lyons Club Eye Bank, 163
Burke, A. A., 199
  appt. steward, 145
Burke, Dr. G., 152
Burn, Robert, 172, 173, 200
  act. CEO, 174
  appt. CEO, 135
  CEO, 205

Burnett, Perry
  architect, 161
Byrant, Gov. Richard
  law to control hosp. charges, 171

## C

C & S Const.
  transplant program, 174
Cafferata, Dr. Treat, 172
Caldwell, Pat, 70
Callahan, Rod, 205
Camp Funston, Kan.
  1918 flu epidemic, 13
Campbell, Dr. Gary, 133
Cancer Center
  est. 1955, 156
Cann, Dr. George
  co. phy., 148
Cantlon, Dr. Edwin
  chief of staff, 201
Cantlon, Dr. Vernon
  chief of staff, 201
Caples, Dr. Byron, 147
Capurro, Ray, 153, 155, 156
  trustee, 75
Caramella, Ben
  Reno Disposal Service, 99
Care Flight
  helicopter service, 122
Carl, Sister, 112
Carlson, Dr. Wm., 174, 197
  trustee, 173
Carson City *Daily Appeal*
  1918 flu, 13, 15
Carson City Nugget, 89
Carson, Evelyn, 70
Carson-Tahoe Hosp., 175
  No. Nev. Hosp. Council, 112
Carter, Alan
  county mgr., 39
Carter, Mr.
  Sierra Oxegen Co., 116
Cashell, Robert
  ch. Univ. Nev. Regents, 121
Cauble, Augus, 197, 199

temp. supt., 151
Cauble, Janet
  nursing direct., 208
  resigns, 150
Chadwick, Bernice, 70
  superv. of nursing, 155
Chalmers, M. Esther, 107
  LPN school, 163
Chamberlain, Carl
  physicist, 133
Chamberlin, Eric
  architect, 160
Child Care Center
  licensed, 173
cholera
  19th century, 6
Christian, Dr. Maynard, 166
  chief of staff, 202
Christmas
  Minneapolis Gen. Hosp., 214
Chrysler Corp.
  convention, 60
Churchill Pub. Hosp.
  No. Nev. Hosp. Council, 112
Churchyard, Mrs. Leland
  Women's League, 209
Civil War cannons
  scrap metal, 22
Clark, Dr. Paul, 134
Cloud, Mrs. Douglas
  Women's League, 209
Co. Hosp.
  old, 11
Co. Plan. Engineer, 137, 138
cobalt therapy, 132
Cody, Larry
  pul. function tech., 129, 163
Cohoon, Mrs. Everett
  Women's League, 209
Colligan, Mary
  dietetic training, 164
Collins, Christy
  labor and del., 206
Conant, Norice
  marriage to Dr. G. Smith, 95
Conkey, Kurt
  storeroom/patient supply, 206

Conran, Dr. Wm., 66
Continental Lodge
  Jim McNeil, Women's League, 168
convalescent unit, 46
Copeland, Dr. Edgar, 151
Corcoran Elementary School
  C. Ogren, 213
Cormier, Mrs. Michael
  Women's League, 210
Cornwall, Dianne
  asst. to CEO, 205
Corona Naval Hosp., Calif., 216
Corvino, Dr. Leo
  trustee, 150
Costa, Rose
  Dr. L. Russell's nurse, 95
Courtyard Center, 132, 134
Coward, Pat, 172, 173, 174, 197
Cowen, Charley
  Reno City Council, 90
Creveling, Dr. Earl, 147
  Nev. Bd. Med. Exam., 139
  suit, 20
Crippled Children's ward
  Elks Club, 149
Crosby, Dr. Robert
  polio team, 29
Crosby, Lyn Milligan
  nurse, cardiac surg., 65
Crosby, Vicki
  Women's League, 209
Crowder, Sadie Tate
  med. neph., 206
Crucilla, Sam
  So. Nev. Memorial Hosp., 113
Crumley, Newt
  plane crash, 74
Cunningham, Jack, 160, 161, 162
  trustee, 76
Cunningham, Mrs.
  central supply, 84
Cunningham, Reva, 70
Curry, Dr. Arrah, 169, 171, 172
  chief of staff, 202

## D

D'Gino, Carl
  *Reno Gazette-J.*, 156
DaCosta, Dr. Albert, 147
  co. phy, 145
Dambro, Dr., 166
Dant, Tom, 2
  benefactor, 90
  Cunard Shipping Lines, 90
  Dant Liquor Co., 90
  Singer Sewing Machine Co., 90
Darlington, Irene
  Washoe Co. Welfare Depart., 85
Daugherty, Dr. Robert
  new dean, 167
Davis, Dr. John M., 133
Davis, Jr., Sammy
  patient, 64
Dawson, Dr. Alson
  co. phy., 143
decontaminate
  mattresses, 37
delirium tremens, 142
DeLonchant, Fred
  architect, 19, 146
Denver Gen. Hosp., 219
Devincinzi, Larry
  caper, Salvadorini and Ogren, 100
Dieter, Deborah
  rehab. therapy ser., 206
Dillard, J. C., 19, 146
  contractor, 18
Dimmick, Maud
  trustee, 147, 148
diphtheria
  19th century, 6
Disneyland Hotel
  designed by Welton Becket, 57
District Attorney
  stops Dillard contract, 18
doctor's divorce
  ER work, 72
Doeden, Dr.
  resident, 167
Dog Valley fire, 50

Dominga, Sister, 111, 112
Donald Cook Assoc., 141
  trauma study, 127, 172
Dondero, Alan
  helps with LPN school, 107
Dondero, Donald
  Reno photo., 107
Drachulich, Ava, 70
drug stores
  Reno in 1901, 9
Drummer, Ben, 106, 159, 161
  trustee, 75, 76, 160
Duke, Dr. Red
  trauma surg., Houston, Tex., 126
Dunlap, Cal
  District Attorney, 129, 168, 169
Durham, John C.
  co. commissioner, 17
Dwyer, Rev. Robert
  concerns about sterilization, 155
Dyer, Mrs., 96
  sec., 158

## E

Earl, Phillip
  Nev. Hist. Soc., 138
East. Plumas Hosp., 131, 171
Edmiston, Claudette
  nurse, cardiac surg., 65
Edmiston, Dr. J. Malcolm
  chief of staff, 202
Edwards, Bea, 36, 75, 156, 157, 160, 161, 162
  trustee, 156
  Women's League, 209
Edwards, Ben, 75
Edwards, Les
  Las Vegas Hosp., 113
Eidem, Joe
  food prod., 206
electroshock therapy
  Minneapolis Gen. Hosp., 214
Elko Gen. Hosp.
  No. Nev. Hosp. Council, 112
Elliott, Dr. Frederick
  polio team, 29

Ellis, Dr. Joseph
   co. phy., 7, 143
Engeseth, Pastor Richard, 55, 56, 163
   appt. Chaplain, 160
English, H. Chester, 157, 199
   purchasing, 82
   temp. supt., 25, 152
Epling, Howard, 159, 181
   pharmacy, 82
Erickson, Dr. John, 172
   chief of staff, 202
Estrin, Dr. Joseph, 151
   co. phy., 150
   radiologist, 154
Eugene, Sister, 111
Evans, Patty
   inform. officer, 205
Evart, Candace
   trustee, 175
Evergreen Helicopter Ser., 126, 167
Explorers Post 117
   Boy Scouts Amer., 168

F

Fahr, Dr. George
   father of EKG, 217
*Fallon Eagle*
   flu, 13
Farmers' Mechanics Bank
   C. Ogren del. baby, 216
Farr, Curtis, 151, 152, 153, 154, 155,
   156, 157
   Trustee, 73
Farr, Mrs. Curtis
   Women's League, 74, 209
Farr, Wm., 165, 168, 173, 174
Faust, C. B.
   1918 undertaker, 14
Feasibility Study Corp. Reorg., 130
Feasibility study of Corp.
   Reorganization, 141, 170
Feldman, Dr. Bernard
   neonatologist, Sunrise Hosp., 166
Feltner, Dr. Wm., 132, 133, 141
Ferguson, Peter, 197
   trustee, 150

Ferris-Erskine and Hellman
   architects, 160
Field, John
   trustee, 158
Fleigh, George
   So. Nev. Memorial Hosp., 113
Fleischmann Foundation, 2, 154, 159,
   163, 168
   $1.2 million to hosp., 166
   benefactor, 88
   cardiac care, 65
   lab. computer, 128, 167
   linear accelerator, 133
   money for NICU, 124
Fleischmann, Max
   benefactor, 88, 89
Florence Crittenden Home, 203
flu
   1918 complications, 14
   1918 prevention, 14
   1918 treatment, 15
   compared to horror of W.W. I, 15
   first wave, 13
   grippe, 15
   pandemic, 12
   second wave, 13
   third wave, Spanish Flu, 13
Folwell Junior High School
   C. Ogern, 213
Ford, Priscilla
   murder trial, 169
Forrester, Jim
   engineer, 78
Foster, Robert
   bus. mgr., 79
Fox, Clyde, 26, 30, 33, 34, 35, 36, 39,
   41, 72, 74, 80, 81, 84, 88, 91, 95,
   153, 154, 156, 158, 199, 219
   Amer. Hosp. Assoc., 40
   appointed, 152
   Assoc. of West. Hosp., 40
   died, 162
   interview for supt., 25
   interviews C. Ogren, 220
   Manhattan Eye and Ear Hosp., 39
   model for hosp. and med. school,
      107

Parma, Ohio, 39
path. contract, 105
recommends hosp. addition, 45
SOM, 107
SOM plans, 157
Women's League, 211
Frank, Dr. Barry, 129, 168
Freeman, Vivian, 169, 172
French Hosp., San Francisco
Earl Horton, 48
Fricke, Dr. Fred, 129
Frinfrock, Dr., 166
Fuller, Dr. John
chief of staff, 201
Furler, Jean
accountant, 78
Furman, Dr. George, 140

## G

Gable, Clark, 50
Gabrielli, Deputy DA John
hosp. attorney, 52
Ganchan, Dr. Richard, 171, 172
chief of staff, 202
Gardner, Alan and Beatrice
UNR researchers, 92
Gardnerville, Nev.
Washoe Meat Co., 59
Garrett, Leon, 181
chief lab. tech., 81
Gastanaga, Mrs. Gene
Women's League, 209
gastroenteritis emergency
airline, 47
Gaunt, Kenneth
trustee, 164
Gen. Rose Hosp., Denver, 219
Georganne, Sister
St. Rose De Lima Hosp., 113
Gerow, Jr., Dr. Lynn, 168, 169
Gerow, Sr., Dr. Lynn, 153
co. phy., 149
resigns as co. phy., 150
resigns as trustee, 154
trustee, 74
Getchell, Noble

lab., 148
Gibson, Dr. Samuel, 11, 145
Nev. St. Hosp., 138
Gilbert, Dr. Harry
radiologist, 153
Gillespie, Dr. Elmer, 151
Gillis, Bill.
*Reno Gazette-J.*, 155
Gleason, Scoop
*S.F. Chronicle*, 112
GNHSA
dialysis, 171
helicopter ser., 167
Gomez, Dr. Myron, 173
direct. trauma, 172
gonorrhea, 216
Gorman, Howard, 162
Gould, JoAnne, 70
bone marrow transplant mgr., 135
oncology, 206
grand jury, 7, 156, 168, 169
Gray, Dr. John
chief of staff, 202
Graybill, Clayton
store room, 77
Great Basin Med. Clinic, 171
Great Depression, 19, 213
economic conditions, 214
Great Lakes Naval Station, 218
Great War
flu pandemic, 12
Green, Daphne, 157, 181
chief nursing superv., 83, 84
nursing direct., 208
retires, 166
Green, Sharon, 113
Green, Shirley
nursing direct., 208
Greenan, Mrs. James
Women's League, 211
Greene, Georganne
asst. admin., nursing, 166
dialysis design, 134
nursing direct., 208
Gregory, Dr. Paul, 65
Griffin, Ed
*Sparks Tribune*, 158

Grow, DeWitt.
  architect, 156
Gruen, Victor
  architect, 160
Guisto, Dr. Donald
  burn unit, 71
Guttman, Dr.
  resident, 167

**H**

Haase, Becky
  peds., 206
Hadley, Deputy DA Wm.
  hosp. attorney, 52, 159, 160, 169
Haily, C., 8
Haislip, Iva, 70
  nurse on cardiac ser., 64
Hall, Helen
  cashier and K. Kakoris' wife, 97
Hall, Jerry
  project coor., 161
Hall, Jr., Dr. Wes
  chief of staff, 202
Hall, Sr., Dr. Wes, 151, 163
  chief of staff, 201
Hall, Teresa
  nurse direct., 20, 208
Hamilton, James
  Univ. Minn. hosp. administration,
  219
Hamway, Marie
  vp admin., 206
Hancock, E. B., 8
Hanssen, Ed J.
  Humboldt Gen. Hosp., 112
Hardy, Brend
  neuro./ortho., 206
Harn, Dr., 166
Harold's Club
  donates iron lung, 28, 154
  slot machine player died, 60
Harrah, Wm.
  visits 1973 building, 64
Harris, Reta
  life skills, 206
Harrison, James
  Veterans Hosp., 113

Hart, Dale, 165
  1st open heart patient, 65
Hartland, Lois, 107
  LPN school, 157
Harvey, Mrs. Thomas
  Women's League, 210
Hatch, A. J.
  sold land where WMC stands, 7
Hatch, Alden
  int. audit, 205
Hawkins, Mrs. Robert Z., 153
  Women's League, 211
Heath, Dr., 166
Heidrich, Ron
  store room, 77
helicopter service
  starts Dec. 16, 1974, 164
Henley, Mr.
  *Reno Evening Gazette*, 152
Henry Kohl Memorial Chapel, 55,
  159
Herliman, Mr.
  C. Ogren employment, 214
Hess, William
  radiological ser., 206
Hickey, John, 197
  trustee, 148, 150
Higgins, Jerry, 173, 174
  trustee, 172
Hilbish, Dr. Judy
  family practice resident, 166
Hill, Fred, 157
  Hill Bro.' Motel, 37
Hill, Wm.
  Shrine Chaplin, 140
Hill-Burton Act, 2, 35, 46, 159
Hillsborough, Calif.
  jewel heist, 114
Hillstrom, Dr. Earl
  chief of staff, 201
HIV
  compared to 1918 flu, 12
Hlubucek, Dr. Donald, 132
HMO, 3
Hoffman, Ruth, 70, 83, 181
  OR superv., 117
Hogan, Dr. Henry, 137, 143
  co. phy., 7

Hogan, Roy "self starter"
  laundry, 81, 159, 181
Hogan, Roy and Lucille, 167
Holcomb, Shorty, 97
  died, 163
Holdridge, James, 168
  morgue diener, 85
Holiday Hotel
  Newt Crumley, 74
Hollar, Jackie
  staff sec., 96, 158
Hollingsworth, Mr., 172
Holstein, Dr. Arthur, 151
Holsworth, G. E.
  plans for hosp,, 145
Hood, Dr. Arthur, 147
  chief of staff, 201
Hood, Dr. Dwight, 147, 149
Hood, Dr. Wm., 147
  Nev. Bd. of Health 1918, 15
Hoover, Linda, 168, 169
  nursing direct., 208
Hoover, Mike
  helicopter service, 126
  soc. service, 86
Hope, Bob
  Children's Miracle TV Network, 171
Horton, Earl, 80, 96, 159, 199
  admin., 48, 158
Hosp. Health Plan
  HMO, 131
Hotchkiss, Gay
  sec., 96
Hotchkiss, Jess
  Kay Martin Band, 96
Houston, John
  movie director, 50
Howell, Dr. Wm., 147
Hudson Hosp., 203
Hulse, James, 156
  journalist, 116
Humboldt Gen. Hosp.
  No. Nev. Hosp. Council, 112
Hume, Dr. Robert, 133
Hummer, Dr. Beth, 133

Humphrey, Mayor Hubert, 219
Humphrey, Mrs. Frank Ellis, 146
  trustee, 17
Humphrey, Neil, 157, 161
  Tax Payers Assoc., 37
Hurd, Gayle
  health cont. ser., 205

I

Infant Care flight
  crash, 167
Inskip, Dr. Richard
  trustee, 173
Invalid's Hosp., 203
Isbell, C. V., 150
  benefactor, 89
  paved parking lot, 23
Isbell, Mabel
  benefactor, 89

J

Jacka, Bart
  Nev. Human Resources, 170
James, George
  *J. Weekly*, 19, 146
JCAH, 103, 140
  Reno Cancer Center, 31
Jeffers, Nurse P., 65
Jeffress, Eileen, 69, 164
  Lou Gehrig's Disease, 70
Jenkins, Mrs. Jess
  Women's League, 210
Johansson, Sharon
  lab. ser., 206
Johnson, Alma, 70, 84
  retires, 164
Johnson, Dr. David C., 133, 134
  trustee, 166
Johnson, Jan
  patient/guest rel., 205
Jones, Jimmy
  cafe, 51
Jones, Stan
  carpenter's union, 46

Joy, Dr.
Nye Gen. Hosp., 113
Joy, Hull, 199
hosp. mgr., 144
Joy, Louise
matron of hosp., 144
Joy, W. H., 144, 199
Juvenile Detention Center
Scott Ditch, 34

K

Kafoury, Mr., 157
Kakoris, Kris, 162
died, 164
orderly, 97
Kakoris, Mrs. Kris
Rose Silva, 148
Kamprath, LuAnn
personnel, 80, 158
Kean, Tom, 157
Sierra Oxygen Co., 116
Keeler, Dr. Wm., 65
Keenan, J. J., 197
Kelley, Dr. Wayne, 151
Kendig, Linda
postpartum, 206
Kennedy, Wm., 20, 146, 147
contractor for 1932 bldg., 19
Kenney, John, 20, 146, 147, 199
1st supt., 17
bus. mgr., 147
Kenny, Sister Elizabeth
polio treat., 217
Keough, Pat, 96, 160, 170
admin, sec 1962, 158
C. Ogren's exec. sec., 95
exec. sec., 97
retires, 174
Kernan, Dr. Francis, 151
chief of staff, 201
Kernan, J. J.
trustee, 147, 148
King, Leon
architect, 160
Kinkade, Mrs. L. Diane
Women's League, 210

Kinney, Ardis
nursing direct., 208
Klaus, Wm. Kelly
co. commissioner, 17
Kleppe, Ernest, 151, 152, 153, 155
trustee, 75
Knapp, Kenneth
no agreement for admin., 158
Kohl family
Piggy Wiggly stores, 56
Kolff dialyzer, 133
Kotter, Mr., 156
Krump Construction
garage const., 174

L

Labuda, Mary, 70
Lakeside Community Hosp., 168
Lamb, James, 170, 171, 172, 173, 200
hired, 130
resigned, 135
Lamb, Senator Floyd, 109
Landers, A. E.
trustee, 150
Landis, Dr. Phil
chief of staff, 202
trustee, 174
Larson, Tess
bus. mgr., 79
Las Vegas Hosp., 113
Las Vegas, *The Age*
flu, 13
Lauer, Carla, 167
planner, 126
Ronald McDonald House, 170
Laws, Evelyn, 70
Laxalt, Gov. Paul
M. Pringle, 94
Laxalt, Senator Paul
helps NICU, 125
Lear, Moya, 63
Lear, Wm., 167
helicopter, 63, 125
Lee, Mrs. Hudson
Women's League, 210
Lees, Dr. Bonnie, 169

neonatologist, WMC, 125
Leftwich, Dr. Wm
  co. phy., 151, 152
Leigh, Joanne, 70
Lenz, Dr. Gilbert, 133
Lewis, Dr. Frank
  ACS ICU inspection, 172
Lewis, Dr. John, 144
Lewis, Joan
  phy. therapy, 85, 157
Licata, Richard, 160
  1st SOM research lab., 45
Lillard, James, 169, 171
Lindh, Barbara, 181
  admitting, 85
  retires, 170
List, Kathy
  health fair, 168
Little, Dr. Dana
  early ER doctor, 127
  house phy., 149
liver transplant
  Dr. R. Simon, 59
Locke, Dr. C. Robert, 151, 153
  manages TB patients, 26
Locke, Mrs. C. Robert
  Women's League, 209
Lohlien, Dr. Harold
  co. phy., 150
Lombardi, Caesar
  gardener, 98
  retiring, 163
Lombardi, Dr. Louis, 108
  regent, Univ. Nev., 160
Long, Art
  journalist, 116
  *Nev. St. J.*, 157, 158
Long, Mrs. Barbara
  Women's League, 210
Longfield, A. L., 199
  temp. mgr., 148
Lown, Dr. Bernie
  Boston cardiologist, 64
Lurie, Dr. Art, 65
Lyon Health Center
  No. Nev. Hosp. Council, 113

## M

MacArthur, Gen. Douglas, 217
Mack Auditorium
  SOM ceremony, 163
Mack's father, Dr. Ernest
  E. D. Mack, photographer, 71
Mack, Dr. Ernest, 25, 92, 108, 109,
  152, 153, 154, 155, 156, 157, 160,
  161, 162, 164, 170, 197
  1973 building dedication, 140
  abortion issue, 117
  chief of staff, 201
  EEG contract, 26, 154
  NSMA, 139
  trustee, 73
Maclean, Dr. Donald, 147
  trustee, 148
Maclean, Dr. Kenneth, 163
  chief of staff, 201
  sec., Nev. Bd. of Med. Exam., 75
MacLeod, John, 181
Macomber-Brunzell Const. Co., 157
MacPherson, Dr. Alfred, 20, 139, 147,
  199
  manager, 20
  resident phy., 148
Maes, G. Sloan
  bone marrow transplant nurse, 135
Magnette, Dr. Jules
  Nev. St. Hosp., 41
Malone, Molly
  U.S. Congress, 90
Manitou Sanitarium Hosp., 204
Manning, Helen
  *Reno Evening Gazette*, 169
Mannino, Dr. Frank
  Univ. Calif. Infant Spec. Care, 124
Manor Care Nursing Home, 70
Mapes Hotel
  Marilyn Monroe's room, 50
  polio study, 28
Mapes, Charles, 154
  Mapes Hotel, 87
Mapes, Geo. W.
  bought 1921 bonds for hosp., 15

Mapes, Mrs. Charles
  Women's League, 87, 209, 211
Martelle, Acel
  Nev. Human Resources, 169
Mason, Olive
  nursing direct., 150, 208
Massey, Karen
  med. staff ser., 205
Matheis, Larry, 172
  Nev. Human Resources, 127
Mathews, Bernice Martin, 70
  LPN school, 107
Mathews, Deputy DA Jack
  hosp. attorney, 52, 158
Matthews, Charlotte
  dialysis nurse, 134
Matthews, Deanna, 70
Mayers Memorial Hosp., 131, 171
Mazzaferri, Dr. Ernie
  act. dean, 167
McCarran, Senator Pat
  helps with Quonset huts, 151
McConnel, Del
  inhalation therapy, 85
McConnell, Delbert, 181
McCormach, Mrs. Roger
  Women's League, 210
McCulley, Ida, 181
  med. records, 84
McCuskey, Dr. Charles
  chief of staff, 202
McDowell, Gene, 169, 171, 172, 173,
  174
McGee, Dr. George
  chief of staff, 201
McGee, Richard
  architect, 161
McKay, Less
  engineer, 77, 78
McKay, Mrs. I., 146
  suit, 20
McKenzie, J. C.
  trustee, 158
McKissick Opera House, 76
McKissick, Sr., Howard, 157, 160, 161,
  162
  resigns, 163

shooting incident, 76
  trustee, 76
McKnight, Wm., 146, 197
  trustee, 17
McLaughlin, Mrs. John, 153
  Women's League, 209, 211
McMullen, Forest
  fac. planning, 206
Meany, George
  labor union boss, 83
measles
  19th century, 6
med. staff appt.
  NSMA membership, 151
  WCMS membership, 151
Medicaid, 2, 3, 113
Medicare, 2, 3, 113, 114, 160
MedLab Computer, 168
Melady, Geraldine
  LPN school, 157
  nurse coor., LPN school, 107
Melner, Mike
  Nev. Human Resources, 165
Melton, Rollan
  journalist, 116
  Women's League, 212
Meranda, Keri
  begin. child care, 206
Meskimen, Karen
  spec. care units, 206
Mettee, Andy
  Wh. Pine Co. Gen. Hosp., 112
Michelson, Wm.
  Care Flight, 168
microbial age, 9
Miercort, Dr. Roger, 133
Miligan, Dennis
  physical ser., 205
Miller, Dr., 147
Miller, James, 174
  CFO, 205
Miller, N. Ed, 108, 161
  chancellor, Univ. Nev., 160
Milstein, Dr. Steve
  non-invasive lab., 168
Minneapolis
  C. Ogren's discharge from Navy,
  217

Minneapolis Gen. Hosp.
  C. Ogren, 214
  polio treat., 217
*Minneapolis Star*, 219
Minola, J.
  patient, 163
Mirabelli, Mike
  trustee, 158
Missall, Dr. Steve, 165
  goes to SMH, 169
  NICU should be at WMC, 124
Mitchell, Mrs. Robert
  Women's League, 209
Modoc Med. Center, 131, 171
Mohler, Dr. Donald, 83, 164
  chief of staff, 202
  invites C. Ogren to dinner, 38
Molde, Jean, 70
  act. nursing direct., 166
  nursing direct., 208
Monaghan, Jeff
  pharmacy, 206
Monibi, Dr. Ali
  plane crash, 124
Monroe, Marilyn, 50
Montgomery, Dr. Eugene, 57, 58
  murdered wife, committed sucide,
    59
Montgomery, S., 58
Mooney, Lawrence, 181
  phy. therapy, 85
Moore, Brian
  human resources, 205
Moore, Robert, 169, 171, 172
  trustee, 168
Mordy, Wendell
  VP UNR, 160
Morgan, Wm.
  architect, 160
Morrison, Dr. Sidney, 147
  chief of staff, 201
  co. phy., 145
Moulton, Dr. Olin, 151, 152, 153, 154,
  197
  trustee, 150
Mount Rose Hosp., 204
Mt. Grant Hosp.
  No. Nev. Hosp. Council, 112

Mulcahy, E. C., 146, 197
  trustee, 17, 147, 148
Mullins, Bertha, 172, 173, 174
Muncie, Betty
  Women's League, 210
Murphy, Dorothy
  nurse, cardiac surg., 65
Murphy, Judy, 172, 173
Myers, Ellen, 70
Myles, Dr. Robert, 59, 62, 168, 169,
  171, 172, 197
  chief of staff, 202
  retires, 173
  SOM public debate, 121
  trustee, 73, 164
Myles, Jean, 59

**N**

Napharsen
  treat. for syphilis, 216
Napp. Ken
  interview for admin., 48
Nash, Sari, 181
  EKG, 85
Nat. Infantile Paralysis Foundation,
  28
  owes hosp. money, 155
Nat. Poison Control Center
  Denver, 66
Naval Hosp., Great Lakes, 218
Neddenriep, Dr.
  resident, 167
Nelson, Dwight, 162
Nev. Bd. of Voc. Ed.
  LPN school, 30
Nev. Hardware and Supply Co., 8, 11
Nev. Health Div., 124, 125
Nev. Hist. Soc.
  1890 lithograph of hosp., 7
Nev. Hosp., 204
Nev. Hygienic Lab.
  bact. and chem. for hosp., 147
  est., 9
  Nev. Pub. Health Lab., 20
Nev. Kidney Foundation, 133, 162
Nev. Legislature
  UNSOM vote, 109

Nev. Pub. Health Board
  est., 9
Nev. Sanitarium, 203
Nev. St. Hosp., 51, 203
*Nev. St. J.*, 123
  C. Ogren leaving, 119
  criticized 1872 hosp., 7
  flu, 13
  hosps. provide good ser., 128
  M. Pringle's career, 94
  patients' names in paper, 147
New London, Minn., 213
Newman, Rich
  employee rel., 205
Newmarker, Jackie
  M. Pringle's granddaughter, 91
Newmarker, Mike, 120, 166, 200
  appt. admin., 119
  asst. admin., 83
  grand jury investigation, 129
  helicopter ser., 126
  M. Pringle's grandson, 91
  resigns, 129, 169
Newmarker, Pat
  M. Pringle's daughter, 91
Nichols, Dr. Robert, 165, 168
  1st heart surg., 65
Nichols, Helen, 157
  med. records, 84
Nightengale, Leon Family
  Cancer Center benefactor, 132
Nightingale, Leon, 90
Nightingale, Mrs. Leon
  peds. nurse, 90
Nitsche, Robert
  journalist, 116
  *Reno Evening Gazette*, 160
Nitz, Dr. Gordon
  chief of staff, 168, 202
No. Las Vegas Hosp., 113
No. Nev. Hosp. Council, 112
Nottingham, G. W., 146, 197
  trustee, 17, 147, 148
NSMA, 139
nursery
  infection, 149
Nurses' Hosp., 11, 203

Nye Gen. Hosp.
  No. Nev. Hosp. Council, 113

## O

O'Boyle, Pearl
  personnel, 80, 157
O'Boyle, Richard
  undersheriff, 80
O'Brien, Dr. Wm., 108, 109, 140, 163
  chief of staff, 201
  polio team, 29
O'Brien, Pat
  heart pump tech., 65
O'Callaghan, Gov. Mike
  M. Pringle, 94
O'Neill, Dr. Wm.
  chief of staff, 202
O'Rourke, Tony
  friend of C. Fox, 40
O'Sullivan, Barry
  patient escort/traction, 206
Odett, Joseph, 9, 138, 199
  appt. steward, 145
  carpenter, 1896 hosp., 8
  steward, 145
  supt., 10
Odett, Linda, 138, 145
  wife of Joseph, 10
Ogren, Carroll, 38, 120, 133, 141, 158,
  160, 161, 164, 181, 199, 200
  appt. act. admin., 159
  helicopter ser., 125
  *Hist. of wmc*, 18, 19, 23, 24, 25, 31,
    140, 161
  leaves WMC, 119
  parking prob., 134
  sick leave, 165
  terminated, 166
  Univ. of Minn., 33
  Wash. Univ., 33
  WMC Hist., 11
Ogren, John
  C. Ogren bro., 213
Ogren, Peter
  C. Ogren father, 213
Ogren, Robert, 218

C. Ogren bro., 213
Ogren, Stuart, 33, 141
  C. Ogern twin bro., 213
  U.S. Naval Hosp., 218
Olmsted, Dr., 166
Olsen, Karen
  dietetic grad., 164
Olsen, Norman
  Washoe Meat Co., 59
Olsen, Ole
  Olsen and Johnson, 63
Orpheum Theater
  Minneapolis, 63
Orvis School of Nursing
  agreement, 157
  UNR, 69
Outcalt, Dr., 166
Owyhee Indian Hosp., 113

P

Paradis, Dr. Henry, 147
Parker, Dr. Steve, 166, 167
  resident, 121
Parker, Leigh
  resp. care, 206
Parsons, Dr. Lawrence, 147, 151
  consulting path., 20
  in charge of lab., 149
  salary terminated, 148
  supervises blood bank, 151
Parsons, Edward
  architect, 149
pathophysio. lab., 159, 160
Patten, Clarence
  trustee, 150
Payne, Mrs. Frank
  Women's League, 211
Pearl, Andy
  trustee, 174
Pecetti, Mrs. Peggy
  Women's League, 210
Peckham, James, 151, 152
  co. commissioner, 17
pediatrics
  ward opened, 152
pediculosis, 142

Peer, Pat, 70
  head OB nurse, 164
People's Hosp., 11, 139, 203
Pepper, Bertha
  C. Ogren's 1st sec., 96
Pepper, Ginger, 97
Peppermill Hotel
  loc. of Hill Bro's. Motel, 38
Pershing Gen. Hosp.
  No. Nev. Hosp. Council, 112
Peter Bent Brigham Hosp.
  coronary care, 64
Peters, Dr. Roy, 161, 162, 168
  trustee, 73, 160
Peterson, Dr. Lowell
  chief of staff, 202
Peterson, Norman, 165, 200
  asst. admin., 83
Peterson, Ray, 153, 155, 156, 158
  trustee, 75
Phalen, Dr. J. Stephen
  cardiology, 64
Phillips, Dr. Percy, 145
Phillips, Dr. Wm., 145
  autopsy contract, 144
Phillips, Eldon, 159, 181
  chief x-ray tech., 81
Phys. Therapy Depart.
  approved, 153
  est., 27
physician licensure
  Nev., 9
Pickering, Dr. Donald, 123, 165
  1st neonatologist, 124
Piersall, Dr. Claude
  radiologist, 147
Platt, Dr. Robert, 121
  int. med. resident, 166
Pleasants, Nancy, 70
Plowman, Jackie, 70
Pokroy, Dr. Michael
  SMH spokesman, 169
polio
  1952-'3 epidemic, 27
Ponciano, Bob
  orderly, 97
Powell, Josephine
  trustee, 165, 168

Powers, Roy, 173, 174
Pringle Way
    named for M. Pringle, 94
Pringle, Jack
    M. Pringle's son, 91
Pringle, John
    M. Pringle's husband, 91
Pringle, Maida, 60, 83, 87, 90, 91, 93,
    157, 158, 160, 161, 162, 168, 169,
    170, 181, 197, 199
    asst. admin., 155
    born in Wheatland, Calif., 93
    ch. of trustees, 165
    direct. nursing, 155
    ER nurse, 127
    friendship with M. Isbell, 89
    laid tile with Ogren and Fox, 40
    liquor ration for Mr. Ratay, 24
    nursing direct., 208
    nursing superv., 23, 150
    office with C. Ogren, 36
    Orvis Nursing Adv. Committee, 94
    Pringle Way named, 163
    resigns as trustee, 166
    retires from hosp., 164
    runs for trustees, 92
    temp. supt., 25, 152
    trustee, 164
    union member, 37
Proctor, Dr. Robert
    chief OB, 169
Prout, John, 172, 200
Prudy, Mrs., 147
Prutzman, Roberta
    health fair, 168
psychiatric unit, 47
pul. physio. lab.
    1st in No. Nev., 128
Putnam, Bud
    architect, 57, 161


Q

Questa, Eddy, 154, 155, 156, 158
    trustee, 74, 155
Quinn, Dr. Walter
    chief of staff, 201

Quonset huts, 44, 165
    blood bank, 30
    bought, 24
    computer depart., 79
    employee living quarters, 35
    Homoja huts, 151
    research of Dr. G. Smith, 77
    retarded children's program, 156
    rheumatic heart patients, 152
    TB ward, 26, 155
    W.W. II surplus, 140
    Women's League, 211
Quota Club Internat.
    M. Pringle, 94


R

Raggio, Senator Wm., 51, 140
    counsel, path. and radiologists, 106
Ratay, Vlad, 24, 25, 199
    appt. supt., 151
    terminated, 152
Ravenholt, Otto
    So. Nev. Memorial Hosp., 113
Rawson, Senator Ray, 172
Raymond, Dr. Mark, 161, 162, 166,
    168, 197
    trustee, 73
Red Cross Hosp., 11, 203
Redfield, Nell Foundation
    Cancer Center benefactor, 132
Redwood Pavilion, 27, 51, 98
    grand jury investigates, 154
    Shorty Holcomb's home, 97
    So. Pacific RR living quarters, 24, 45
Reed, B. A., 197
    trustee, 148
Reed, Wm.
    Aetna Insurance Co. and Medicare,
    114
Regional Dialysis Center
    grand opening, 173
Reid, Rene
    co. commissioner, 131
Reitz, George
    So. Nev. Memorial Hosp., 113
Remedee's Restaurant, 131

Reno Cancer Center, 31
Reno Civic Band
  1973 dedication, 64
*Reno Evening Gazette*, 10
  flu, 13
  public losing confidence, 129
*Reno Gazette-J.*
  1906 hosp. photo, 11
  Women's League, 212
Reno Gen. Hosp., 204
Reno Hosp., 203
Reno HS Adult Ed. Div.
  LPN school, 30, 156
Reno Mill Lumber Co.
  lumber for 1896 hosp., 8
Reno Rodeo, 25, 153
Reno Rotary Club
  C. Ogren, 88
Reno Surg. Center, 135
Reno, Dr. Elwood, 147
Resource Center
  opens, 172
Reveley, J., 124, 166
  admin., SMH, 110, 165
  merge OB units to SMH, 123
Rhea, Sigmun
  Pres. Korea, 74
rheumatic fever
  19th century, 6
Rhodes, Bryce, 108, 156, 158, 160, 197
  Nev. Bd. of Med. Exam., 75
  NSMA, 75
  trustee, 74, 75, 155
Rhodes, Cornelia
  Women's League, 209
Rhyno, Richard, 169
  pub. relations, 85
Rich, Sue
  NICU, 206
Rigelhuth Maternity Hosp., 203
Rimington, Claytha
  1st dialysis tech., 133
Rimington, Doug
  dialysis patient, 133, 163
Ripsom, Ruth
  nursing oper., 206

Risser, Stephanie
  dietetic training, 164
Ritzlin, Dr. Roger, 173, 174
  chief of staff, 202
Riverside Convalescent Center
  Sylvia Rundio, 57
Rix, Edna., 70
Robbins, Roy, 172, 173, 174
Roberts, Sam
  pharmacist, 82
Robinson, Dr. LaRue, 138, 146
  trustee, 17
Robison, Dr. Martin, 147
Rogers, Edith, 70
  LPN school, 107, 163
Rogers, Richard
  purchasing, 82
Rolfs, Diane
  ER, 206
Ronald McDonald House, 170
  opens, 171
Roosevelt High School
  C. Ogren, 213
Roosevelt Hosp., 11, 204
Rose De Lima Hosp.
  Bill Sthultz, 83
  cobalt machine, 52
Rose Pavilion, 44
Rosenauer, Mrs. Adolf
  Women's League, 210
Rosenow, Dr. Edward
  Mayo Clinic, 155
  studies Reno's polio epidemic, 28
Ross, Dr. George, 36, 151
  Nev. Bd. of Med. Exam., 140
Roush and Belz
  contractor, 146
Rowe, Dr. Peter
  starts cardiology, 64
  trustee, 158
Royal Hartung Hosp., 204
Rundio, Billie, 59
Rundio, Sylvia
  wife of Wm., 57
Rundio, Wm., 57, 161
  Portsmouth, Va., 57

Rusk, Robert
    trustee, 164
Russell, Dr. Frank, 151
Russell, Dr. Larry, 26, 95, 99, 139,
    158, 181
    clinic direct., 153
Russell, Gov. Charles, 94
Russell, Louise
    Dr. L. Russell's wife, 95
Russell, Rick
    heart pump tech., 65

## S

Saibini, Mrs. John
    Women's League, 209
Salk, Dr. Jonas E.
    polio vaccine, 28
Salvadorini, Dr. V. A., 60, 66, 81, 85,
    99, 108, 160, 162, 163, 170
    1951 contract, 153
    blood bank, 30
    NSMA and WCMS, 139
    path. contract, 26
    research lab, 159
    retiring, 165
Sampson, Roy, 181
    personnel, 80
Samuels, Dr. Frank
    anesthesia, 148
Samuels, Dr. Wm., 147
San Francisco
    C. Ogren Navy, 217
San Quentin Prison
    1918 flu epidemic, 13
Sandars, Dr. Leibert, 132, 139, 154,
    163
    radiology contract, 26
    research lab., 159
    retires, 173
    WCMS, 140
Sande, Dr. John
    chief of staff, 202
Sannella, Dr. Lee, 151
Sauer, Leo, 160, 161, 162
    trustee, 76

Sauls, Dr. Carl
    chief of staff, 202
Savage and Sons, 11
    plumbing contractor, 145
Schaff, W. W., 8
Schaffer, George
    lumber for 1896 hosp., 8
Schmaltz, Dean
    cardiopul. ser., 206
Schurz Indian Hosp., 113
Scott Ditch, 11, 34
Scott, Dr. Arthur, 108
    chief of staff, 202
    polio team, 29
Scott, Dr. John
    chief of staff, 202
Scott, Richard
    trustee, 163
Scully, Dr. Thomas, 109, 161, 165,
    166, 167
    asst. admin., 162
    director ed., 57
    SOM public debate, 121
Sebbas, Mildred
    Pershing Gen. Hosp., 112
Seevers, Leo, 174
Seher, Dr. Richard, 121, 166
    resident, 167
Sellers, Mrs. Silas
    Women's League, 209
Semenza, Lawrence
    auditor, 149
Seraphine, Sister, 110, 111
    SMH, 112
Servoss, Dr. George, 147
    co. phy., 146
SFH
    CON, 3
    dumping patients, 172
Shane, Dr. Stan, 135
Shaw, Dr. David, 147
Shaw, Rev. James, 160
    Episcopal Church, 56
Shea, Martha, 70
Shelly, Carl, 151, 152
Sheppard, Laurine
    chief nursing superv., 155

Sheppard, Maurice
Harrah's Club, 66, 67
Sheppard, Mrs. Laure
Women's League, 209
Shields, Fred
reporter, 153
Shull, Mrs. Meta, 199
Sieber, Wm., 154, 155
trustee, 155
Sierra Hosp., 204
Sierra Nev. Labs., 131
Sierra Oxygen Co., 116
Sierra Pacific Power
Scott Ditch, 34, 35
Sierra Valley Community Hosp.,
131, 171
Simon, Dr. Robert, 59, 60
asst., cardiac surg., 65
Simpson and Beckett
architects, 160
Simpson, Dr. Wm.
polio team, 29
Simpson, Roger
architect, 57, 161
Sister's Hosp.
became SMH, 11
Sisters of St. Dominic, 11
Skaggs, Juanita, 159
med. records, 84
smallpox
vaccination, 6
Watson's Mill, Nev ., 5
Smart, Clyde
bus. office, 158
SMH, 3, 12, 110, 125, 126, 155, 165,
169, 204
agree to same room rates, 153
dumping patients, 172
est. 1908, 11
fights WMC trauma designation,
128
Fleischmann Foundation, 88
gov. coop. during war, 150
hires attorney for baby war, 170
laundry by WMC, 50
liaison committeee with WMC,
170

NICU, 122, 124
No. Nev. Hosp. Council, 112
opens ER in 1972, 123
trauma ser., 127
uses dialysis ser., 134
WMC's relationship, 27
Smith, Audrey
Mt. Grant Hosp., 112
Smith, Dr. Esmond
Calif. Children Services, 124
Smith, Dr. George, 60, 64, 108, 110,
159, 160, 161, 165
1st research lab., 45
CICU, 160
dean, SOM, 57
research in Quonset hut, 77
wedding, 95
Smith, Dr. Jesse, 151
Smith, Helen
nurse, poison center, 66
Smith, Lloyd
husband of Louise K. Smith, 55
Smith, Loretta, 70
Smith, Louise Kohl, 55
donates chapel, 159
Women's League, 209
Smith, Phil
asst. admin., 160
Smith, Sr., Harold
helps with C. Fox's salary, 25
So. Nev. Memorial Hosp., 113
burn unit, 71
Van De Graff accelerator, 53
So. Pacific RR, 152
dorms, 152
Emergency Hosp., 204
living quarters to WMC, 24
Redwood Pavilion, 45
Sohn, Dr. Anton, 170, 172
chief of staff, 202
trustee, 171
vice chief of staff, 168
Sontag, Ed, 77, 157, 159
chief engineer, 45
leukemia, 159
Soo, Kit
phy. therapy, 159

Sourwein, Dr. Mary
  family practice resident, 166
Spann, John, 154, 155
*Sparks Tribune*
  1918 flu, 13, 15
Spoon, Eugene
  photo. depart., 86
  tele./security, 205
Spreckels, Kay
  Clark Gable's wife, 50
St. George Hosp., 11, 12, 204
St. Mary's Convent and School, 11
St. Michael Med. Center
  Dr. Scully, 57
St. Rose De Lima Hosp., 112, 113
Stadtherr, Dr. Anthony, 147
Staggs, Jack, 114
  So. Nev. Memorial Hosp., 113
Stahr, Mrs. Roland
  Women's League, 211
Staples, Geraldine, 168
  "Poison Lady", 66
Starzl, Dr. Thomas
  impt. liver transplant surg., 59
Stead Air Base
  Quonset huts, 140
Steele, Helen
  nurse, poison center, 66
Stevenson, June, 70
Stewart, Rod
  food ser., 206
Sthultz, Bill, 160, 181
  controller, 83
Stingley, D. D., 149, 199
  admin., 22
  resigns, 150
Stock, Private Wilbourn
  1918 flu death, 14
Stone and Mulloy
  architects, 154
Stone, Douglas
  architect, 23, 150
Stouder, Dr. Mike
  family practice resident, 166
Strasser, Dr. Hans, 151
  co. phy., 152

Streeter, Richard
  trustee, 158
Sturr, D. R., 143
  bought hosp. bldg., 7
Sullivan, Dr. John, 147
Summerfield, L.
  Fleischmann Foundation, 154
Sumner, Hall
  1918 flu death, 13
Sunrise Hosp.
  Las Vegas, 135
Supple, Catherine, 181
Sutherland, Elaine Sue
  bus. office/admitting, 205
Sutter Gen. Hosp.
  Earl Horton, 48
Sutton, Dr. Jennifer, 133
SW Blood Bank, 30, 140, 156, 157
Swain Hosp., 204
Swinney, Gloria
  surg. acute, 206
Swope, Mrs., 157
syphilis, 216

T

Tahoe Forest Hosp.
  Tuckee, Calif., 62
Tainter, Dr. Eugene, 151
Talbot, Claendel, 181
Talbot, Clare
  EEG, 85
Tapogna, Steve
  materials management, 206
Tappan, Dr. Wm.
  chief of staff, 202
Taylor, Dr. Horace
  chief of staff, 201
Taylor, Ruby, 70
Telecky, Duane
  plant ser., 206
Thoma, Dr. George, 11, 145
  Nev. St. Hosp., 138
Thomas, Bruce, 151, 152, 197
Thomas, Corinne
  Washoe Co. Welfare Depart., 85

Thompson, Dr. Alice, 139, 147
  1st path., 20
  Nev. Hygienic Lab., 139
Thompson, Dr. David
  cardiology, 64
Thompson, Wm.
  1876 const. hosp., 7
Thomsen, Dr., 147
Thorne, Christine
  med. records/case coord., 205
Thorpe, Dr. Moreton
  radiologist, 149, 154
Tillim, Dr. Sidney, 151
  Nev. St. Hosp., 41
Timerlake, Alice, 70
Tinkham, N. A.
  Reno Municipal Band, 140
TOMBOLA
  Women's League, 211
Tors, Jane
  marketing communications, 206
toxicology capabilities
  lab., 157
trauma center require., 127
Treanor, Dr. Wally, 70
Trinity Episcopal Church, 160
Truckee pharmacy
  unpaid Oympians' bills, 49
tuberculosis, 26, 27
  19th century, 6
Turlarski, Lura
  Reno Cancer Center, 31
Twaddle, Alice
  matron, 145
Twaddle, Eben, 199
  supt., 145, 146
typhoid fever
  19th century, 6

U

U.S, Congress, 2
U.S. Army, 23
U.S. Depart. of Labor
  certifies Dr. B. Lees, 125
U.S. Navy
  sold Quonset huts, 24

U.S. Pub. Health Ser., 23
  gov. coop. during war, 150
U.S. Secret Service
  inspection for President's visit, 47
*U.S.S. Coral Sea*, 78
  Aircraft Carrier, 218
*U.S.S. Hope*
  E. Phillips, 81
*U.S.S. Missouri*, 217
*U.S.S. New Jersey*, 217
*U.S.S. Pittsburgh*, 142, 216
*U.S.S. Quincy*, 142, 216, 217
*U.S.S. Wisconsin*, 217
Underwood, James, 168, 169
  trustee, 166
Univ. Comm. College Sys. Nev.
  LPN school, 107
Univ. Hosp., 204
Univ. of Mich. Hosp.
  Dr. P. Rowe, 64
Univ. of Nev.
  1918 flu, 14
Univ. of Nev. Bd. of Regents, 161
Univ. of Nev. *Sagebrush*
  flu, 13
UNR nurse's cap
  cowboy hat, 69
UNSOM, 160
  bone marrow transplant, 135
  directs Nev. Pub. Health Lab., 20
  opposition by med. staff, 120

V

Valenta, Dr. Henry
  co. phy., 152
  home loaned to Clark Gable, 50
Verhey, Jim
  Schurz Indian Hosp., 113
Veterans Hosp., 113, 135, 204
  uses dialysis ser., 134
VFW Portola, Calif., 28
  donates portable iron lung, 155
Vhay, David
  architect, 156, 158
Vhay, Mrs. David
  Women's League, 209, 211

Vietnam
  helicopter service, 126
virus, H1N1
  flu, 15
virus, Swine Iowa 30
  related to flu virus, 15

**W**

Wadsworth, Nev.
  hosp., 8, 144
Wagensteen, Dr. Owen
  impt. surg., 217
Walker Boudwin Construct. Co,, 159
Walker, Dr. Moris, 137
  1901 Reno descrip., 9
Wallace, Henry, 151, 199
  supt., 24
Walsh, David
  Dep. Attn. Gen., 161
Walsh, empoyee, 60
Walters, Dr.
  resident, 167
Walther, Key, Maupin, etc.
  hosp. attorney, 170
Walton's Funeral Home
  advertisement, 160
Wangsness, Elaine
  housekeeping, 156
Warren, Dr. Stafford
  consultant, 161
Warren, Everett
  flies blood to Fallon, 155
Warren, Wallie, 153
  *Nev. St. News*, 155
Wash. Univ., St. Louis, 219
Washoe City
  county seat, 5
  hosp. bldg., 7
Washoe Co. Bank
  financed 1903 hosp., 11
Washoe Co. Hosp.
  1918 flu, 14
  old, 148
Washoe Co. Pub. Hosp., 9, 11, 146
  new, 148

Washoe Gen. Hosp., 17, 18, 19, 139,
  146, 150
  1924 No. Wing, 15
  1943 blood bank, 23
  1947 Annual Report, 152
  new wing, 21
  Washoe Co. Pub. Hosp., 18
Washoe Health Sys., 131, 135, 171,
  174
Washoe Health Sys. Network
  participating hosp., 171
Washoe Pregnancy Center, 123
Washoe Professional Center, 131
Washoe Professional Pharmacy, 131
Washoe Valley, 5
Washoe West. School Pract. Nursing,
  94
Washoe, Chimpanzee
  M. Pringle, 92
Watson's Mill, Nev.
  smallpox, 5
Waugh, Laura
  nursing direct., 208
WCMS, 147, 166
  Auxiliary (AWCMS), 211
  blood bank, 30
  bylaws of Washoe Co. Gen. Hosp.,
    20
  organizes team for polio, 28
  polio equip. fund, 29
  voted on SOM, 120
WCMS Auxilary (AWCMS)
  scholarships for LPNs, 107
Weed, Dr. A. Gideon, 137
  1st Washoe co. phy., 6
Wehrli, Kathryn
  VP fin., 205
Welton Beckett and Assoc.
  architect, Santa Monica, 57
  architects, 160
Wentworth Hosp., 204
Wescott, Gary
  imaging center, 205
Wessel, Joanne
  cardiac nurse, 64
West. Clinical Labs, 163

West. Med. Supply, 131
Wh. Pine Co. Gen. Hosp.
    No. Nev. Hosp. Council, 112
Wheeler, Sessions
    Fleischmann Foundation, 88
Whisman, Coach Ray
    1918 flu death, 14
Whitaker Hosp., 204
Whiting, Glen, 159
    housekeeping, 157
Whitlock, David
    polio patient, 29, 154
Whomes, Willeta
    Churchill Pub. Hosp., 112
Wilkerson, Bertha, 146
    nursing direct., 20, 148, 208
Wilkerson, Mary Ellen
    health cont. ser., 205
Williams, Anita, 70
Williams, Belie, 169, 171
Wilson, E. B., 143
    owns 1864 printing office, 6
Wilson, Thomas
    advertising, 160
Winikow, Dr. Wm., 151
Winn, Benjamin
    trustee, 158
Winters, Kimberly
    labor and del., 206
WMC
    1st CAT scanner, 53
    East Wing, 23, 37
    hosp. farm, 22
    malpractice, 72
    named, 152
    So. Wing, 18
    So. Wing, SOM offices, 109
Wohleen, Mabel
    C. Ogren mother, 213
Wolfe, Dr. Clare, 151
Wolfe, Mrs. Victor
    Women's League, 210
Women's Relief Corps, 145
Women's Auxiliary, 154
    organized, 25, 153

Women's League, 2, 38, 75, 76, 107,
    155, 158, 168, 171
    benefactor, 88
    bought TVs for hosp., 44
    bylaws, 156
    dinner for Marilyn Monroe, 50
    gift to Shorty Holcomb, 98
    Ladies Auxiliary, 151
    linear accelerator, 133, 163
Work, Mrs.
    nursing direct., 208
World War II, 22
    hosp. in good financial shape, 20
    Pearl Harbor blackouts, 149
Wright, Aurora
    dialysis, 206
Wright, Ethel
    1st cardiac cath. patient, 65
Wyman Pavilion, 138, 140
    incresed to 39 beds, 158
    psychiatry ward, 51
Wyman, Dr. Rodney, 138, 147, 149
    chief of staff, 201
    Nev. St. Hosp., 140
    Women's League, 211
    Wyman Pavilion, 140
Wyman, Mrs. Rodney
    Women's League, 211

Y

Yerg, Dr. Raymond
    temp. co. phy., 151
Young, Bud
    sheriff, 78
Young, Genevieve
    bus. mgr., 78, 157
    personnel, 156

Z

Zamboni, Joe
    laundry, 81
Zamboni, Rose
    laundry, 81